Edgar M Williams
May, 1984

Physics and Chemistry of Porous Media
(Schlumberger-Doll Research, 1983)

AIP Conference Proceedings
Series Editor: Hugh C. Wolfe
Number 107

Physics and Chemistry
of Porous Media

(Schlumberger-Doll Research, 1983)

Edited by

D. L. Johnson and P. N. Sen
Schlumberger-Doll Research

American Institute of Physics
New York   1984

L.C. Catalog Card No. 83-73640
ISBN 0–88318–306–4
DOE CONF-8310216

Foreword

Porous materials are ubiquitous and constitute perhaps the most complex of disordered systems. Attempts to understand these materials date back to Lucretius, 1st century B.C.(see Kendall's article in these proceedings). Much of the theoretical understanding derives from a host of effective medium theories produced in the last century. Lord Rayleigh's pioneering work still remains an inspiration to go beyond these approximations. Models for which the effective medium theories are exact have been proposed, but topological limitations of simple effective medium theories, and methods to go beyond them for intermeshed systems, are now appreciated. This is due in large measure to the development, within the last 5-10 years, of the ability to perform carefully controlled experiments. As a result, several striking experimental effects that occur when the solid and fluid phases both form infinite spanning clusters have been observed.

The understanding of fundamental scientific issues relevant to porous media requires the participation of scientists from different disciplines and environments; this realization was the motivation for the first symposium on the Physics and Chemistry of Porous Media which was held at Schlumberger-Doll Research on October 24 and 25, 1983. The purpose of this symposium was to bring together a diverse group of people who do not normally interact with each other. Indeed, several speakers commented to us that they were surprised that they were invited to speak. This was intentional on the part of the Organizing Committee. Thus, the talks (and the articles reproduced herein) cover aspects of Chemistry, Physics, Geology, and Fluid Dynamics. The porous media themselves are gels, superleaks, sedimentary rocks, and a wide variety of artificially manufactured materials. It is apparent, even from the table of contents of this small volume, that porous media do indeed exhibit a wealth of diverse physical phenomena.

The planning of this Symposium required the efforts of many individuals. The meeting would not have taken place without the encouragement and support of Michel Gouilloud and Michael Ekstrom. The local Organizing Committee was chaired by Larry Schwartz and was assisted and advised on essentially a daily basis by Elyse LeRoy; the success of the symposium is a reflection of their extraordinary organizational abilities. Thanks are also due to Karen Kavanagh for many important suggestions. During the meeting, the four sessions were presided over efficiently by Gene Simmons, Etienne Guyon, Monroe Waxman, and by Morrel Cohen who also gave an excellent summary talk at the end of the symposium. We were fortunate to have a distinguished list of paticipants who enlivened the symposium by vigorous discussions.

David Linton Johnson
Pabitra N. Sen   December 12, 1983

Participants

D. Alpert, Harvard University
P. Baker, Schlumberger-Doll Research
J. Banavar, Schlumberger-Doll Research
S. Battacharya, Exxon Research and Engineering Co.
M. Batzle, Arco Oil and Gas Company
J. R. Beamish, University of Delaware
S. Berko, Brandeis University
Y. Bernabe, M.I.T.
J. G. Berryman, Lawrence Livermore National Lab
B. Bonner, Lawrence Livermore National Lab
A. Booer, Schlumberger Well Services
C. Boyeldieu, Etudes et Productions Schlumberger
A. Brie, Schlumberger-Doll Research
F. Brochard, College de France
R. Burridge, New York University, Courant Inst.
A. E. Bussian, Texaco
J. Byerlee, U.S. Dept. of the Interior - Geological Survey
A. Callegari, Exxon Research and Engineering Co.
G. S. Cargill, IBM
R. Chandler, Schlumberger Well Services
J. -D. Chen, Schlumberger-Doll Research
W. Chew, Schlumberger-Doll Research
C. Clavier, Etudes et Productions Schlumberger
G. R. Coates, Schlumberger Well Services
M. Cohen, Exxon Research and Engineering Co.
R. Cohen, Exxon Research and Engineering Co.
B. De, Chevron Oilfield Research
P. G. de Gennes, College de France
J. M. Deutch, M.I.T.
K. J. Dunn, Chevron Oilfield Research
N. Dutta, Shell Development Co.
P. Eisenberger, Exxon Research and Engineering Co.
R. Ehrlich, University of South Carolina
M. P. Ekstrom, Schlumberger-Doll Research
S. Feng, Harvard university
W. R. Foster, Mobil Research and Development Corp.
M. R. Frisinger, Schlumberger-Doll Research
D. Fuerstenau, University of California, Berkeley
F. Gamble, Schlumberger-Doll Research
N. Goins, Mobil Research and Development Corp.
M. Gouilloud, Schlumberger Ltd.
G. S. Grest, Exxon Research and Engineering Co.

J. Gubernatis, Los Alamos National Laboratory
E. Guyon, ESPCI (Paris)
T. Hagiwara, Shell Development Co.
C. Hall, Schlumberger Cambridge Research
B. Halperin, Harvard University
K. E. Hanson, Amoco Production Company
A. Heim, Schlumberger-Doll Research
D. C. Herrick, Amoco Production Company
J. Hinch, University of Cambridge
R. M. Holt, Petroleum Technology Research Inst.
A. H. Jageler, Amoco Production Company
R. Jenkins, Core Laboratories
D. L. Johnson, Schlumberger-Doll Research
D. Johnston, Exxon Production Research Co.
J. V. Jose, Northeastern University
S. Katayama, Nippon Schlumberger K.K.
K. Kendall, ICI Corporation
W. E. Kenyon, Schlumberger-Doll Research
T. Keyes, Yale University
P. R. King, B. P. Research Centre
W. Klein, Boston University
R. Knight, Stanford University
H. Kojima, Rutgers State University
J. Koplik, Schlumberger-Doll Research
M. Lax, City College
P. Leath, Rutgers State University
R. Lenormand, Schlumberger-Doll Research
H. Levine, Schlumberger-Doll Research
M. Lipsicas, Schlumberger-Doll Research
T. Lubensky, University of Pennsylvania
T. Madden, M.I.T.
P. C. Martin, Harvard University
J. L. McCauley, Jr., University of Houston
D. McConnell, Schlumberger Cambridge Research
J. J. McCoy, The Catholic University of America
J. Melrose, Mobil Research and Development Corp.
K. Mendelson, Marquette University
G. Milton, Cornell University
S. Moss, University of Houston
W. Murphy, Schlumberger-Doll Research
M. Muthukumar, University of Massachusetts
M. Myers, Shell Development Co.
S. R. Nagel, University of Chicago
C. Nicholson, New York University Medical Center
A. Obuchi, Nippon Schlumberger K.K.

R. O'Connell, Harvard University
Y. Oono, University of Illinois
M. Orton, Schlumberger-Doll Research
N. Pallatt, B. P. Research Centre
A. Pearson, Schlumberger Cambridge Research
E. Pittman, Amoco Production Company
T. J. Plona, Schlumberger-Doll Research
J. P. Poirier, Institut de Physique du Globe
V. Polciauskas, Chevron Oilfield Research
Y. Pomeau, Schlumberger-Doll Research
W. E. Preeg, Schlumberger-Doll Research
R. Raythatha, Schlumberger-Doll Research
S. Redner, Boston University
G. Reiter, University of Houston
J. Reppy, Cornell University
J. Roberts, Schlumberger-Doll Research
P. Rossi, Dowell Schlumberger
C. Roulet, Etudes et Productions Schlumberger
I. Rudnick, University of California, Los Angeles
W. B. Russel, Princeton University
K. A. Safinya, Schlumberger-Doll Research
L. Schwartz, Schlumberger-Doll Research
P. N. Sen, Schlumberger-Doll Research
L. Shen, University of Houston
P. Sheng, Exxon Research and Engineering Company
R. W. Siegfried, Arco Oil and Gas Company
G. Simmons, M.I.T.
R. S. Simpson, Texaco
J. Singer, Schlumberger Well Services
E. Sprunt, Mobil Research and Development Corp.
H. E. Stanley, Boston University
M. Stephens, Rutgers State University
C. Straley, Schlumberger-Doll Research
J. R. Tabanou, Schlumberger Well Services
T. Tanaka, Massachusetts Institute of Technology
D. Tanner, University of Florida
B. Tittman, Rockwell Science Center
M. Tomkiewicz, Brooklyn College, CUNY
A. Thompson, Exxon Production Research Co.
L. A. Thomsen, Amoco Production Company
J. P. Tomanic, Schlumberger-Doll Research
M. Tomkiewicz, Brooklyn College, CUNY
V. V. Varadan, Pennsylvania State University
V. K. Varadan, Pennsylvania State University
C. Varma, Bell Laboratories

H. J. Vinegar, Shell Development Co.
N. Wada, Schlumberger-Doll Research
J. Walsh, M.I.T.
M. H. Waxman, Shell Development Co.
I. Webman, Exxon Research and Engineering Co.
A. Weinrib, Cornell University
R. Wiggins, Schlumberger-Doll Research
D. J. Wilkinson, Schlumberger-Doll Research
J. Willemsen, Schlumberger-Doll Research
K. W. Winkler, Schlumberger-Doll Research
P. -Z. Wong, Schlumberger-Doll Research
T. Wong, State University of NY at Stony Brook
B. Zinszner, Institut Francais du Petrole

CONTENTS

CHAPTER IV: Chemical Aspects

THE PORE GEOMETRIES OF RESERVOIR ROCKS

Edward D. Pittman
Amoco Production Company, Research Center, Box 591, Tulsa, OK 74102

ABSTRACT

A ternary pore geometry classification scheme for reservoir
rocks places intergranular and intercrystalline porosity at a common
pole. These porosity types tend to have well interconnected pores
and usually are good reservoirs. Intragranular, moldic, and vuggy
porosity are grouped at another pole of the classification triangle.
Rocks with these porosity types usually have poorly interconnected
pores and low permeability. Rocks with microporosity are grouped at
the final pole of the triangle. These may be argillaceous sandstones, finely textured carbonates, diatomites, or tripolitic
cherts. Water-wet microporous rocks hold bound water. Rocks with
significant amounts of microporosity and/or intragranular, moldic,
and vuggy porosity need fractures, either natural or induced, to
make an attractive reservoir. Fracture porosity may occur by itself
or combined with any other porosity type. Reservoirs typically contain multiple pore types, although one type often predominates.
Large scale cavernous features in carbonates occasionally contain
oil.

INTRODUCTION

Pore geometry, the three-dimensional network of pores, determines the quality of a reservoir rock; that is, the volume of fluids
and the capability to transmit fluids. Of course, fluid factors
such as viscosity also play a role. Pore geometry is controlled
primarily by mineralogy, fabric, and diagenetic history. The purpose of this paper is to provide an overview of some of the practical aspects of pore geometry and to show examples of the major
pore geometry types.
     In this paper sandstone is used to mean terrigenous sandstone.
Carbonate rocks composed of sand-sized components will be referred
to as carbonate sand. Some workers believe that carbonate and sandstone reservoirs have little in common. However, to the contrary,
these two major reservoir categories have many similarities and can
be accommodated with a common pore geometry classification scheme.
     The major differences between carbonate and sandstone reser-
voirs result from: (1) mineralogy; (2) origin of grains; (3) size
and shape of grains; and (4) influence of early diagenesis on carbonate rocks. The differences in these features are summarized in
Table I. Carbonate rocks in general have a more complex heterogeneous pore system than sandstones, although the differences are not
as great as was believed 10 or 15 years ago.
     Porosity in reservoirs has either a primary (initial or orig-
inal) or secondary origin. Primary pores tend to be destroyed with
burial because of compaction and cementation. Petrologists have
long recognized that secondary porosity in carbonate rocks is

Table I Comparison of differences between carbonates and sandstones

factor	carbonates	sandstones
mineralogy	relatively soluble carbonate minerals	relatively insoluble silicate minerals
origin of grains	biological and non-biological; formed near site of deposition	grains originate through weathering and erosion of existing rock with transportation to site of deposition
size and shape of grains	many grains are large with shapes like twigs, branches, rods, or flakes, which pack more loosely than ellipsoidal grains	ellipsoidal
influence of early diagenesis	major changes may occur within 125,000 years	little effect

common; whereas, the importance of secondary porosity in sandstones has only recently been recognized.[1] Secondary porosity in carbonates often is fabric selective because of differences in solubility attributable to mineralogy or crystal size variation. In sandstones secondary porosity most commonly results from dissolution of carbonate cement and silicate grains, particularly feldspars and lithic fragments.

METHODS OF STUDYING POROSITY

A variety of methods are used to study porosity and to gain information on pore geometry. Some methods contribute only indirectly to an interpretation of pore geometry. An approach that integrates results from various methods is used in this paper. A visual examination of the core is the best method to obtain information on large features such as fractures and location of porous intervals. Such an examination will provide a basis for selecting samples for more detailed studies.

Thin sections of rocks provide the most common means of studying porosity. This technique yields useful but essentially two-dimensional information on pores. Pores of the rock must be saturated with dyed epoxy resin prior to thin sectioning in order to be able to recognize real pores from any artifacts produced by the thin section preparation technique.

Pore casts are replicas of pore systems and can be made for any
reservoir rock by injecting an acid-resistant medium into the pores
and then dissolving the rock. Early efforts at using pore casts
utilized Woods metal, which is an alloy of bismuth, tin, and cadmium
having a melting point of 70°C.[2] Later studies have used epoxy
resin.[3] The sequence of acids used to dissolve the rock is important if both carbonate and silicate minerals are present. The carbonate minerals must be dissolved first in HCl or $C_2H_4O_2$ and then
the silicate minerals can be dissolved in HF. If $CaCO_3$ (calcite)
comes in contact with HF, a calcium fluoride is produced that will
not dissolve in HCl. Pore casts of microporous rocks often are dis-
rupted by the desiccation process. This can be prevented by using a
freeze drying or critical point drying technique. A variation of
the pore cast technique is to impregnate the pore cast with a con-
trasting colored epoxy resin then make serial sections with a micro-
tome.[4]

Scanning electron microscopy is useful for studying rocks and
pore casts, especially if microporous. This technique provides
information that compliments the study of pores in thin section.

Mercury injection tests have been used by many workers to study
or characterize the pore systems of rocks.[5] This technique provides
a calculated distribution of effective pore apertures (throats).

Pore aperture size can be calculated from:

$$Pc = \frac{2\ \gamma\ \cos\ \theta}{r} \tag{1}$$

where Pc = capillary pressure (atm), γ = surface tension of mercury
(480 dynes/cm), θ = contact angle for mercury (140°), and r = radius
of pore aperture (μm).

Mercury ejection tests have received less attention, but provide an indication of how readily a rock will yield a nonwetting
fluid during a pressure drop.[6] This does not mean there is a direct
correlation with oil production because there are large rheologic
differences between mercury and less viscous, pressure dependent
natural pore fluids often containing dissolved gas. In general, low
porosity rocks eject mercury less efficiently during pressure reduction than high porosity rocks.

Molten Woods metal has been utilized as the injection medium in
a porosimeter.[7] The pressure can be maintained at any level while
permitting the Woods metal to cool and crystallize. Examination of
the sample then allows good visualization of the pore space occupied
by the nonwetting phase under various capillary pressures.

The study of porosity using image analysis techniques is a
relatively new and promising area of future research.[8] Another
developing technique is the use of computed tomography.

CLASSIFICATION OF PORE GEOMETRY

This classification is adapted from a scheme devised for sandstones that was previously published by the author.[9] It is a

pragmatic approach that groups fabric related pore types at the
poles of a ternary diagram (Fig. 1). End member reservoir types are
not unusual, but most reservoirs are mixtures of two or more
porosity types. Fracture porosity may occur with any of the
porosity types or by itself. This classification makes no distinc-
tion between primary and secondary porosity.

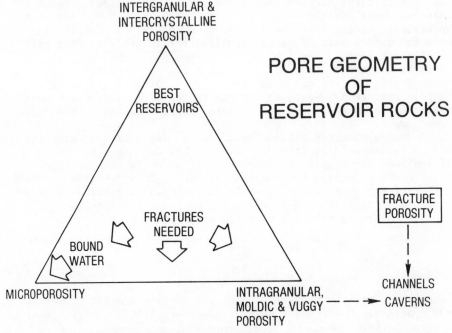

Fig. 1. Classification of pore geometry for reservoir rocks. Best
reservoirs plot in upper part of triangle. Reservoirs plotting in
lower one-third need fractures, either natural or induced, to make
an attractive reservoir. Reservoirs plotting near microporosity
pole have high-bound water saturations if the rock is water-wet.
Fracture porosity occurs by itself or with any other pore type.
Channels and caverns are large-scale features associated with carbonate rocks.

The position of a reservoir in the classification triangle is
helpful in predicting reservoir behavior. Generally, the best reservoirs will plot in the upper part of the triangle. Rocks that
plot in about the lower third of the triangle need fractures to make
an attractive reservoir. These rocks may have sufficient porosity
based on core analysis but the macropores are either poorly interconnected or else the pore system is predominantly microporous.
Water-wet reservoirs with abundant micropores have high water saturation because of bound water held by capillary forces in micropores
and because of water adsorbed on the high surface area. This water
is not mobile, and if hydrocarbon-bearing macropores occur with
micropores then the rock may yield water-free hydrocarbons despite
unusually high water saturations.

A description of selected reservoir rocks will illustrate the
classification concept and the significance of pore geometry types
to productive capabilities. We will start at the top of the triangle and move clockwise before considering fractured reservoirs.
Intergranular porosity (i.e., pore space among grains) occurs in
sandstone and carbonate sand reservoirs. Considerable theoretical
and experimental work on grain shape and packing has been done to
develop concepts of pore geometry for rocks with intergranular
porosity.[10]

Nugget Sandstone, the major reservoir in the overthrust play of
Utah and Wyoming, is an example of a rock with predominantly intergranular porosity (Fig. 2). The sample shown in the photomicrograph
is cemented by the clay mineral illite, which is not readily apparent at this magnification but is prominently displayed as crinkly
films in the scanning electron micrograph (Fig. 3A). An epoxy resin
pore cast reveals the intergranular pores that are well interconnected by tabular shaped pore apertures (Fig. 3B). The impression
of the illite crystals in the pore cast is visible within the
sockets from which sand grains were dissolved.

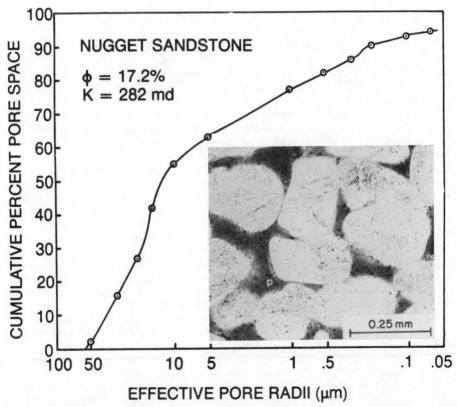

Fig. 2.   Sandstone with intergranular porosity (p). Mercury injection curve indicates large well-sorted pore throats indicative of a
good reservoir rock.

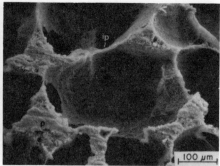

Fig. 3.   Scanning electron micrographs of Nugget Sandstone.
A.   Short fibers of illite (i) line intergranular pores (p). Areas
without illite represent pressure solution grain contacts (gc).
B.   Pore cast showing intergranular pores (p) and tabular interconnecting pores (ip). The impression of the illite plates provides a
pitted appearance where sand grains once existed.

A mercury injection test indicates the Nugget Sandstone has
large pore apertures (Fig. 2). The mercury entry point is approximately 50 μm. Between 50 and 10 μm the pores are relatively well
sorted as shown by the steepness of the curve. At the limits of the
test (1800 psi; 0.06 μm) 94% of the pore space was filled by mercury. The qualities making for a good reservoir rock are large and
well-sorted pore apertures.
The Baker Dolomite represents a carbonate rock with intercrystalline porosity. The original rock, a limestone, has been dolomi-
tized leading to the development of pores among the dolomite rhombohedra (Fig. 4). The mercury injection curve indicates an entry
point of about 11 μm with well-sorted pore apertures between 11 and
4 μm (41% of the pore throats). This curve has a hump indicative of
a bimodal pore system. The micropores, which have pore radii that
are mostly between 1 and 0.25 μm, are visible in the scanning electron micrographs of the rock (Fig. 5A) and pore cast (Fig. 5B).
This sample has 20% porosity of which 12.5% is macropores and 7.5%
micropores based on a point count of the thin section.
The various porosity types grouped at the lower right pole of
the classification triangle (Fig. 1) are characterized by isolated
macropores and are dependent on microporous interconnections among
crystals or grains to provide matrix permeability.
Feldspar grains in many sandstones are partially dissolved to
produce intragranular porosity (Fig. 6A-B). In other sandstones,
for example the Tuscarora of the Appalachian province, the feldspar
has been essentially totally dissolved to produce moldic porosity
(Fig. 7A). Pores in the Tuscarora are poorly interconnected
resulting in a permeability of only 0.05 md. The pore cast shows
thin films of epoxy resin representing minute pores through which
fluids would have to flow to move from one moldic pore to another
(Fig. 7B). The mercury injection curve also indicates the presence
of small pore apertures with only 58% of the pores penetrated by

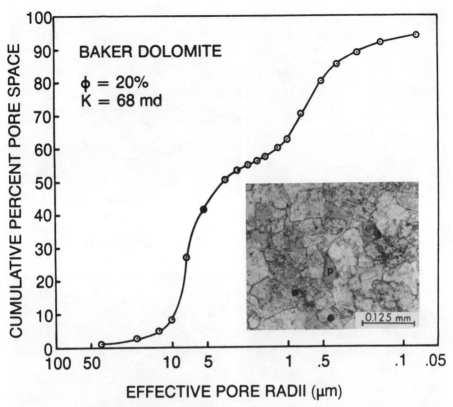

Fig. 4. Dolomite with intercrystalline porosity (p). Note bimodal
nature of mercury injection curve.

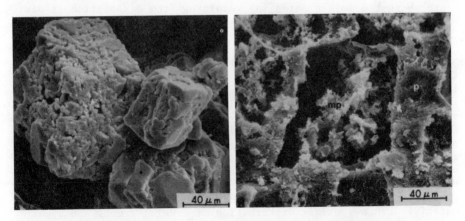

Fig. 5. Scanning electron micrographs of Baker Dolomite.
A. Dolomite rhombohedra with micropores. B. Pore cast showing
large intercrystalline pores (p) and micropores (mp) within dolomite
rhombohedron.

8

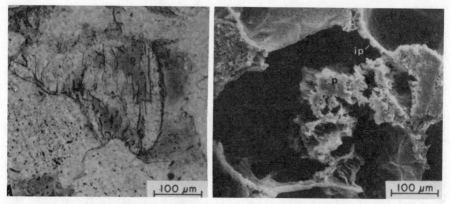

Fig. 6. A. Photomicrograph showing intragranular macropore (p)
formed by partial dissolution of feldspar. B. Pore cast illus-
trating intragranular macropore (p) and tabular pore interconnections (ip).

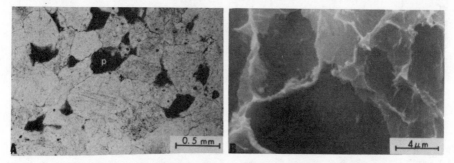

Fig. 7. Tuscarora Sandstone. A. Photomicrograph showing poorly
interconnected moldic pores (p) resulting from dissolution of disseminated feldspars. B. Pore cast depicting microporous interconnections among grains and crystals.

mercury at the limit of the test (Fig. 8). The largest pore apertures have a radii of only about 1 μm. The pore cast and mercury
injection test data support the low permeability measurement.
     Moldic pores are also common in carbonate reservoirs, particu-
larly those containing appreciable oolites. The Drum Limestone of
Kansas contains oolites, peloids, and skeletal grains (Fig. 9). The
oolites have been dissolved and the molds partially to completely
infilled by calcite cement. The distribution of calcite cement is
sporadic with some pores totally infilled, while adjacent pores have
very little cement. The same is true for the epoxy resin, which
penetrated some moldic pores, while adjacent pores lack the
material. This sporadic distribution of mineral cement and epoxy
resin reflects the heterogeneous nature of the pore system and the
fact that the calcite cement among the moldic pores consists of
tightly interlocked crystals (Fig. 10A-B). Even at 1800 psi, epoxy
resin was unable to penetrate the pore apertures between some moldic

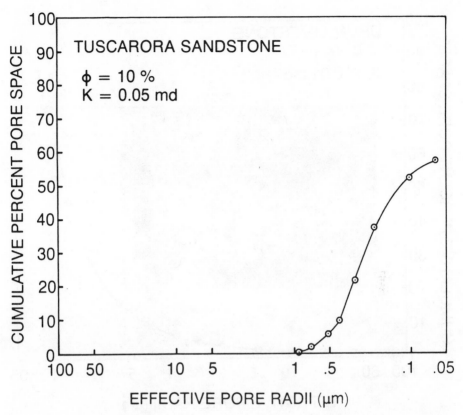

Fig. 8.   Mercury injection curve indicates small pore apertures
with only 58% of pores occupied by mercury at limits of test.

pores.   Pore casts of the Drum reveal micropores within oolite
grains (Fig. 11A) and micropores among calcite crystals along which
fluids must move through the rocks (Fig. 11B).   The mercury injection curve for the Drum Limestone shows a wide range in sizes with a
few percent of relatively large pore apertures (>5 μm) but with 87%
of the pore apertures less than 0.5μm.   A permeability of only
0.01 md makes sense for this pore geometry (Fig. 9).
        Vuggy carbonate rocks can be either limestone or dolomite.
Vuggy limestones nearly always have low permeability because of poor
interconnections among vugs.   Vuggy dolomites may be attractive reservoirs if sufficient intercrystalline porosity is associated with
the vugs.   Limestones that plot at or near the vuggy porosity pole
may have large obvious pores that give the appearance of a highly
porous rock, although the porosity is usually not high (5-10%) and
the permeability is quite low.   In fact, a limestone with disconnected vugs is the seal for the trap at Clear Creek Field, South
Dakota.[11]
        Irregular vugs form from selective dissolution of carbonate
grains from the surrounding matrix because of solubility

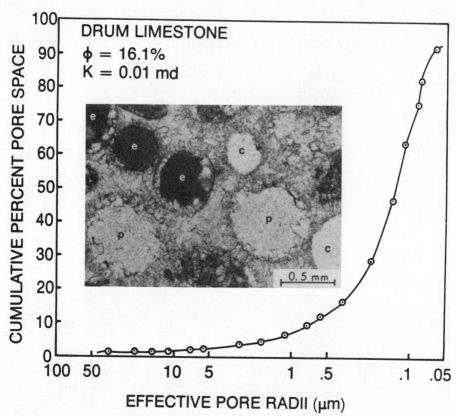

Fig. 9.   Photomicrograph reflects the sporadic distribution of open moldic pores (p), cement-filled moldic pores (c), and epoxy-filled moldic pores (e). The mercury injection curve shows a wide range in pore aperture radii that is skewed toward the finer sizes.

differences. If the solutions continue to be undersaturated with respect to carbonate minerals, the matrix is dissolved expanding the vug while losing the distinctive shape of the mold.

The Coban Dolomite from Guatemala is a vuggy dolomite (Fig. 12). The mercury injection curve is strange appearing because of the edge effects of vugs. The low pressure (large pores) part of the curve is probably meaningless. It is significant, however, that 60% of the pore apertures have radii <0.06 μm. Scanning electron microscopy confirms that the dolomite crystals fit tightly together and that some micropores also occur within the dolomite crystals (Fig. 13A-B). This sample has a permeability of only 0.046 md.

Sandstone and carbonate reservoirs with abundant micropores plot in the lower left corner of the classification triangle (Fig. 1). Diatomite and tripolitic chert fit in this category also. Micropores in reservoirs usually hold water but may hold hydrocarbons under certain conditions. If a large oil column is present then buoyancy pressure can overcome capillary pressure and displace

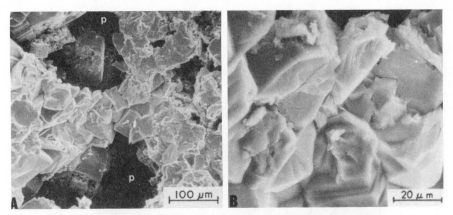

Fig. 10. Scanning electron micrographs of Drum Limestone.
A. Moldic porosity (p) formed by dissolution of oolites.
B. Closeup of cement-filled intergranular area showing tightly
interlocking calcite crystals and lack of pore openings.

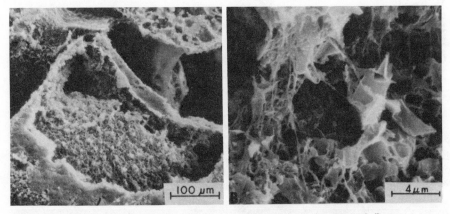

Fig. 11. Scanning electron micrographs of pore cast of Drum
Limestone. A. Micropores occurring within an oolite.
B. Tabular-shaped interconnecting pores between moldic pores.

water in micropores creating a high oil saturation. Fractures are
required, however, to produce oil from this type of rock at an eco-
nomic flowrate.
    Micropores in sandstone are usually associated with clay min-
erals occurring as authigenic growths in pores or as detrital clays
present in layers or in grains. Authigenic clays within the pore
system have the greatest impact on the reservoir because the clay is
in a position to restrict fluid flow and react with fluids in the
pore system. Clay minerals, like finely textured carbonates, have
micropores and high surface areas to hold water, but some clays

12

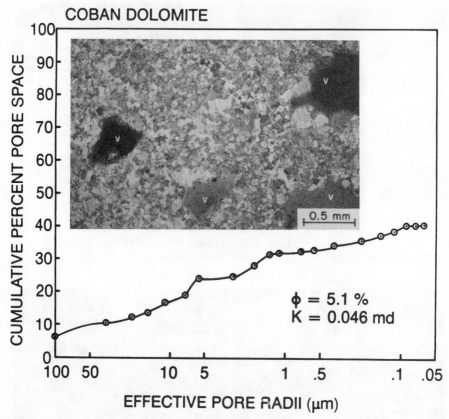

COBAN DOLOMITE

Fig. 12. Vuggy porosity (v) gives a misleading representation of large pore apertures because of the edge effect of the vugs in mercury injection tests. It is significant that only 40% of the pores were occupied by mercury at the limits of the test.

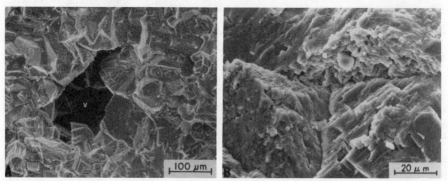

Fig. 13. Scanning electron micrographs of Coban Dolomite showing: A. vug (v) surrounded by tightly packed crystals; B. higher magnification view of contact between crystals. Note micropores within crystals.

because of high cation exchange capacity and the development of an ionic double layer have even greater conductance of electrons.

The San Miguel Sandstone from south Texas has detrital as well as authigenic clay (Fig. 14). The rock has good porosity (17.1%)

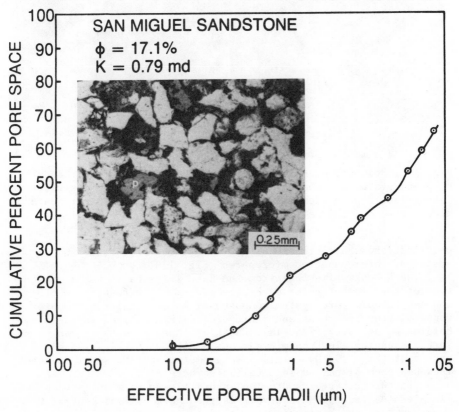

Fig. 14. Clay-bearing sandstone has a few moldic macropores (p) but is mostly microporous. The mercury injection curve suggests the pore radii have a polymodal size distribution.

but low permeability (0.79 md) because authigenic clays are restricting the pore throats (Fig. 15A). Microporosity created by the clay minerals is visible in the intergranular areas of the pore cast (Fig. 15B). The mercury injection curve suggests the pore system is at least bimodal and possibly trimodal, although the finest mode is subtle.

Chalks from the North Sea are good examples of microporous carbonate reservoirs. The mercury injection curve (Fig. 16) indicates that the pore apertures are all less than 0.5 μm. However, the pore apertures are well sorted. Macropores exist within the chambers of foraminifers, which are not abundant enough to significantly augment the porosity (Fig. 16). At high magnifications it is apparent that the chalk is composed of fragments of coccoliths (Fig. 17A). The

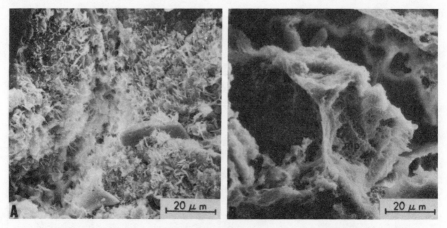

Fig. 15. Scanning electron micrographs of the San Miguel Sandstone.
A. Sand grains are coated with authigenic clay, which restricts the
intergranular pore (center). B. Pore cast reveals the presence of
micropores (mp) in the intergranular areas.

pore cast shows a macropore within a foraminifer chamber and a
system of interconnected micropores (Fig. 17B).

The Rodessa Limestone from the East Texas basin has a common
type of pore geometry for carbonate rocks. This rock has a pronounced bimodal pore system composed of intergranular macropores
containing hydrocarbons and micropores within oolites and peloids
holding bound water (Fig. 18). Both of these pore types can be seen
in the scanning electron micrographs of the rock (Fig. 19A-B) and
pore cast (Fig. 19C-D). This pore geometry and its significance to
logs has been discussed in detail elsewhere.[12]

Fracture reservoirs develop in brittle rocks of all types. An
example of a fractured reservoir is the chert of west central Okla-
homa known as the Mississippian Solid. Entry pressure on the mercury injection curve is approximately 0.14 μm with 94% of pore apertures less than 0.14 μm (Fig. 20). Fractures are not plentiful, but
open fractures occur in cores and sometimes are visible in thin section (Fig. 20A). The porosity is only 2.1% with essentially all of
this porosity attributable to micropores (Fig. 20B). Matrix permeability is less than 0.05 md. These reservoirs behave as typical
fracture reservoirs without significant storage space other than
fractures: high initial flow rate with a rapid decline as oil is
produced from the fracture system.

Carbonate rocks sometime develop channels and caverns which are
nonfabric selective, large scale, porous features (Fig. 1). Planar
structures, such as fractures, faults, and joints, are conduits for
fluid flow. Through extensive dissolution these features may
develop into channels and even caverns. Continued development of
extensive vuggy porosity could also lead to cavernous voids. These
large scale porous features are associated with underground water
flow and karst areas. Occasionally oil fields are found in caverns.

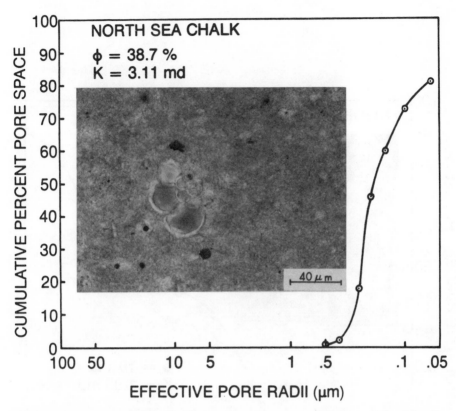

Fig. 16. This is essentially a microporous reservoir with all of the pore apertures <0.5 md. Macropores within chambers of foraminifers are sparsely disseminated.

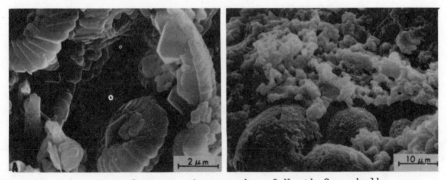

Fig. 17. Scanning electron micrographs of North Sea chalk.
A. Micropores among coccolith fragments. B. Pore cast showing macropores within foraminfer chambers (bottom) and complex of micropores.

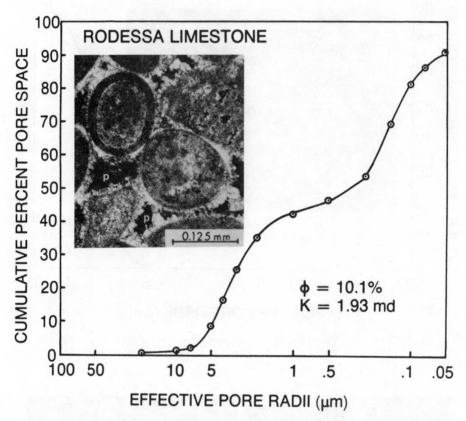

Fig. 18.   This limestone has intergranular pores (p) visible in the photomicrograph.   The mercury injection curve indicates a bimodal distribution of pore aperture sizes, which influences fluid distribution and production.

The Dollarhide pool, Andrews County, Texas, had nine wells drilled on 40-acre spacing that encountered an oil-filled cavern up to 16 ft thick in the Fusselman Limestone.[13]

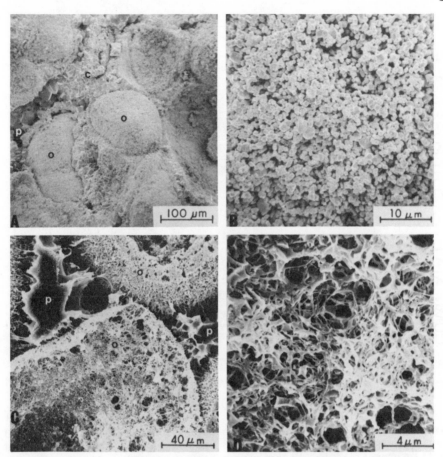

Fig. 19. Scanning electron micrographs of Rodessa Limestone.
A. Rock consists predominantly of oolites (o) cemented by calcite
(c) with retention of some intergranular porosity (p). B. At
higher magnification the microporous nature of the oolites is
visible. C. Pore cast shows intergranular pores (p) and micropores
within oolites (o). D. At higher magnification, the microporous
nature of the pore cast is distinct.

18

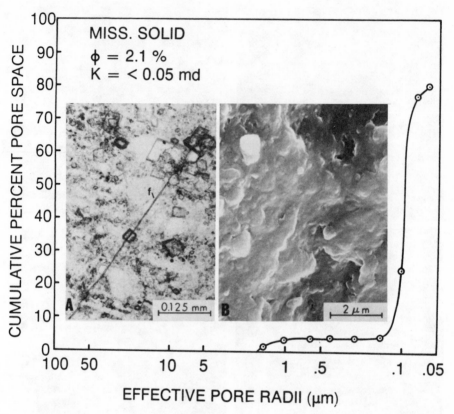

Fig. 20. Ninety-six percent of the pore apertures in this fractured chert reservoir have a radii <0.013 µm. A. Hydrocarbons are stored in fractures (f). B. Micropores, which contain bound water, are shown in this high magnification view.

REFERENCES

1. B. K. Proshlyakov, Geol. Nefti i Gaza, $\underline{4}$, 24 (1960);
    K. R. Chepikov, E. P. Ermolva, and N. A. Orlova, Dokl. Akad.
    Nauk. SSSR, $\underline{144}$, 435 (1962); J. B. Hayes, Soc. Econ. Paleon.
    and Mineral. Spec. Pub., $\underline{26}$, 127 (1979); V. Schmidt and
    D. A. McDonald, Soc. Econ. Paleon. and Mineral. Spec. Pub., $\underline{26}$,
    175 (1979).
2. W. O. Winsauer, H. M. Shearin Jr., P. H. Masson and
    M. Williams, Am. Assoc. Petrol. Geol. Bull., $\underline{36}$, 253 (1952).
3. E. D. Pittman and R. W. Duschatko, J. Sed. Petrol., $\underline{40}$, 1153
    (1970).
4. C. Straley and M. M. Minnis, J. Sed. Petrol., $\underline{53}$, 667 (1983).
5. W. R. Purcell, Trans. AIME, $\underline{186}$, 39 (1949); J. H. M. Thomeer,
    J. Pet. Tech., Mar., 73 (1960); R. B. Robinson, Am. Assoc.
    Petrol. Geol. Bull., $\underline{50}$, 547 (1966).
6. N. C. Wardlaw, Am. Assoc. Petrol. Geol. Bull., $\underline{60}$, 245 (1976);
    N. C. Wardlaw and R. P. Taylor, Bull. Can. Petrol. Geol., $\underline{24}$,
    225 (1976).
7. B. F. Swanson, J. Pet. Tech., Jan., 10 (1979).
8. C. Lin and J. Hamaski, Jour. Sed. Pet., $\underline{53}$, 670 (1983).
9. E. D. Pittman, Ann. Rev. Earth Planet. Sci., $\underline{7}$, 39 (1979).
10. L. C. Graton and H. J. Fraser, J. Geol., $\underline{43}$, 785 (1935).
11. J. L. Stout, Am. Assoc. Petrol. Geol. Bull., $\underline{48}$, 329 (1964).
12. B. D. Keith and E. D. Pittman, Am. Assoc. Petrol. Geol. Bull.,
    $\underline{67}$, No. 9, in press (1983).
13. D. H. Stormont, Oil and Gas J., April 7, 66 (1949).

RADIAL DISTRIBUTION FUNCTIONS AND MICROGEOMETRY
OF DENSE RANDOM PACKINGS OF HARD SPHERES

G. S. Cargill III
IBM Thomas J. Watson Research Center
Yorktown Heights, New York 10598

ABSTRACT

This paper describes the generation, analysis, and some applications of dense random packings of hard spheres. Particular attention is given to descriptions of the microgeometry of these packings in terms of density, radial distribution functions, and polyhedral analysis.

INTRODUCTION

Dense random packing has been the subject of interest and study since well before the discovery of dense periodic packing of atoms in simple crystalline solids, but many questions about dense random packing still remain unanswered. In fact, the very definition of "dense random packing" is not very precise. J. D. Bernal, a leader of work in this area in the 1950's and 1960's, defined dense random packing of hard spheres as "a homogeneous, coherent and essentially irregular assemblage of spheres containing no crystalline regions."[1] J. L. Finney, a student and co-worker of Bernal who has made many original contributions in this field, has pointed out that Bernal's definition is inadequate, since it uses imperfectly defined terms such as "homogeneous" and "essentially irregular."[2]

Bernal himself noted that the study of irregular space filling had a long history, and he cited the experimental work on the packing and swelling properties of peas described by the Reverend Stephen Hales in his book "Vegetable staticks" published in 1727:

"I compressed several fresh parcels of Pease in the same Pot with a force equal to 1600, 800 and 400 pounds; in which Experiments, tho' the Pease dilated, yet they did not raise the lever, because what they increased in bulk was, by the great incumbent weight, pressed into the interstices of the Pease, which they adequately filled up, being thereby formed into pretty regular Dodecahedrons."

It has also been pointed out[2] that even earlier authors were concerned with random packing of particulate materials and the differences between dense and loose random packings, e.g., St. Luke (VI, 38):

"Give, and it shall be given unto you; good measure, pressed down and shaken together, and running over, shall men give into your bosom. For with the same measure that ye mete withal it shall be measured to you again."

Although the definition of "dense random packing" remains largely an operational one, in which particulate materials are "pressed down and shaken together . . . ," dense random packing of hard spheres (DRPHS) produces a porous medium which has been a useful model for atomic arrangements in metallic glasses,[3,4] for particle packing in unfired ceramics,[5] and for structures in packed bed reactors;[6] and which should find applications in modelling other physical systems of densely packed particles which are not periodic in arrangement.

The remainder of this article describes how dense random packings have been produced and how their structural properties and characteristics have been determined, described, and understood.

GENERATION OF DENSE RANDOM PACKINGS

Most research on "dense random packing" has been experimental rather than theoretical in emphasis. The experiments have consisted of filling containers with ball bearings and then squeezing or shaking, taking precautions to prevent nucleation of periodic arrays at the container surfaces, or using computer algorithms to generate structures which resemble those obtained with the ball bearings. With the ball bearings packings, and with the computer generated packings, the structures are dense in the sense that they contain few internal holes large enough to accommodate another sphere but are random in that there are only weak correlations between positions of spheres separated by five or more sphere diameters and they contain no recognizable regions of crystalline-like order.

Mechanically packed ball bearings. The most ambitious ball bearing packing study was carried out by J. L. Finney. Fig. 1, taken from his Ph.D. thesis,[7] illustrates how a dense random packing of 8,000 ball bearings was prepared: a rubber bladder was filled with the small balls, wrapped with rubber strips, and kneaded to maximize the density of the packing. The structure was frozen by pouring hot wax into the bladder and allowing the wax to harden. Coordinates of the individual ball bearings were measured with a travelling microscope, working down from the top of the model, removing each ball after its position had been determined. The density and other structural properties of the packing were determined from these coordinates.[7] Fig. 2 shows the dense random packing part way through the measuring process.

Computer-generated packings. Dense random packings similar in many ways to those obtained with ball bearings have been generated with a number of different computer algorithms by the sequential addition of spheres onto triangular sites on the surface of a cluster. The procedure first employed by Bennett[9] and by Adams and Matheson[10] begins with a triangular seed and additional spheres are added at triangular surface sites, chosen to be as close as possible to the center of the original seed. Structural models containing thousands of spheres have been generated in this way.

Tetrahedron perfection. A modification of this algorithm, proposed by Ichikawa,[11] limits the acceptable triangular surface sites to those for which the three spheres comprising the triangle nearly touch one another. The "tetrahedron perfection" of the pocket formed by spheres 1, 2, and 3 is defined as

$$k = \max_{\{12,13,23\}} r_{ij} / (R_i + R_j) \qquad (1)$$

22

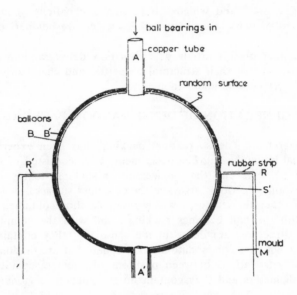

Fig. 1. Apparatus used in constructing dense random packings (from ref. 7).

Fig. 2. Dense random packing of hard spheres part way through the measuring process (from ref. 7).

where r_{ij} is the separation between centers of spheres i and j, and R_i and R_j are their radii. Spheres are added to the cluster at sites that satisfy the chosen tetrahedron perfection requirement, $k \leq k_{max}$, always taking the acceptable site that is closest to the center of the cluster. Perfect tetrahedra are formed when $k_{max}=1$, i.e., when only k=1 sites are allowed. For models with one size of sphere, all pockets have $k \leq 2$, so $k_{max}=2$ corresponds to no tetrahedron perfection requirement.

Sections through DRPHS structures for $k_{max}=2$ and $k_{max}=1.2$ are shown in Fig. 3. The $k_{max}=1.2$ structure contains large cracks and voids and is less dense than the $k_{max}=2$ structure, although the former contains large numbers of nearly perfect tetrahedra, which represent very high *local* packing density.

Other computer-generated random packings. In contrast to the growth of spherically shaped models by isotropic sequential addition, other models have been produced by growth from a two-dimensional, thin film seed. Again, spheres are added sequentially at triangular sites, but different rules have been used in choosing the sites to be filled, e.g., the lowest triangular site or, for the case shown in Fig. 4, triangular sites selected based on proximity to the arrival points for spheres incident on the growing surface in a unidirectional flux at angle α with respect to the overall surface normal.[12] Note the aligned, anisotropically shaped voids which are grown with this procedure.

Another computer-based method uses co-operative rearrangement rather than sequential addition.[13,14] The method starts with a random set of sphere coordinates. In a stepwise process, the sphere radius is increased from zero until overlap occurs between two spheres. These two spheres are moved apart to remove the overlap. Other pairs of spheres are checked for overlap and are moved apart if necessary. When all overlaps have been removed, the radius is further increased until overlap occurs, and the procedure is repeated until the rate of densification drops below a chosen cutoff value.

Molecular dynamics[15] and Monte Carlo[16] methods have also been used to generate dense random packed structures, but generally with smaller numbers of particles than the other methods.

Relaxation of hard sphere packings. A variation of DRPHS which is particularly relevant in modelling atomic arrangements in metallic glasses involves "relaxation" of the hard sphere structures with pairwise central forces, usually of the Lennard-Jones or Morse types.[17,18] The relaxation allows displacements of atoms that reduce the energy of the structure

$$E = \frac{1}{2} \sum_{i \neq j} \sum_j E_{ij}(r_{ij}) \tag{2}$$

Most relaxations of large models have been carried out using the conjugate gradient method with free boundaries. Results obtained by relaxing the DRPHS structures of Fig. 3 are shown in Fig. 5.[18] Changes are more apparent for the k=1.2 structure, where relaxation removed most of the voids and cracks, than for the k=2 structure, where significant changes also occurred in short range order. The relaxed structures can no longer be thought of as hard sphere packings, since there is no discrete distance of closest approach with either the Lennard-Jones or Morse potentials.

24

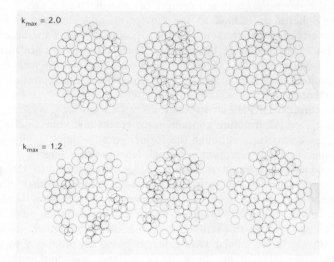

Fig. 3. The circles represent spheres in orthogonal slices, one sphere diameter in thickness, passing through the center of DRPHS structures with k_{max} = 2.0 and 1.2. Note the increasing porosity which accompanies increasing tetrahedron perfection (from ref. 18).

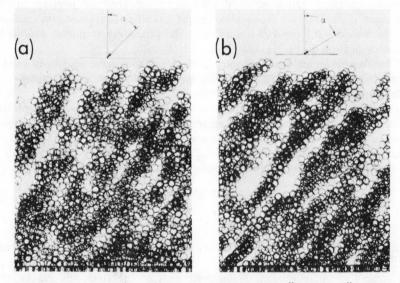

Fig. 4. The structure of amorphous hard sphere films "deposited" at (a) α=45° and (b) α=60° The circles represent spheres within a slice five sphere diameters in thickness which is parallel to the plane of incidence (from ref. 12).

MICROGEOMETRY OF DENSE RANDOM PACKINGS

Dense random packings have been characterized by their packing fractions and by their radial distribution functions. The topologies of dense random packings have been described in terms of polyhedra (Bernal holes) with vertices defined by the sphere centers and in terms of Voronoi polyhedra (or Wigner-Seitz cells), having surfaces defined by the envelope of planes which perpendicularly bisect lines drawn from a sphere's center to the centers of other nearby spheres. The faces of the Voronoi polyhedron about a given sphere define its "geometrical neighbors."

Packing fraction. The packing fraction η represents the occupied volume divided by the total volume for a hard sphere structure. The ball bearing structures of Finney[7] and of Scott and Kilgore[19] have $\eta=0.6366$ with reported uncertainties of ±0.0004 and ±0.0005 respectively. From these and other measurements, the density of mechanically constructed DRPHS structures appears to be very reproducible. For "loose random packing of hard spheres," obtained by pouring ball bearings into a container with rough sides without shaking or squeezing, less reproducible packing fractions $\eta\approx0.60$ have been obtained;[20] this is thought to be close to the lower limit of mechanical stability for a random packing. For periodic close packing, $\eta=(\pi/6)2^{1/2}=0.7405$.

Computer generated DRPHS structures generally have lower packing fractions than the DRPHS structures made with ball bearings. Isotropic sequential addition algorithms produce structures in which the density decreases with increasing cluster radius, with a limiting value of $\eta\approx0.61$ for k=2.[9] Higher values of η have been obtained for structures generated with cooperative rearrangement algorithms.[13]

Using two or more particle sizes. Packing fractions for dense random packings with more than one size of sphere have been studied empirically, and in limiting cases also theoretically. Westman and Hugill[4] in 1930 examined the "apparent volumes" V_a of mixtures of two sizes of "round, washed sand" particles. Values of V_a were given corresponding to the "real volumes" of material being unity, so the packing fraction η is simply $1/V_a$. Results obtained in some of their experiments are reproduced as data points in Figs. 6(a) and 6(b), for two binary systems having diameter ratios of 6.3 (coarse/medium) and 50.5 (coarse/fine), with different volume fractions for the larger and smaller particles. Westman and Hugill commented that the sand grains were approximately spherical, but that the fine sand was more angular than the coarse sand. This is probably the reason that V_a for the fine sand was found to be somewhat larger than for the coarse or medium sand.

To interpret their observed dependences of V_a on diameter ratios and on volume fractions, they considered the expected dependence of V_a on volume fraction for three limiting cases: (i) a diameter ratio of unity; (ii) a diameter ratio which approaches infinity with addition of a few of the small particles, which reside in the interstitial regions of the packing of large particles; and (iii) this same limiting diameter ratio with addition of a few large spheres within the packing of small particles. For case (i), V_a is expected to follow the straight line CM in (a) or CF in (b), i.e., there will be no particle size effect on packing

26

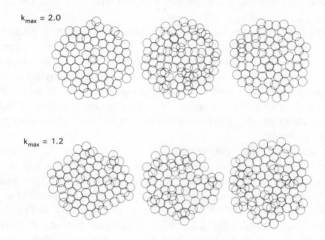

Fig. 5. As for Fig. 3, but for relaxed structures (from ref. 18).

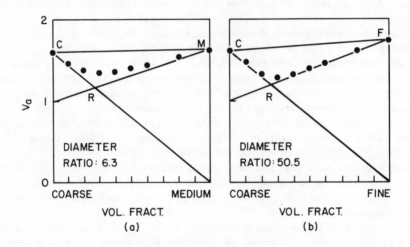

Fig. 6. Apparent volume V_a observed (data points) and calculated for limiting cases (straight lines), as described in text, for binary dense random packings with diameter ratios of (a) 6.3 and (b) 50.5 (from ref. 5).

fraction. For case (ii), V_a is expected to decrease from C following the line connecting C to the lower right, $V=0$, corner of the diagrams, since adding the small particles does not increase the apparent volume of the packing although it increases the real volume. For case (iii), V_a is expected to decrease from F or M following the line to the $V=1$ point at the middle left of the diagrams. The case (ii) and case (iii) lines cross at point R at between 20 and 30 volume percent of the larger particles.

As expected, the experimentally determined values of V_a fall within the triangle CFR or CMR, and they approach the lines CRF and CRM as the diameter ratio become larger and as the values of volume fraction of large or small particles approaches zero. For systems of two or more sizes of particles having very large diameter ratios and packing individually to $V_a=1.605$ ($\eta=0.624$), considerations along the above lines lead to estimates of the minimum V_a (or maximum η) for optimum mixtures of 1.166 (0.859), 1.057 (0.947), 1.021 (0.978), and 1.008 (0.994) for 2, 3, 4, and 5 different sizes respectively.

Local structures around spheres--Voronoi polyhedra. The nearest neighbor order of random packings can be characterized by tabulating various properties of the collection of Voronoi polyhedra, of which one is associated with each particle in the packing. The three properties which have most often been considered are the number of faces per polyhedron, the number of edges per face, and the volume per polyhedron. Distribution plots of these properties for Finney's[7] DRPHS structure are shown in Fig. 7 and 8. The volume per polyhedron has been normalized by the average polyhedron volume, giving the reduced volume ΔV^* as plotted in Fig. 7. The average polyhedron volume is simply related to the packing fraction η. The data in Fig. 8 were calculated from the measured sphere coordinates. However, earlier information of this type was obtained by Bernal by packing together powdered, 'plasticene' balls irregularly and pressing them into one solid lump.[1] He disassembled the packing to examine the polyhedral shapes formed by the balls in the packing. A wide variety of different polyhedra were obtained. From Finney's measurements, there are average values of 14.2 faces per polyhedron and 5.16 edges per face. The data of Bernal and of Finney show that the Reverend Hale was mistaken in his assertion that most of his polyhedra were "pretty regular Dodecahedrons," since no twenty-faced polyhedra were found, c.f. Fig. 8(a). However, there is a preponderance of faces with five edges, c.f. Fig. 8(b), which the Reverend Hale probably mistook as representing dodecahedra. The variety of Voronoi polyhedral volumes and shapes are indicative of the random character of these packings; they contain a wide spectrum of different nearest neighbor environments. The behavior of these quantities has also been examined in computer generated and relaxed DRPHS structures.

Local structures between spheres--interstitial or Bernal holes. Bernal also examined the polyhedra surrounding interstitial regions in DRPHS structures.[1] The vertices of these polyhedra are centers of spheres surrounding the interstitial region. The corresponding polyhedra in simple, close packed periodic packings are regular tetrahedra and octahedra. For the DRPHS structures, Bernal identified five types of interstitial polyhedra, allowing two spheres to define the edge of a polyhedral cavity even if their centers were somewhat more than a sphere

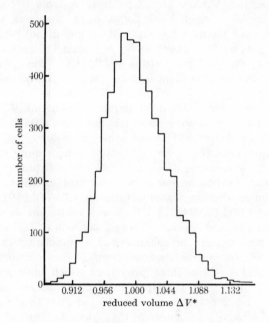

Fig. 7. Cell volume distribution for Finney's large DRPHS model (from ref. 8).

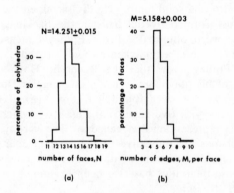

Fig. 8. Finney's results for (a) the distribution of faces per Voronoi polyhedron and (b) the distribution of edges per face for the Voronoi polyhedra, obtained for his 8000 sphere DRPHS model (from ref. 8).

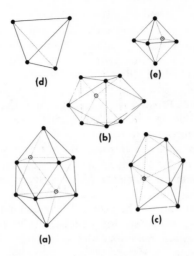

Fig. 9. Bernal's five "canonical holes" of dense random packing (from ref. 1).

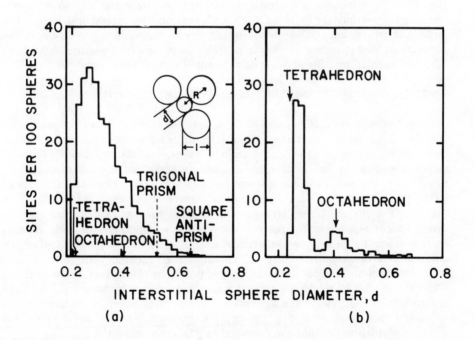

Fig. 10. Distribution of interstitial sphere sizes for the Finney DRPHS model (from ref. 22) on the left and for the same model relaxed with a Morse potential (from ref. 24) on the right. Sizes corresponding to various "Bernal holes" are indicated.

diameter apart. He reported that almost all the volume of the DRPHS structure could be divided into five canonical holes. The regular versions of these five polyhedra are shown in Fig. 9: (a) Archimedian antiprism, shown capped with two half octahedra; (b) trigonal prism, shown capped with three half octahedra; (c) tetragonal dodecahedron; (d) tetrahedron; and (e) half-octahedron, shown as full octahedron.

Whittaker[21] and Frost[22] have reexamined the interstitial polyhedra in DRPHS structures, finding that the five Bernal holes, with or without octahedral caps, with small distortions, were inadequate to describe the DRPHS, and that additional polyhedra must be introduced. Frost also investigated the size of interstitial regions in both Finney and Bennett type DRPHS structures, by determining the maximum diameter which a sphere occupying each interstitial site could have. His results for the Finney model are shown in Fig. 10. Interstitial site statistics were about the same for the Bennett model. Arrows indicate the interstitial sphere diameters for various regular polyhedral interstitial sites. As expected, there were no interstitial sites large enough to accommodate a sphere of unit diameter.

Finney and Wallace[24] carried out similar investigations of relaxed DRPHS structures. Their results for relaxation with a Morse potential are also shown in Fig. 10. They indicate a bimodal distribution of interstitial site sizes, corresponding approximately to those for tetrahedral and for octahedral sites. The larger interstitial sites have been squeezed out during the relaxation. The connectivity and correlations of interstitial holes in DRPHS structures have been been investigated by Ahmadzadeh and Cantor[23] and by Finney and Wallace.[24]

RADIAL DISTRIBUTION FUNCTIONS FOR DENSE RANDOM PACKINGS

Radial distribution functions, RDF(r), provide another means for measuring and describing the arrangements of particles in dense random packings. Radial distribution functions can be determined experimentally to describe atomic arrangements in liquids, in amorphous solids, and in polycrystalline solids, by using x-ray, electron, or neutron scattering measurements.[3] The basic features of RDF(r) for "crystalline" and "amorphous" arrays of "atoms" are illustrated in Fig. 11. For the crystalline arrangement, RDF(r) consists of delta functions at distances corresponding to discrete atom-atom separations and with weights corresponding to the average number of neighbors at each separation. For the amorphous arrangement, RDF(r) is a continuous function, with contributions from all atom-atom separations and with peaks corresponding to separations which occur with particular frequency, e.g., the nearest neighbor peak. At large separations r, RDF(r) for the amorphous arrangement becomes featureless and approaches the parabola $4\pi r^2 \rho_0$, where ρ_0 is the average atomic density. G(r) is a "reduced distribution function," related to RDF(r) as shown in Fig. 11.

G(r) for the Finney DRPHS structure[7] is shown by the histogram in Fig. 12. The continuous curve in Fig. 12 is the reduced distribution function for an amorphous $Ni_{76}P_{24}$ alloy determined from x-ray scattering measurements and plotted together with the DRPHS G(r) by using the the sphere diameter as an adjustable parameter.[25] The remarkable agreement between features in these two

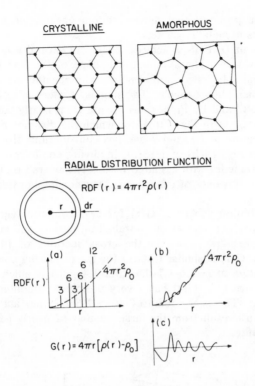

Fig. 11. Radial distribution functions shown schematically for (a) crystalline and (b) amorphous materials. Also shown is the reduced distribution function (c) for the amorphous material.

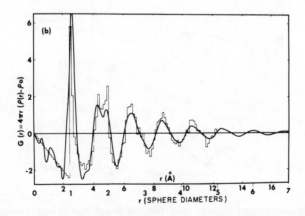

Fig. 12. Comparison of reduced radial distribution functions G(r) for Finney's DRPHS structure (histogram) and for amorphous $Ni_{76}P_{24}$ (from ref. 25).

curves supports the proposal that dense random packing be used to describe atomic arrangements in metallic glasses.

Special features of DRPHS structures. There are several singularities in $G(r)$ for the DRPHS structure. The asymmetrical shape of the first DRPHS peak at $r \geq 1$ dia. comes from spheres in hard contact, with the fall off at larger r from pairs of spheres which almost touch. The singular feature at $r \leq 2$ dia. has been explained by Bennett[9] and by Finney[8] as arising from nearly colinear groups of three touching spheres, as in Fig. 13(a), for which the distance r can be no more than 2 dia. The feature at $r = 1.6$-1.7 dia. has contributions from configurations like those shown in Fig. 13(b) and 13(c), involving equilateral triangles with a shared edge and tetrahedra with a shared base. The overall oscillatory behavior of $G(r)$ with increasing values of r has been given no simple explanation in terms of local configurations.

Reduced distribution functions $G(r)$ for two computer generated DRPHS structures having different degrees of "tetrahedron perfection" are shown in Fig. 14. These structures are shown in the cross sections of Fig. 3. For the $k_{max} = 2.0$ structure, $G(r)$ is similar to $G(r)$ for the physically constructed model, except that the feature at $r = 1.6$-1.7 dia. (3.2-3.4 rad.) is much less prominent. For the $k_{max} = 1.2$ structure, $G(r)$ has a very prominent amplitude of oscillation at larger distances. The sharp features at $r = 1.6$-1.7 dia. and 2 dia. for the $k_{max} = 1.2$ model must result from the large number of nearly perfect tetrahedra built into this structure.

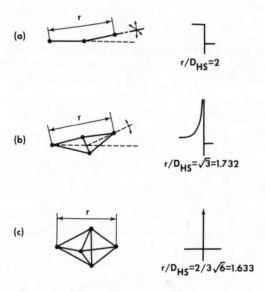

Fig. 13. Simple connected groups and their discontinuous contributions to the radial distribution function. Two darkened circles connected by a solid line denote two particles in hard contact and D_{HS} is the sphere diameter (from ref. 9).

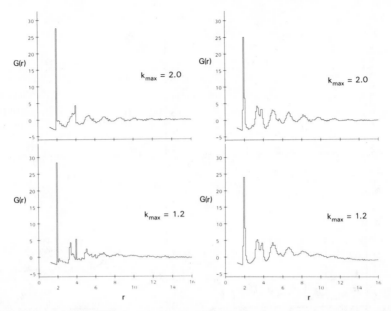

Fig. 14. Reduced distribution functions for DRPHS structures of 500 spheres for tetrahedron perfection k_{max}=2.0 and 1.2 (left), and reduced distribution functions for the same structures after relaxation with Lennard-Jones potentials (right) (from ref. 18).

Also shown in Fig. 14 are G(r) curves for the same two models after relaxation with Lennard-Jones potentials, corresponding to the cross sections shown in Fig. 5. Relaxation has made G(r) curves for the two models essentially identical, and they are more similar to G(r) for the mechanically constructed DRPHS model, Fig. 12. Finney has examined relaxation effects on radial distribution functions for a wider variety of potentials and starting structures, as well as relaxation effects on Voronoi and interstitial polyhedral distributions.[16]

Binary RDF's and metallic glasses. Radial distribution functions have also been determined for several binary dense random packings, because of interest in these structures as models for atomic arrangements in two component metallic glasses. Results are shown in Fig. 15 for a computer generated (k_{max}=1.1) binary dense random packing with 76% small spheres and 24% large spheres, a diameter ratio of 1.405, and relaxation with simple Lennard-Jones potentials.[26] The plots of $G_{AA}(r)$, $G_{AB}(r)$, and $G_{BB}(r)$ are partial distribution functions, including only AA, AB, and BB contributions respectively, $G_{ij}(r)=4\pi r[\rho_{ij}(r)-x_j\rho_0]$, where x_j is the fraction of spheres of type j in the packing. The distance scales correspond to a small sphere radius of 1.235Å and a resulting large sphere radius of 1.735Å, to represent cobalt and gadolinium atoms respectively. Introducing two different sizes of spheres reduces the strength of features in the partial distribution functions outside of the nearest neighbor region.

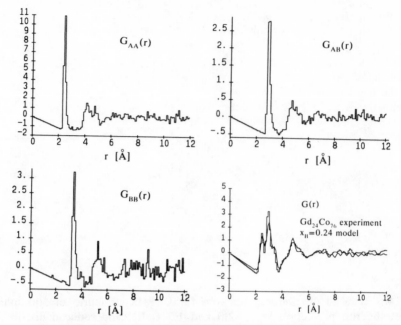

Fig. 15. Partial distribution functions $G_{ij}(r)$ for a relaxed binary DRP model, and comparison of composite distribution function obtained from x-ray scattering measurements on an amorphous Gd-Co alloy with a composite distribution function calculated from the relaxed DRP model (histogram) (from ref. 26).

Also shown in Fig. 15 is the histogram plot of $G(r)=4\pi r(\rho(r)-\rho_0)$, the composite distribution function, a weighted sum of the partial distribution functions

$$\rho(r) = \sum_{i=1}^{2} \sum_{j=1}^{2} W_{ij} \rho_{ij}(r)/x_j \qquad (3)$$

where the weighting factors W_{ij} depend on the concentrations and on the x-ray scattering factors of elements represented by the two sizes of spheres: $W_{AA}=0.33$, $2W_{AB}=0.49$, and $W_{BB}=0.18$. The plotted $G(r)$ histogram has been broadened by convolution with a Gaussian of r.m.s. width $\sigma=0.1$Å Also plotted with the histogram is the experimentally determined distribution function for an amorphous $Gd_{24}Co_{76}$ alloy, demonstrating that relaxed DRPHS structures may be useful models for atomic arrangements in these amorphous materials.

Recent developments and present directions. Two emerging areas of thought about dense random packing focus on the long recognized difficulty in close packing tetrahedra. Kleman, Sadoc, et al.,[27-29] have argued that this difficulty can be avoided by carrying out the packing in a hyperspace of appropriately chosen curvature, rather than in the flat, 3d laboratory space. These constructions in curved space are then mapped onto the zero curvature, laboratory space, leading to various kinds of defects, which Kleman, Sadoc, et al., argue are unavoidable in three dimensional dense random packings.

Another related development concerns the occurrence of orientational correlations in computer simulations of supercooled liquids. Icosahedral type orientational order was found to persist over much longer distances than the more familiar positional order.[30] Nelson has argued that "the defects introduced by the incommensurability of flat space with the tiling of tetrahedra are in fact disclination lines in a state of perfect icosahedral bond orientational order."[31]

These new views of DRPHS should stimulate further experimental and modelling work in this area.

CONCLUSIONS

Dense random packings of hard spheres produced physically with ball bearings or generated by various computer algorithms represents a special class of porous media. Arrangements of particles in dense random packings have been described using several different approaches: Voronoi polyhedra, interstitial polyhedra, and radial distribution functions. Some aspects of nearest neighbor microgeometry can be associated with particular features of the distribution functions. Although no comprehensive theory for the statistical geometry of these types of structures is now available, recent developments involving curved space mappings, disclination type defects, and bond orientational order may lead the way to further progress.

REFERENCES

1. J. D. Bernal, Proc. Roy. Soc. Lond. A. *280*, 299 (1964).
2. J. L. Finney, J. Phys. (Paris) *36*, C2-1 (1975).
3. G. S. Cargill III, Solid State Physics *30*, 227 (1975).
4. G. S. Cargill III, Atomic Energy Review, Supplement No. 1, 63 (1981).
5. A. E. R. Westman and H. R. Hugill, J. Am. Ceram. Soc. *13*, 767 (1930).
6. D. P. Haughey and G. S. G. Beveridge, Can. J. Chem. Eng. *47*, 130 (1969).
7. J. L. Finney, Ph.D. Thesis, University of London, 1968.
8. J. L. Finney, Proc. Roy. Soc. Lond. A. *319*, 479 (1970).
9. C. H. Bennett, J. Appl. Phys. *43*, 2727 (1972).
10. D. J. Adams and A. J. Matheson, J. Chem. Phys. *56*, 1989 (1972).
11. T. Ichikawa, Phys. Status Solidi A *29*, 293 (1975).
12. D. Henderson, M. H. Brodsky, and P. Chaudhari, Appl. Phys. Lett. *25*, 641 (1974).
13. J. L. Finney, Mater. Sci. Eng. *23*, 207 (1976).
14. D. C. Koskenmaki, Mater. Sci. Eng. *23*, 207 (1976).
15. A. Rahman, J. J. Mandell, and J. P. McTague, J. Chem. Phys. *64*, 1564 (1976).
16. F. F. Abraham, J. Chem. Phys. *72*, 359 (1980).
17. J. L. Finney, in **Diffraction Studies on Non-Crystalline Substances**, I. Hargittai and W. J. Orville-Thomas, eds. (Elsevier, Amsterdam, 1981), p. 439.

18. G. S. Cargill III, in **Diffraction Studies on Non-Crystalline Substances**, I. Hargittai and W. J. Orville-Thomas, eds. (Elsevier, Amsterdam, 1981), p. 781.
19. G. D. Scott and D. M. Kilgour, Brit. J. Appl. Phys. (J. Phys. D) 2, 863 (1969).
20. G. D. Scott, Nature 188, 908 (1960).
21. E. J. W. Whittaker, J. Non-Cryst. Solids 28, 293 (1978).
22. H. J. Frost, Acta Met. 30, 889 (1982).
23. M. Ahmadzadeh and B. Cantor, J. Non-Cryst. Solids 43, 189 (1981).
24. J. L. Finney and J. Wallace, J. Non-Cryst. Solids 43, 165 (1981).
25. G. S. Cargill III, J. Appl. Phys. 41, 2248 (1970).
26. G. S. Cargill III, in **Amorphous Materials: Modelling of Structure and Properties**, V. Vitek, ed. (The Metallurgical Soc. of AIME, Warrendale, PA, 1983), p. 15.
27. M. Kleman and J. F. Sadoc, J. Phys. (Paris) 40, L569 (1979).
28. J. F. Sadoc and R. Mosseri, Phil. Mag. B 45, 467 (1982).
29. M. Kleman, J. Phys. (Paris) 43, 1389 (1982).
30. P. J. Steinhardt, D. R. Nelson, and M. Ronchetti, Phys. Rev. B 28, 784 (1983).
31. D. R. Nelson, Phys. Rev. Letters 50, 982 (1983).

PHASE TRANSITIONS OF BINARY MIXTURES IN POROUS MEDIA

F. Brochard and P.G. de Gennes
Collège de France, 75231 Paris Cedex 05, France

ABSTRACT

We consider a porous solid, or a gel, saturated by a two fluid system A+B, in the limit where the thickness ξ of the AB interface is smaller than the pore size D. The solid prefers to be in contact with one of the fluids (A). But, if we decrease the chemical potential of B, the B fluid enters the structure. We discuss the reversible penetration process.

1) A relatively simple, but instructive, case is obtained when the solid is periodic, and is reduced to thin, equidistant, sheets or rods.

a) for sheets ...n, n+1, n+2... of alternate preferences (n preferring A, n+1 preferring B,...) we find a well defined first order transition below the wetting transition T_w of the walls : the critical point is brought down to T_w

b) with sheets which are all identical (or for all cases with rods) we expect that the critical point is only weakly shifted from it's unperturbed value.

2) For random porous media, or for gels, with preference for A, we define 2 types of behavior when the chemical potential of B is decreased :

a) "capillary invasion" with clusters of B regions growing progressively

b) "flip process" where all pores are abruptly invaded by B (except possibly for a thin sheath of thickness ξ near the walls). The "fields" H (= chemical potential changes) required to perform capillary invasion (H_c) or flip (H_f) are in ratio :

$$H_f/H_c \simeq (\xi/D)^{2-d_f}$$

where d_f is the fractal dimension of the pore surface. Gels made with rod like molecules have $d_f = 1$, while flexible chains in good solvents have $d_f = 5/3$. For all gels the flip process should dominate and we expect a sharp transition. On the other hand, porous solids ($d_f = 2$) require a special discussion. Modeling the pores as long, interconnected capillaries of random diameter D, we find that capillary invasion dominates in this case, and we expect no sharp transition.

ELECTROMAGNETIC PROPAGATION IN RANDOM COMPOSITE MATERIALS

K.D. Cummings and J.C. Garland
Ohio State University, Columbus, Ohio 43210

D.B. Tanner
University of Florida, Gainesville, Florida 32611

ABSTRACT

Measurements of the reflectance of composite materials consisting of random mixtures of Ag and KCl small particles have been made for frequencies from 10–43000 cm^{-1}. The metal volume fraction in these samples was between 5% and 100%. The optical constants of the samples, obtained from Kramers–Kronig analysis, are shown to agree qualitatively with calculations based on Bruggeman's effective medium approximation.

INTRODUCTION

The electromagnetic properties of inhomogeneous media have been studied for substantially more than 100 years[1] and exact solutions to the problems of the interaction of light with a small particle were first worked out at the beginning of this century.[2] In recent years interest in this topic has revived; there have been lively discussions about the correct model for the optical response of inhomogeneous systems[3-8] and a number of anomalies in the properties of these materials have been discovered.[9-13]

This paper describes experimental studies of composite systems consisting of mixtures of small metal and insulating particles. The goal of these experiments was to understand the ways in which the effective properties of the inhomogeneous material were determined by the properties of the constituents. The experiments consisted of reflection measurements at frequencies between the far infrared and the near ultraviolet. The results will be compared to the predictions of simple theories of inhomogeneous materials.

THEORY OF INHOMOGENEOUS MEDIA

The optical response of a pure homogeneous medium is in general well characterized by a complex permeability μ and dielectric function ε. The former quantity is typically unity at infrared and optical frequencies while the latter may be written as

$$\varepsilon(\omega) = \varepsilon_1(\omega) + \frac{4\pi i}{\omega}\, \sigma_1(\omega) \;, \qquad\qquad (1)$$

where $\varepsilon_1(\omega)$ is the real dielectric function and $\sigma_1(\omega)$ the frequency-dependent conductivity.

That such a characterization also describes an inhomogeneous medium is not immediately obvious because the properties of the medium are functions of position: $\varepsilon=\varepsilon(\vec{r},\omega)$ and $\mu=\mu(\vec{r},\omega)$. Generally, the idea of a spatially varying response function is not very useful because to employ it would mean solving a formidable boundary-value problem which requires knowing the exact geometric arrangement of the constituents. This information is usually unavailable; in addition, what is interesting is the average response of the inhomogeneous medium to external fields, not the local response. Fortunately, so long as the scale on which measurements are made (the wavelength) is large compared to the scale of the fluctuations of the dielectric function (the particle size), the inhomogeneous medium appears to be uniform in its response to external fields and can thus be described by an effective dielectric function $\varepsilon_{eff}(\omega)$ and permeability $\mu_{eff}(\omega)$. The problem with which theories of inhomogeneous media are confronted, therefore, is in its most general terms the following: Given a inhomogeneous medium that has a well-defined local dielectric function $\varepsilon(\vec{r},\omega)$ and permeability $\mu(\vec{r},\omega)$, how can the effective response functions of the entire medium be determined?

Historically, this problem has been addressed from two rather different points of view. The first is a molecular field model originally developed by Clausiaus, Mossotti, Lorentz, and Lorenz to calculate the local field in a crystal[1] and applied to the optical properties of an inhomogeneous medium by Garnett[14]. This model has become known as the Maxwell-Garnett theory (MGT). The second point of view is a symmetrical effective medium approach, initially developed by Bruggeman[15]. This model is generally called the effective medium approximation (EMA), although both it and the MGT are in fact effective medium theories, providing expressions for the dielectric function of a homogeneous medium which has properties effectively identical to those of the inhomogeneous medium.

Each theory (and most subsequent developments[5-8,16-18]) begins with a major simplification. The local dielectric function $\varepsilon(\vec{r},\omega)$ of the inhomogeneous medium is assumed to take on a limited number of discrete values (typically two) rather than being allowed to vary over a continuous range. This simplification clearly applies to the samples which we have studied, which are disordered composites, random mixtures of many grains each of which by itself has spatially uniform properties. The composite is characterized by specifying the volume fraction, dielectric function, shape, and size of each grain type. Each grain is then taken to be a polarizable entity, with dipole moment induced by fields from external sources as well as from the fields of the polarized grains in the outside medium.

The principal difference between the MGT and the EMA is the way in which the medium surrounding the grain under consideration is treated. In the MGT it is assumed that the medium surrounding the grains is one of the constituents of the mixture (for example, the one with the largest volume fraction) while in the EMA is assumed that the surrounding medium is characecized by the effective properties of the inhomogeneous medium.

The initial step in either model is to find the electromagnetic fields inside and outside of a single particle when that particle is subjected to plane wave field. In the long-wavelength limit, $c/\omega \gg a$, the applied fields appear to be spatially uniform and to have

$e^{-i\omega t}$ time dependence. The particle in this quasistatic limit has only dipole moments; these moments are time varying so that there are electric currents flowing; the electromagnetic power dissipation would be proportional to the integral of $\vec{J} \cdot \vec{E}$ thoughout the volume of the particle.

The electric dipole moment is given by the solution to the static boundary value problem of a dielectric sphere in a uniform far field[19]. The electric field outside is that of a dipole. Inside, the field $\vec{E}_p$ is spatially uniform:

$$\vec{E}_p = \frac{3\varepsilon_o}{\varepsilon_p + 2\varepsilon_o} \vec{E}_o \, e^{-i\omega t} \, , \qquad (2)$$

where ε_p is the complex dielectric function of the particle, ε_o is the dielectric function of the medium outside the particle, and $\vec{E}_o$ is the uniform far field.

Although it may seem that the electric dipole term would specify fully the response of the particle to the applied plane waves[2], it turns out that in the far infrared region magnetic dipole (or eddy current) behavior is often even more important. This effect, which causes the medium to have a nonzero magnetization even though the constituents are nonmagnetic, has been discussed by Russell et al[11], Carr et al[12], and Stroud and Pan[8]. For most of the samples described in this paper, however, the metal concentration and the frequency of the light are large enough that the magnetic dipole response has negligible effect on the calculated optical properties. Our model calculations show that we may safely take $\mu_{eff} = 1$ for these samples.

We will define the effective dielectric function of the inhomogeneous medium in terms of volume-averaged fields. For simplicity we will assume a two component composite and label these constitutents type a and type b materials. If f is the volume fraction of type a, then (1-f) will be the volume fraction of type b, so that the average fields are:

$$\langle\vec{E}\rangle = f\vec{E}_a + (1-f)\vec{E}_b \, , \qquad (3)$$

$$\langle\vec{D}\rangle = f\varepsilon_a \vec{E}_a + (1-f)\varepsilon_b \vec{E}_b \, , \qquad (4)$$

where we have used the local relationship $\vec{D}_i = \varepsilon_i \vec{E}_i$. The effective dielectric function is defined by

$$\langle\vec{D}\rangle = \varepsilon_{eff} \langle\vec{E}\rangle \, . \qquad (5)$$

When we write equation (5), we take the point of view that the interesting property of the medium is the average response to external fields; the external field is just $\langle\vec{E}\rangle$ while $\langle\vec{D}\rangle$ is the responses to that field. (Note that by our definition of the complex dielectric function, equation (1), we have included the current density $\langle\vec{J}\rangle$ in $\langle\vec{D}\rangle$.)

The Maxwell-Garnett theory is implicitly a model for a dilute system. According to the MGT, a single grain of dielectric function ε_a is assumed to lie at the center of a cavity (the Lorentz cavity) carved out of the interior of the inhomogeneous medium. All other type a grains are excluded from this cavity, whose remaining space is assumed to be filled with a medium with dielectric function ε_b. Thus, the local field at the grain is the superposition of the uniform applied field and the uniform field from the charge located on the cavity surface. (As discussed by Landauer[1] in his review of inhomogeneous materials, one way to exclude other grains from the cavity is to use a small cavity, which encloses tightly the grain. Another approach is to assume that the dipolar fields from those neighboring grains which are inside a large cavity sum to zero in the vicinity of the central grain.) With this assumption, the electric field inside the grain is uniform and given by substitution of $\varepsilon_p = \varepsilon_a$ and $\varepsilon_o = \varepsilon_b$ into equation (2):

$$\vec{E}_a = \frac{3\varepsilon_b}{\varepsilon_a + 2\varepsilon_b} \vec{E}_b e^{-i\omega t} . \tag{6}$$

Combining equations (3)-(6) gives, after some algebra, the Maxwell-Garnett expression for ε_{eff} which we label ε_{MGT}:

$$\varepsilon_{MGT} = \varepsilon_b + \varepsilon_b \frac{3f(\varepsilon_a - \varepsilon_b)}{(1-f)(\varepsilon_a - \varepsilon_b) + 3\varepsilon_b} . \tag{7}$$

Equation (7) illustrates two properties which are characteristic of the MGT approach to inhomogeneous media. First, the equation is inherently asymmetric in its treatment of the two constitutents: different values are obtained for ε_{MGT} depending on whether, for example, we regard the composite as consisting of metal grains embedded in insulator or the other way around. Second, the equation gives a smooth variation of ε_{MGT} with volume fraction, from ε_b when f=0 to ε_a when f=1; thus, there is no percolation transition. Such a transition is, in fact, specifically excluded by the assumption that the embedded grains do not contact one another. In applications of the MGT the asymmetry and the absence of a percolation transition can be handled in an ad hoc fashion by assuming that as the volume fraction of one constituent increases from zero to unity its role changes from that of inclusion to that of host[3]. Despite its shortcomings, the MGT is generally believed to work for well separated particles. More generally, Hashin and Shtrikman[20] have shown that the MGT expression in its zero-frequency limit represents bounds to the actual conductivity of a two-component heterogeneous medium, an upper bound if $\sigma_a < \sigma_b$ and a lower bound if $\sigma_b < \sigma_a$.

In contrast to the MGT, the EMA has the attractive feature of treating all constituents of the medium in an equivalent way. It achieves this symmetry by regarding an individual grain (which may be either type of material) as being embedded in an otherwise homogeneous "effective" medium which is assumed to possess the average properties of the medium. When placed in an external field, the grain in question will be polarized; the field inside is given by equation (2), with ε_o equal to the effective dielectric function ε_{EMA}.

$$\vec{E}_p = \frac{3\varepsilon_{EMA}}{\varepsilon_p + 2\varepsilon_{EMA}} \vec{E}_{eff} e^{-i\omega t} \, , \tag{8}$$

where $\vec{E}_{eff}$ is the effective field in the surrounding medium. This field is chosen in a self-consistent way: so that the electric field in the medium, when summed over all the grains in the medium, equals $\vec{E}_{eff}$. This self-consistency condition may be incorporated into the theory in a number of ways; the simplest is to set $\vec{E}_{eff}$ equal to the definition of the average field,

$$\vec{E}_{eff} = f\vec{E}_a + (1-f)\vec{E}_b \, , \tag{9}$$

and then substitute equation (8) evaluated for the fields inside the two kinds of grains. After a little algebra, this procedure yields a quadratic equation for ε_{EMA}. The solution is

$$\varepsilon_{EMA} = \frac{B}{4} \pm \frac{1}{4} \sqrt{B^2 + 8\varepsilon_a \varepsilon_b} \, , \tag{10}$$

where $B = \varepsilon_a(3f-1) + \varepsilon_b(2-3f)$ and where the sign of the square root is chosen such that $Im(\varepsilon_{EMA}) \geq 0$.

The EMA differs from the MGT in two important ways. First, the equations treat each of the constituents of the medium on an equal basis. The EMA is thus a symmetric theory and is not restricted to a particular range of concentrations. Second, the EMA predicts a metal-insulator transition at a critical volume fraction (for spherical grains) of 1/3. To demonstrate this second point, we assume that the imaginary part of the complex dielectric function dominates the real part as $\omega \to 0$, so that $\varepsilon_a \simeq 4\pi\sigma_{1a}/\omega \gg 1$. If, in addition, $\sigma_{1b}=0$, equation (10) may be solved to find

$$\sigma_{1EMA} = \begin{cases} 0 & f \leq 1/3 \\ \dfrac{3f-1}{2} \sigma_{1a} & f \geq 1/3 \end{cases} \tag{11}$$

EXPERIMENTAL TECHNIQUES

Metal "smoke" particles were produced by the method of evaporation in a noble gas. This technique produces single crystalline, nearly spherical small particles with a relatively narrow size distribution[21,22]. For our samples, Ag metal was evaporated from an aluminum oxide coated molybdenum boat in an ordinary evaporator while a mixture of 75% argon and 25% oxygen was

flowing through the system. The pressure of the system was stablized
to approximately 1 Torr by adjusting the pumping speed. In the
evaporation process the metal vapor loses energy to the noble gas
atoms, causing the metal to cool and coalesce into small particles.
The oxygen was introduced into the apparatus to produce a thin oxide
coating on the metal particles. This coating prevented the particles
from cold-welding together during evaporation, but was thin enough to
allow metal-to-metal contact between the particles under sufficient
pressure.

Electron microscopy showed the particles to be spherical with a
mean radius of 120 Å and a log-normal size distribution with a
geometric standard deviation of about 1.5.

The composite samples were manufactured by mixing the metal
smoke with powered KCl. This mixture was compressed (9 kbar) in an
evacuated (1 mTorr) die to make a wafer-shaped sample. A cyclic
technique, which involved adding a small increment of Ag smoke to the
KCl, pressing a pellet, grinding up the pellet at 77 K, adding more
smoke, re-pressing, and repeating the process, was used. This stepwise increase of the metal volume fraction allowed the Ag and KCl to
mix well. The final volume fractions were determined by elemental
analysis in a scanning electron miscroscope.

The surface of the composite sample was polished smooth and
flat. Final polishing was done using isoproponal and 0.3 μm alumina
powder. Even though the composite surface was shiny after polishing,
the samples showed signs of diffuse scattering. The scattering
increased as the sample was attacked by water vapor in the air. The
rough surface scattered the high frequency light, causing the
reflectance to be smaller than it should be at high frequencies. To
compensate for this scattering, the samples were coated with Au
immediately after the reflectance was measured. A comparison between
the gold coated surface and the uncoated surface allowed correction
of the reflection spectrum for scattering.

The reflectance in the 10 to 700 cm^{-1} (1 to 90 meV) region was
measured with a Michelson interferometer and 1 K bolometer detect-
or.[23] A vacuum spectrometer built around a Perkin-Elmer model 16U
grating monochromator[23] was used to measure reflectance in the 500 to
45000 cm^{-1} (.06 to 5.6 eV) region.

EXPERIMENTAL RESULTS

Because the reflectance measurement covered an extremely large
frequency region (10 to 45000 cm^{-1}), Kramers-Kronig analysis[24]
provides accurate values of the phase shift on reflection. With the
reflectance and phase shift known, all the usual optical functions
can be calculated. Conventional extrapolation procedures were used
in the Kramers-Kronig analysis[24]. Samples having low dc
conductivities were assumed to have a constant low-frequency
reflectance between zero frequency and 10 cm^{-1} (1 meV). In samples
with large dc conductivities, the low-frequency reflectance was
assumed to follow the Hagen-Reubens relation[25]

$$R(\omega) = 1 - A\omega^{1/2} \tag{12}$$

where A is chosen to make the relation fit the first few data points. The approximation is valid for the low frequency reflectance of metals when the dc conductivity (in esu units) is much greater than the frequency.

A second extrapolation was done in the region just above the last data point (45000 cm^{-1} or 5.6 eV) to 400000 cm^{-1} (50 eV). This region was assumed to contain contributions from interband transitions and the reflectance was extrapolated as ω^{-s}. The exponent used was s=0.8, because bulk Ag[26] has $R \approx \omega^{-0.8}$ between 50000 and 400000 cm^{-1}. Other experiments, $0 \leqslant s \leqslant 2$, gave very similar results, particularly for $\omega < 35000$ cm^{-1}. Above 400000 cm^{-1} the reflectance was assumed to follow ω^{-4}, appropriate for free-electron behavior.

Figure 1 shows the real part of the dielectric function for several Ag/KCl samples. Notice the low frequency values of ε_1 are postive for small volume fractions and negative for higher volume fractions. This change is due to the insulator to metal (percolation) transition. The sharp decrease at low frequencies is from the free electrons reflectivity and conductivity in the infrared. Measurements[22] of the static dielectric constant indicate the percolation transition occurs at a volume fraction of 0.2. The structure in ε_1 at 32000 cm^{-1} is from the electrons of the d states[27], which lie 4 eV below the Fermi surface in Ag.

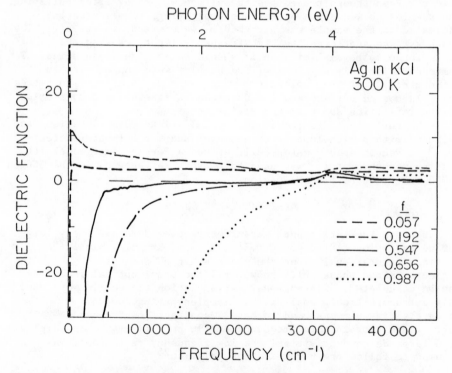

Figure 1. Real part of the dielectric function obtained by Kramers-Kronig analysis of the reflectance of Ag-KCl composites

Figure 2 shows the Kramers-Kronig result for the frequency dependent conductivity, $\sigma_1(\omega)$. Notice the large change in the low frequency values of the conductivity as the volume fraction of Ag increases. There is a minimum in the conductivity just above 30000 cm^{-1} (3 eV) followed by a sharp rise in the conductivity at the onset of the interband transitions. The appearance in our composite samples of the interband transitions at the same energy as in the bulk metal indicates that the electronic structure of Ag is not altered drastically from its bulk behavior in the small (120 Å radius) particles. Figure 3 shows the low frequency conductivity for three low concentration samples in detail. For samples with f>0.3, the conductivity in this frequency range is off scale. The peak in the figure is from the transverse optical phonon[25] in KCl. The strength of this peak actually increases with increasing volume fraction of metal. This effect is predicted by the theories of composite materials[28]. At higher concentrations (f>0.3) we no longer see the optic phonon.

DISCUSSION

We have used semi-classical models for the dielectric response of KCl and Ag in the MGT and EMA. KCl is a diatomic crystal with a fundamental lattice-vibration in the far infrared[29] and its lowest electronic transition[30] above 7eV. We choose a Lorentz oscillator model[24] to represent this transverse optic phonon mode in the dielectric function of KCl (ε_{KCl}):

$$\varepsilon_{KCl}(\omega) = \varepsilon_\infty + \frac{\omega_L^2}{\omega_{TO}^2 - \omega^2 - i\gamma\omega} . \qquad (13)$$

In equation (12), the constant $\varepsilon_\infty = 2.1$ is the electronic contribution to the dielectric function; $\omega_{TO} = 141$ cm^{-1} is the resonance frequency of the vibrational mode of the ions; $\omega_L = 206$ cm^{-1} is the oscillator strength of this vibration; and $\gamma = 5$ cm^{-1} is the full width at half maximum for the oscillator. The oscillator strength ω_L^2, calculated from the Lyddane-Sachs-Teller relation[25], is

$$\omega_L^2 = \varepsilon_\infty (\omega_{LO}^2 - \omega_{TO}^2) \qquad (14)$$

where $\omega_{LO} = 200$ cm^{-1} is the longitudinal polariton frequency, the zero of the real part of the dielectric function.

Ag is a metal with d bands lying 4 eV below the Fermi energy[27]. Therefore, at frequencies lower than 32000 cm^{-1} (4 eV) only intraband transitions can also occur. The dielectric function of Ag (ε_{Ag}) can be represented as a combination of a free-electron Drude model[24,25] for low frequency behavior and tabulated data[26] for the higher frequency bound behavior.

$$\varepsilon_{Ag}(\omega) = \varepsilon_b(\omega) - \frac{\omega_p^2}{\omega^2 + i\omega/\tau} \qquad (15)$$

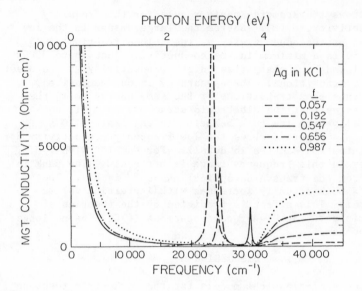

Figure 4. Conductivity of Ag-KCl composites as calculated by the Maxwell Garnett theory.

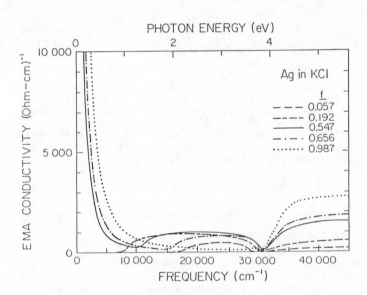

Figure 5. Conductivity of Ag-KCl composites as calculated by the effective medium approximation.

Here $\varepsilon_b(\omega)$ is the high frequency value of the dielectric function for bulk Ag, $\omega_p = 73100$ cm^{-1} is the unscreened plasma frequency[27] for Ag and τ is the relaxation time of the electrons in the particle. Because the Ag particles are small (r=125 Å), this time is dominated by surface collisions even at room temperature. To account for this size effect, we write the scattering rate as

$$\frac{1}{\tau} = \frac{v_F}{\ell_{Ag}} + \frac{v_F}{r} , \qquad (16)$$

where v_F is the Fermi velocity and ℓ_{Ag} the bulk mean free path. Using $\ell_{Ag} = 300$ Å, we calculate $1/\tau = 740$ cm^{-1} (90 meV) for our 120 Å radius Ag particles. (Note that in converting from sec^{-1} to cm^{-1}, one divides by $2\pi c$.)

Figure 4 and 5 shows the calculated frequency-dependent conductivity for several volume fractions obtained from the EMA and MGT. To obtain reasonable results from the asymmetric MGT, samples with f<0.5 were assumed to have Ag grains embedded in a KCl host while those with f>0.5 were assumed to consist of KCl grains in a Ag host. This switch from an insulating host to a conducting host artificially produces a percolation transition at f=0.5 in the MGT calculations. In contrast, the percolation transition occurs automatically in the EMA when f=1/3. A comparison of figure 4 and 5 with figure 2 shows that the EMA correctly predicts a broad peak in the conductivity with a maximum value of 1000 Ω^{-1} cm^{-1}. The sharp peaks predicted by the MGT at 25000 cm^{-1} (KCl host) or 30000 cm^{-1} (Ag host) are not seen in our data.

In the low-frequency, low volume fraction conductivity calculations, Figure 6, the transverse optic mode of KCl is enhanced with increasing volume fraction of Ag. The magnitude of the phonon peak is in good agreement with experiment (Figure 3) for volume fractions up to 0.2. Above f=0.2 the experimental system shows a large enhancement over the EMA, because the EMA has a higher critical volume fraction than the experimental system. The EMA agrees qualitatively with the low-frequency measurements when both the model and the specimens are above (or below) the critical volume fraction.

Figure 7 shows the absorption coefficient for some of our samples. At low frequencies and small volume fractions it has been shown[12] that $\alpha(\omega)$ can be written as

$$\alpha(\omega) = Kf\omega^\beta \qquad (17)$$

where K depends upon the particle radius and other properties of the composite system. At low values of f and ω, $\beta=2$. As either f or ω is increased, β is expected to change from 2 to a value less than 1. This qualitative behavior is seen in our data. Notice that as the volume fraction increases the change becomes more pronounced.

48

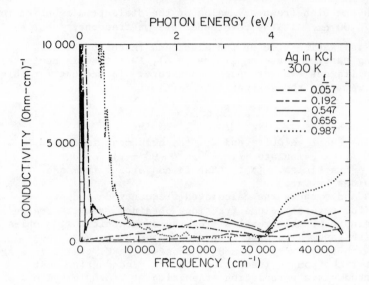

Figure 2. Frequency dependent conductivity obtained by Kramers-Kronig analysis of the reflectance of Ag-KCl composites.

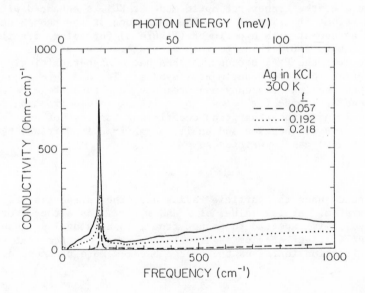

Figure 3. Frequency dependent conductivity showing low frequency detail.

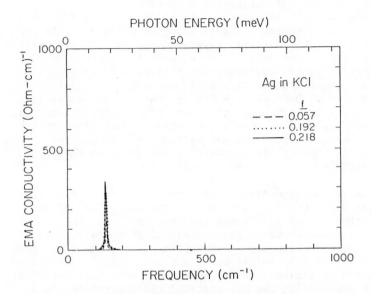

Figure 6. Effective medium approximation calculation of the conductivity showing the low frequency detail.

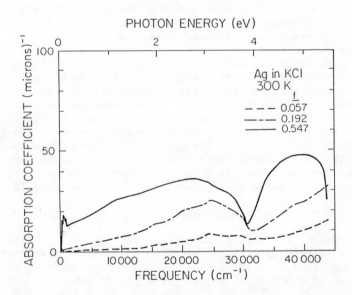

Figure 7. Absorption coefficient obtained by Kramers-Kronig analysis of the room temperature reflectance. 1 micron^{-1} equals 10000 cm^{-1}.

SUMMARY

In summary, the optical properties of Ag-KCl composites are in qualitative agreement with calculations based on the effective medium approximation. This agreement includes both the effects of the percolation transition on the optical properties and the characteristics (width and strength) of the broad infrared peak in the frequency-dependent conductivity. In addition, the data satisfy several sum rules[31] for the effective conductivity. These sum rules will be discussed elsehwere[32]. Our measurements are in poor agreement with the Maxwell-Garnett theory because that theory is applicable only to systems far from percolation. Materials which are described by the Maxwell-Garnett theory, such as cermet systems,[3,4] are generally understood to do so because strong correlations exist in the locations of the particles; thus, these materials are non-random composites.

In contrast to the reasonably good agreement between experiment and theory found here, the far-infrared absorption in low-volume-fraction composites ($f < 0.05$) is mysteriously large[9-13]. The discrepancy between the observed absorption and model calculations which consider only electric dipole absorption (i.e., the dielectric functions of equations 7 or 10) is about a factor of 10^6. When eddy current absorption is included in the model (and when the most favorable parameters are used in the calculation) the discrepancy is a factor of 10 to 100, although the eddy current absorption does predict a correct frequency, concentration, and size dependence for the absorption. Note that at small concentrations and low frequencies, both the MGT and the EMA given essentially identical numerical values for the absorption, so that the anomaly is not dependent upon the effective medium model chosen. Finally, in superconducting samples the frequency dependence of the observed absorption also disagrees with calculations[13].

We note in conclusion that there are two qualitative differences between the experiments described in this paper and those where anomalies are observed. First the present experiments are made at metal concentrations which either are near to or above the percolation point, so that the electric dipole contribution to the optical properties is much stronger. Second, the measurements have been made at much higher frequencies, so that the skin effect makes the magnetic dipole contribution weaker. Whether these differences are significant is unclear, however, because if the magnetic dipole term were ignored, the discrepancy between experiment and theory would be 10^6.

ACKNOWLEDGEMENTS

We thank D. Stroud for several useful discussions and S. Miller and B. Farrar for assistance with the electron microscopes. Work at Ohio State was supported in part by the U.S. DOE though contract DE-AS02-78ER04914 and by the OSU MRL though grant DMR-8119368.

REFERENCES

1. For a review see R. Landauer, Electrical Transport and Optical Properties of Inhomogeneous Media, ed. by J.C. Garland and D.B. Tanner, (AIP, New York, 1978) p 1.

2. H.G. van de Hulst, Light Scattering by Small Particles, (Dover, New York, 1981).

3. R.W. Cohen, G.D. Cody, M.D. Coutts, and B. Abeles, Phys. Rev. B8, 3689 (1973).

4. J.I. Gittleman and B. Abeles, Phys. Rev. B15, 3273 (1977).

5. C.G. Granqvist and O. Hunderi, Solid State Commun. 19, 939 (1976); Phys. Rev. B16, 1353 (1977); ibid 16, 3513 (1977).

6. I. Webman, J. Jortner and M.H. Cohen, Phys Rev. B15, 5712 (1977); B16, 2539 (1977).

7. D. Stroud and F.P. Pan, Phys. Rev. B17, 1602 (1978).

8. P. Sheng, Phys Rev. Lett. 45, 60 (1980).

9. D.B. Tanner, A.J. Sievers and R.A. Buhrman, Phys. Rev. B11, 1330 (1975).

10. C.G. Granqvist, R.A. Buhrman, J. Wyns and A.J. Sievers, Phys. Rev. Lett. 37, 625 (1976).

11. N.E. Russell, J.C. Garland and D.B. Tanner, Phys. Rev. B23, 632 (1981).

12. G.L. Carr, R.L. Henry, N.E. Russell, J.C. Garland and D.B. Tanner, Phys. Rev. B24, 777 (1981).

13. G.L. Carr, J.C. Garland and D.B. Tanner, Phys. Rev. Lett. 50, 1607 (1983).

14. J.C.M. Garnett, Phil. Trans. Roy. Soc. A203, 385 (1904); A205, 237 (1906).

15. D.A.G. Bruggeman, Ann. Physik. (Leipz.) 24, 636 (1935).

16. D. Stroud, Phys. Rev. B12, 3368 (1975).

17. D.M. Wood and N.W. Ashcroft, Philos. Mag. 35, 269 (1977).

18. P.N. Sen and D.B. Tanner, Phys. Rev. B26, 3582 (1982).

19. J.D. Jackson, Classical Electrodynamics, 2nd ed., (John Wiley and Sons, Inc., New York 1975), p. 149.

20. A. Hashin and S. Shtrikman, J. Appl. Phys. 33, 3125 (1962).

21. C.G. Granqvist and R.A. Buhrman, J. Appl. Phys. 47, 2200 (1976).

22. D.M. Grannan, J.C. Garland and D.B. Tanner, Phys. Rev. Lett. 46, 375 (1981).

23. K.D. Cummings, D.B. Tanner and J.S. Miller, Phys. Rev. B24, 4142 (1981).

24. F. Wooten, Optical Properties of Solids, (Academic Press, New York, 1972).

25. C. Kittel, Introduction to Solid State Physics, 5th ed., (John Wiley and Sons, Inc., New York, 1976).

26. H.J. Hagemann, W. Gudat and C. Kunz, internal report DESY SR-7417, Deutsches Elektronen-Synchrotron, Hamburg, (1974); H.J. Hagemann, W. Gudat and C. Kunz, J. Opt. Soc. Am. 65, 742 (1975)

27. H. Ehrenreich and H.R. Philipp, Phys. Rev. 12B, 1622 (1962).

28. E. Simanek, Phys. Rev. Lett. 38, 1161 (1977).

29. K.W. Johnson and E.E. Bell, Phys. Rev. 187, 1044 (1969).

30. H.R. Philipp and H. Ehrenreich, Phys. Rev. 131, 2016 (1963).

31. D. Stroud, Phys. Rev. B19, 1783 (1979).

32. K.D. Cummings, J.C. Garland and D.B. Tanner, to be published.

DIELECTRIC ENHANCEMENT DUE TO GEOMETRICAL
AND ELECTROCHEMICAL EFFECTS

Pabitra N. Sen , W. C. Chew, and David Wilkinson

Schlumberger-Doll Research, P. O. Box 307
Ridgefield, CT 06877

ABSTRACT

The conductivity and dielectric constant of water-filled rocks depend on geometrical and interfacial effects. The grain shape determines both Archie's exponent for the d.c. conductivity and the frequency dependent dielectric constant. Large values of dielectric constant can arise from platey grains. Platey grains also lead to large frequency and salinity dependences of the dielectric constant. Interfacial effects are particularly important in clayey systems.

INTRODUCTION

At low frequencies, around the KHz range, the dielectric constant of water-saturated rocks can be as great as 10,000.[1-8] These gigantic values are remarkable - considering that the dielectric constant of any of the constituent components does not exceed 80. In this paper, we summarize our current understanding of how the dielectric constant and the conductivity of sedimentary rocks depend on: clay, salinity, frequency, textural variables.

The electrical properties of a rock/water mixture depend on the bulk electrical properties of the constituents, and on (a.) Electro-chemical/Interfacial Effects (b.) Geometrical arrangement of the constituents. The interfacial effect is particularly prominent in clayey samples. In most cases in practice these two effects are present simultaneously. First we will consider the geometrical aspects, and then the interfacial effects. This paper is organized as follows. We first consider the cross-term effect, which is as follows: If the host material is conducting, the out-of-phase part of the induced polarisability of the inclusion can drive a conduction current that appears as a displacement current i.e. a real dielectric constant. Then we consider the iterated dilute limit theories and point out the difficulties and possible uses of them. Next we consider how large values of dielectric constant arise specifically from the platey grains. In the subsequent section, we discuss relations between dielectric enhancement, and the well known enhancement near a percolation threshold. The section after that deals with similar ideas on partially oil/partially water saturated rocks. In the final section we summarize our current work on double layer effects.

0094-243X/84/1070052-14 $3.00 Copyright 1984 American Institute of Physics

Let us close this section with a note on notation. Maxwell's equations entail the complex dielectric constant $\epsilon(\omega)$, which is a function of frequency. In this paper, we write $\epsilon(\omega) = \epsilon'(\omega) + i\,\sigma(\omega)/\omega\epsilon_0$, where ϵ' and σ are real-valued functions of frequency ω, and ϵ_0 is the permittivity of the vacuum. The real part, $\epsilon'(\omega)$, and the imaginary part, $\sigma(\omega)/\omega\epsilon_0$, of $\epsilon(\omega)$ are related by the Kramers-Kronig relations.[9]

CROSS-TERM EFFECT

The cross-term effect is a mechanism that gives rise to large values of the dielectric constant of a mixture. When there is a conducting host, as well as an out of phase part of the induced polarizability α of the inclusion, the out-of-phase induced field can drive a conduction current which appears as a displacement current to the experimentalist.[6,8] This can be understood easily using even the simplest mixing formula, for example the Maxwell effective medium theory.[10] The dielectric constant of a mixture depends on the product of the dielectric constant of the host ϵ_H and the induced polarization α, of the inclusion. According to Maxwell's formula, the effective dielectric constant is $\epsilon_e \approx \epsilon_H(1+3\eta\alpha)$ where η is the fractional volume of the spherical inclusions. The imaginary part of the dielectric constant of the host is proportional to the conductivity of the host σ_H divided by frequency ω. As $\omega \to 0$, this diverges, thus the cross-term, which is proportional to $(\mathrm{Im}\alpha)\,(\sigma_H/\omega)$, gives a large value to the real part of the dielectric constant of the mixture. Physically, this implies that an out-of-phase part in α, the induced polarization, will give rise to an out-of-phase electric field. This field in turn will drive an out-of-phase conduction current proportional to σ_H. This out-of-phase current is interpreted to be a macroscopic displacement current implying a large dielectric constant for the mixture. We will mention below how a large $\mathrm{Im}\alpha$ can come about from either textural or surface effects in specific cases.

GEOMETRIC EFFECTS

The importance of geometrical effects can be simply illustrated by the following *exact* results. If we apply an electric field parallel to the interface of a layered medium (with thicknesses smaller that the wavelength) or a medium consisting of tubes, the effective dielectric constant is given by

$$\epsilon_e = \sum_i f_i \epsilon_i , \tag{1}$$

where f_i denotes the volume fraction of the i-th phase of dielectric constant ϵ_i. But when the field is applied perpendicular to the interface of the layered medium, ϵ_e is given by

$$\epsilon_e = [\sum_i f_i/\epsilon_i]^{-1} . \tag{2}$$

If some of the materials are conductors and some insulators, in the first case we obtain a non-zero $\sigma(0)$, whereas $\sigma(0)$ is zero for the latter. Similarly, the dielectric constants are drastically different in two cases. In the latter case, one can obtain a divergent $Re\epsilon$ for a mixture of conductors and insulators. If a volume fraction ϕ of a conducting phase of dielectric constant $\epsilon_w = \epsilon'_w + i \sigma_w/\omega\epsilon_0$ is mixed with an insulating material ϵ'_m, then for low frequencies,

$$\omega << \left[\frac{1-\phi}{\phi} \frac{\sigma_w}{\epsilon'_m\epsilon_0} \quad , \quad \frac{\sigma_w}{\epsilon'_w\epsilon_0} \right] \tag{3}$$

one finds from Eq. (2) that

$$\epsilon'_e(0) = \epsilon'_m/(1-\phi) \rightarrow \infty \qquad \text{as} \quad \phi \rightarrow 1 \tag{4}$$

But, the system is insulating as a whole, i.e.

$$\sigma_e(0) = 0 \tag{5}$$

When one punctures these insulating layers, the system becomes conducting as a whole, but the large value of the dielectric constant remains. This case of insulating layers with holes punched onto them, as well as other cases of random geometry cannot be solved exactly, and approximation schemes have to be applied judiciously.

The effective medium type mixing laws (see references cited in Ref. 1) can handle rather simple situations in which the concentration of impurities is small and/or the contrast in the properties of constituents is small, *and* the inclusions or the constituents have simple shapes. None of these limitations apply for brine saturated rocks. In rocks, each of the solid and fluid components is part of an infinite percolating cluster. The method of iterated dilute limit, which preserves the continuity of the fluid phase, has proven to be successful in predicting many electrical properties and some acoustic properties of brine saturated rocks and other porous media. In particular, for spherical grains one finds

$$\left[\frac{\epsilon_m - \epsilon_e}{\epsilon_m - \epsilon_w} \right] \left[\frac{\epsilon_w}{\epsilon_e} \right]^{1/3} = \phi \tag{6}$$

Here ϵ_e is the effective dielectric constant, ϵ_w is that of water, and ϵ_m is that of the matrix, and ϕ is the porosity.[1]

When the rock grains are nonconducting, the d.c. limit of equation (6) gives Archie's law,

$$\sigma(o) = \sigma_w(o) \phi^m \; ; \quad \text{with} \quad m = 3/2. \tag{7}$$

For a spherical grain shape, the value $m = 3/2$ agrees well with the experimental data, as shown in Fig. 3 of Ref. 11. The value of m was obtained by electrical and acoustical methods on fused glass bead samples. At low porosities, the beads are strongly fused together and the shape is nowhere near spherical. Thus deviation from a result devised for spherical grains is to be expected, as observed. At extremely low values of porosity, one could be near a percolation threshold. There, one may expect a scaling law which is to be discussed below.

The key ingredient in deriving the iterated dilute limit is that the water phase must remain inter-connected. Our method is to build up the solid phase in increments, by adding an infinitesimal amount of solid and computing the dielectric constant in a self-consistent manner at each step.[1] These derivations are somewhat obscure about the actual geometry that corresponds to the mathematical derivation, and thus rather unsatisfactory. The three key ingredients in this theory are that (a) the inclusions are added by infinitesimal amounts into a (b) continuum host obtained at the previous step, and (c) the size of the inclusion is small compared to the wavelength. If the size of inclusion at a given step is much greater than the particle sizes in any previous step, condition (b) will be met. One can envision cutting a big hole that may pass through previously placed grains and installing a large inclusion of the solid grain to fit it. The dilution of the new inclusion can be kept as low as desired, and their sizes small compared to the wavelength. This line of argument can be made more precise by taking proper limits, in appropriate order, perhaps along the same lines as the work of Milton.[12] In any event, it will be more desirable to have a tractable geometrical model which has a closer resemblance to real pore spaces.

Next, consider rocks made up of spheroidal grains. For an isotropic rock, in which the grains are randomly oriented, we need to average over the orientation distribution. This has been done in Refs. 13-14. For spheroids, we find the cementation exponent m is given by

$$m = \int \frac{5 - 3L}{3(1 - L^2)} P(L)dL \qquad (8)$$

Here $P(L)$ is the probability distribution for the depolarization factor L along the symmetry axis. The full equation for the dielectric constant is complicated and is given in Ref. 13. For the fully water saturated case, the dielectric properties of many rock samples can be very well described by a bi-modal distribution of rock grain shape.[15-17] In this model grains are taken to be spherical ($L=1/3$) with a probability p and platey ($L = 1-\delta$, $\delta << 1$) with probability 1-p. Using only two adjustable parameters, p and δ, the frequency dependence of ϵ' from 0.5 MHz to 1.3 GHz can be fitted satisfactorily. Also, we have prepared glass bead samples with microscope cover-slides embedded in them. We find that the experimental data can be described satisfactorily without any adjustable parameters.

LARGE VALUES OF DIELECTRIC CONSTANT: THIN PLATE EFFECTS

As shown above, the low-frequency dielectric constant of a material made up of a layer of insulating material covered with a layer of conducting material can be extremely large when the concentration of the insulating phase becomes small. This is known as the Maxwell-Wagner effect.[10,4] In this case, the material as a whole has a zero d.c. conductivity because the layer of insulating material blocks the current path. The iterated dilute limit model shows that under certain circumstances $\text{Re}\epsilon_e$ can be enormously large even when the sample remains conducting. This model is more appropriate to sedimentary rocks which remain conducting to very low values of porosity.[4,5] The algebraic details showing enhancement for platey grains can be found elsewhere.[13,18] Here we show how the cross-term effects can explain the phenomenon.

It is easy to show[6] that the polarizability of a thin plate-like object of dielectric constant ϵ_m imbedded in ϵ_R is given by a complex quantity

$$\alpha = \frac{\epsilon_m - \epsilon_R}{L\epsilon_m + (1-L)\,\epsilon_R} \tag{9}$$

Since α has both real and imaginary parts, the induced dipolar fields from the inclusions will have an in-phase as well as an out-of-phase term. This complex dipolar field will drive a displacement current in addition to the conduction current in the medium, as discussed above.

ENHANCEMENT OF DIELECTRIC CONSTANT NEAR A PERCOLATION THRESHOLD UNIVERSALITY/CORRELATED PERCOLATION

The Maxwell-Wagner effect described above is one example of dielectric enhancement near a conductivity threshold. Another well known case is the dielectric enhancement which occurs in inhomogeneous mixtures of metals and insulators when the conducting metallic phase is close to a percolation threshold (see Ref. 19, and references therein). Notable progress has been made for such systems in developing scaling theories to predict the behavior of the conductivity σ and the dielectric constant ϵ' as functions of the volume fraction ϕ of the conducting material and the frequency ω. Results of interest here are that the low frequency conductivity vanishes at the percolation threshold ϕ_c according to a power law of the form

$$\sigma \sim \sigma_w(\phi-\phi_c)^t \quad , \quad \phi > \phi_c \tag{10}$$

$$= 0 \qquad \phi < \phi_c \quad ,$$

where σ_w is the conductivity of the conducting phase, which is the water in the case of brine saturated porous media. The real part of the dielectric constant is predicted to diverge as ϕ approaches (from below or above) ϕ_c

$$\epsilon' \sim \epsilon_m' \,|\,\phi-\phi_c|^{-s} \quad , \tag{11}$$

where ϵ'_m is the dielectric constant of the matrix. The above results (10) and (11) hold for low frequencies

$$\omega \ll |\phi - \phi_d|^{(s+t)} \frac{\sigma_w}{\epsilon'_m \epsilon_0} \quad , \qquad (12)$$

For $\omega \gg |\phi - \phi_c|^{(s+t)} \sigma_w / (\epsilon'_m \epsilon_0)$, the dielectric constant ϵ' increases as frequency is lowered

$$\epsilon' \sim \epsilon'_m \left(\frac{\sigma_w}{\epsilon'_m \epsilon_0 \omega} \right)^{s/s+t} \quad . \qquad (13)$$

In the scaling laws (10)-(13), the exponents t and s are known as the conductivity and superconductivity exponents.[19] These exponents are universal for random systems, i.e., do not depend on details of the geometry such as coordination number, but only on the space dimension of the system. However, correlations in the geometry will in general change the exponents.

Random systems always exhibit a non-zero percolation threshold ϕ_c below which the d.c. conductivity vanishes. In real rocks, however, the empirical law known as Archie's Law, see Eq. (7), indicates that $\phi_c = 0$, i.e., the water in the pore space remains conducting down to arbitrarily low concentrations. If we assume that the pore space is completely filled with water, this means geometrically that the pore space remains connected even in samples with very low porosity. The extension of scaling laws to such correlated geometries will be interesting. The analogue of the dielectric enhancement for real rocks will presumably occur at the limit $\phi \to 0$ i.e , in the low porosity limit.

Even if we argue that $\phi_c = 0$, i.e., the percolation threshold is zero, it remains to be seen whether the scaling laws would be useful for rocks. There are obvious temptations due to the power law form of Archie's law and the dielectric enhancements. But, most sedimentary rocks have porosities in the range of 10-20 percent i.e., far from the critical region. Also, the experimentally usable frequencies cannot be too low. The scaling laws would be useful if they turn out to be valid far beyond the expected asymptotically small region near the threshold. Furthermore, it will be useful only if a finite number of universality classes exists with respect to variations such as grain shape and packing geometry.

We are currently investigating several computational schemes and several geometries. A model of packed spheres, like an Apollonian pack,[20] would be a realistic model for the geometry. A particular calculational scheme which may be useful is the position space renormalization group (PSRG). This method has not so far been used to calculate electrical properties either of continuous media or of correlated systems. It is known[19] that PSRG treats statistical fluctuations more carefully than the effective medium theories, and thus should give reasonable results both inside and outside the critical region $\phi \sim \phi_c$, $\omega \sim 0$ described above. In preparation for an extension of PSRG to the continuum situation, we have applied this method to a capacitor - resistor network, with the capacitors representing the insulating rock grains and the resistors the conducting

58

water.[19] Perhaps the greatest advantage of this scheme is that it can be used to compute numerical approximations to the complex conductance at values ϕ and ω which are finite distances away from the critical point. In principle, this means that the technique might be used in a practical way for more realistically complicated models.

We also found that the full non-linear iteration scheme gives a power law behavior for a range of concentrations far away from the critical value (see Fig. 1). This is similar to the behavior observed experimentally.[21] We do not understand why the power laws, which are believed to hold asymptotically near the critical point, hold for values of p and ω which are finite distances away from the critical point. In practice this may imply that there are only a few universality classes, and a single power law may apply over a large range of porosity in each class.

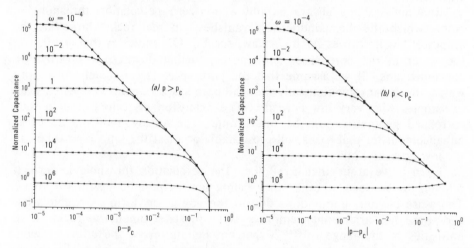

Fig. 1.   Variation of effective capacitance c_{eff} with concentration p of the conducting elements for various ω, showing the critical behavior and crossover. The quantity plotted is the normalized capacitance c_{eff}/c. For $\omega > 10^6$ the results break down because $\omega c/\sigma > 1$. The results are for a 2D square network where bonds are randomly occupied by a conductor of conductance σ with probability p and capacitance c with probability 1-p. In this case $p_c = 0.5$ (from Ref. 19).

It would be extremely useful for geophysical prospecting if there did exist universal laws governing dielectric enhancement for the case of real rocks. However, we know from calculations of Weinrib and Halperin that the exponent ν giving the correlation length can vary continuously with the degree of long-range correlation.[22] We expect that the conductivity exponents t and s would also vary, and Feng et. al.[23] have made some progress in that direction. The second step is to determine what kind of short-range and long-range correlations are present in porous rocks. This is currently being investigated by studying micrographs of serially sectioned rocks. It may turn out that the correlation in the pore space will depend on the grain shape. We are also investigating the numerical solution of Maxwell's equations for real rock geometries, since it may turn out that the correlation in the pore space may not have a simple power law behavior as used in the schemes mentioned above.[22,23]

ROCKS SATURATED WITH OIL AND WATER

Although we believe that the percolation theories are not good models for the pore space, when two fluids are present the percolation ideas have been applied with success to dielectric enhancement in porous media, because they can describe the topology of the fluid phases.[24] The essential reason for this is that surface tension forces cause the wetting fluid to occupy the smaller pores, and the non-wetting fluid the larger ones. While the wetting fluid probably always maintains continuity via surface films, the non-wetting fluid can become completely disconnected. For example, in an oil-wet rock, which is non-wettable by the brine, there is a threshold water saturation S_{wc} below which the water phase is disconnected. The conductivity as a function of water saturation S_w near threshold is given by

$$\sigma(S_w) \sim \sigma(S_w=1)(S_w-S_{wc})^t \qquad (14)$$

where t is the conductivity exponent. A more sophisticated description which takes account of the fluid configurations produced by an actual displacement experiment is under consideration. The above considerations should not be confused with the experimental results for the water-wet case, which are often fitted by a law of the form

$$\sigma = \sigma_w \phi^m S_w^n. \qquad (15)$$

In summary, we find that the currently available computational schemes and the currently employed geometrical models are rather unsatisfactory. Combination of numerical solution of Maxwell's equation for small cells with renormalisation may prove useful. In addition to actual serial sections of rocks, randomly packed grains of different shapes and sizes will provide useful geometries.

SURFACE EFFECTS

A charged particle, such as a clay particle, immersed in an electrolytic solution acquires a charge cloud, known as the electrochemical double layer.[25-31] Polarization of the double layer in an external electric field has been invoked, for the last twenty years, as the mechanism responsible for large ($\sim$ 1000) values of low frequency dielectric constant in rocks

60

containing clay particles, as well as in other colloidal and biological systems. Recently, there has been a great deal of theoretical interest in this area-- numerical solutions have been obtained by Fixman,[25] Delacey and White,[26] and O'Brien and White,[27] and analytical solutions of varying degree of accuracy and applicability have been obtained by Dukhin and Shilov,[28] Fixman,[29] Chew and Sen,[7] Hinch, Sherwood, Chew and Sen,[30] culminating with the work of Chew.[31] The main deficiency of all these results is that they are valid only for a dilute suspension. In addition, theory has to be extended to non-spherical (platey shapes) to be applicable to clays. The most glaring difficulty in this area is the lack of experimental data. We summarize the theoretical results obtained here.

The model used is the diffuse double layer model which assumes that the charge distribution is given by the Boltzmann distribution in terms of the potential. The potential Ψ is given, self consistently, in terms of these charges by Poisson's equation.

$$\nabla^2\Psi = -\frac{N_+ - N_-}{2N_0\delta^2} \tag{16}$$

Here $e\Phi/k_BT=\Psi$, $\delta^2 = \epsilon'_w k_BT/(e^2 2N_0)$, δ is the Debye screening length, ϵ'_w is the dielectric constant of the solution, N_0 is the ambient ionic density, and $N_\pm$ are ionic densities of positively and negatively charged particles. In the absence of the external electric field, the Boltzmann distribution gives a nonlinear equation

$$\nabla^2\Psi = \frac{\sinh\Psi}{2N_0\delta^2} \tag{17}$$

This equation was solved by us using matched asymptotics techniques using δ/a as the small parameter, a being the particle radius. The result, to second order in δ/a, agrees extremely well with the numerical solution,[32] even when this ratio is as large as 1, and Ψ as large as 10.

The equations for the ionic currents are

$$\vec{j}_\pm = \vec{v}N_\pm^t + D_\pm\left[-\nabla N_\pm^t \mp \frac{e}{k_BT}N_\pm^t\nabla\Phi^t\right], \tag{18}$$

and the Stokes equations governing solvent flow are

$$\mu\nabla^2\vec{v} - \rho^t\nabla\Phi^t - \nabla P^t = 0,$$

$$\nabla\cdot\vec{v} = 0, \tag{19}$$

Here μ is the viscosity, and, $D_\pm$ are the diffusion coefficients for the positive and negative ions. The equations are linearized with respect to the applied field E_0 by setting

$$N_\pm^t = N_\pm + n_\pm,$$

$$\Psi^t = \Psi + \psi,$$

$$\rho^t = \rho_0 + \rho,$$

$$P^t = P + p. \tag{20}$$

In the above, ρ_0, P, $N_\pm$ and Ψ are the unperturbed charge density, pressure, ionic densities and potential respectively around the charged particle before the application of an electric field, and $\vec{v}$, ρ, p, $n_\pm$ and ψ are the velocity, perturbed charge density, pressure, ionic densities and potential respectively, each proportional to E_o. The linearized equations for the ionic currents and Stokes equation are given by

$$\vec{j}_\pm \sim \vec{v} N_\pm + D_\pm \left[-\nabla n_\pm \mp \frac{e}{k_B T} (N_\pm \nabla \phi + n_\pm \nabla \Phi) \right] + O(E_o^2), \ E_o \to 0$$

$$\mu \nabla^2 \vec{v} - \rho_0 \nabla \phi - \rho \nabla \Phi - \nabla p = 0, \tag{21}$$

$$\nabla \cdot \vec{v} = 0. \tag{22}$$

Furthermore, the currents satisfy the continuity equation

$$\nabla \cdot \vec{j}_\pm = i\omega n_\pm \tag{23}$$

The time dependence $\exp(-i\omega t)$ of the perturbed quantities is implied. The perturbed potential satisfies Poisson's equation in terms of the perturbed charge densities. This, along with Equations (21)-(23) constitute five equations for the five unknowns $\vec{v}$, p, $n_\pm$ and ϕ.

These equations have been solved by various methods.[7,28,29] In Ref. 7 we solved these equations using the method of matched asymptotics but neglecting the flow, to second-order in δ/a. The term giving enhancement in the real part ϵ'_e of the effective dielectric constant of the ensemble is second order in δ/a; the series converges if $(\delta/a)t^2/(1 - t^2) \ll 1$, where $t = \tanh(e\Phi_0/k_B T)$, and Φ_0 is the surface potential. The static value of ϵ'_e, to this order, is $\epsilon'_e \sim 36 f \epsilon'_w t^2/(1 - t^2)^2$, where f is the volume fraction of particles, and ϵ'_w the real part of the dielectric constant of the solution. When $\Phi_0 \to \infty$, $t \to 1$, ϵ'_e diverges as $\epsilon'_e \sim \frac{9}{4} f \epsilon'_w \exp(e\Phi_0/k_B T)$. When applicable, the theory agrees well with experiments[33] over three decades in frequency, with one adjustable parameter, Φ_0, as shown in Fig. 2.

The perturbative approach adopted by us contributes to a new understanding of the mechanism that gives rise to the dielectric enhancement. In this case the enhancement depends critically on a neutral induced diffusion cloud that extends far beyond the original double layer. In the unperturbed double layer, charges fall off exponentially as $\exp[-(r-a)/\delta]$. The induced cloud falls off rather slowly, as $\exp[-\lambda(r-a)]$, $\lambda \sim \sqrt{\omega/2D}$, and enhancement disappears when ω becomes so large that $\lambda a \gg 1$. The counterion current in the double layer

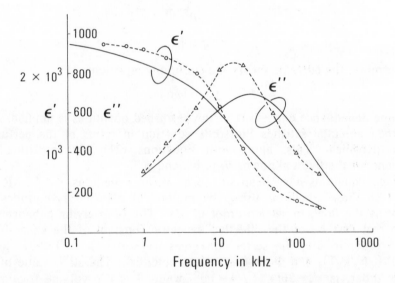

Fractional Volume = 30%

——————— Theory
－－－－－－ Experimental

$\Psi_0 = 3.85$

$D_+ = D_- = 2 \times 10^{-5}\ cm^2/sec$

$\epsilon_w = 80\ \epsilon_0,\ \epsilon_p = 3\epsilon_0$

$\delta/a = 1/60,\ a = 0.094\mu$

$N_0 = 2.08 \times 10^{25}\ m^{-3}$

Fig. 2. **The comparison of theoretical and experimental values of the real and imaginary parts of the dielectric constant of polystyrene particles suspended in electrolyte solution.**

region in the presence of an externally applied field is large. This strong counterion current causes charges to pile up at the ends of the particle. The excess charges discharge into the bulk solution through a diffusion process, in addition to a conduction process. At low frequencies, a large diffusion cloud of size $\lambda^{-1} = \sqrt{2D/\omega}$ is set up by the diffusion process (here we have set $D_+ = D_- = D$). The diffusion current in the diffusion cloud is out-of-phase with the applied field. This out-of-phase diffusion current has a "back-up" or "cushion" effect on the circumferential current in the double layer - causing the circumferential current to be out-of-phase. Hence, the dipolar field has an out-of-phase component. On the other hand, when the frequencies are high, the rapid oscillation of circumferential current in the double layer does not allow the build up of a large diffusion cloud outside the double layer. In fact, the diffusion cloud is smaller, both in extent and in amplitude. Hence the out-of-phase component of the circumferential current in the double layer is small, resulting in little or no enhancement.

Our analysis gives a dependence on ω which is much broader than the frequency dependence of the Debye equation

$$\epsilon_e \sim \frac{1}{1 - i\omega\tau} .$$ (24)

We find[33]

$$\epsilon_e \sim \frac{1}{1 + \sqrt{-2i\omega\tau} - i\omega\tau},$$ (25)

where $\tau = a^2/2D$ Eq. (25) (which corresponds to the theoretical curve in Fig. 2) has a more gradual transition than Eq. (24). The physical explanation for such a broader than Debye type relaxation, which is commonly encountered in electrochemistry, is that the diffusion cloud, which controls the relaxation, shrinks slowly as $\omega^{-1/2}$ as $\omega \to \infty$.

The solvent flow effects were taken into account by Hinch et al.[30] and by Chew.[31] The main effect of the flow is to further increase the dielectric enhancement. This additional increase can be understood as follows: The external electric field exerts a force on the double layer, which is not neutral. Although the flow velocity is zero right on the surface, it is non-zero just outside the double layer. Since the double layer is thin, the net effect is like a slip boundary condition, which in turn implies a flow in the bulk. The total current depends on drift (or flow), diffusion, and the conduction current. Above, we argued how the mismatch of conduction currents inside and outside the double layer gave rise to the diffusion cloud. This effect is further exaggerated by the flow induced by the electric field inside the non-neutral double layer. As a side effect, the solvent flow causes a charged particle suspended in the fluid to move with a velocity V which is the source of electrophoresis or electrokinetic effect. Finally, Chew's[31] results are valid for high surface potential.

REFERENCES

1. P. N. Sen, C. Scala, and M. H. Cohen, Geophysics *46*, 781 (1981).
2. N. C. Lockhart, J. Colloid and Interface Sci. *74*, 509 (1980).
3. J. H. Scott, R. D. Carroll, and D. R. Cunningham, J. Geophys. Res, *72*, 5101 (1967).
4. P. N. Sen, Appl. Phys. Lett. *39*, 667 (1981).
5. P. N. Sen, Geophysics, *47*, 1714 (1981).
6. P. N. Sen, in *Macroscopic Properties of Disordered Media*, p. 226, Ed. R. Burridge, S. Childress, and G. Papanicolau (Springer-Verlag, N.Y., 1982).
7. W. C. Chew, and P. N. Sen, J. Chem. Phys. *77*, 4683 (1982).
8. P. N. Sen, and W. C. Chew, Microwave Power *18*, 1 (1983).
9. L. D. Landau and E. Lifshitz, *Electrodynamics of Continuous Media,* (Pergamon, N.Y., 1960).
10. J. C. Maxwell, *A Treatise on Electricity and Magnetism: (1873),* (Dover, N.Y., 1954).
11. T. J. Plona and D. L. Johnson, (in these proceedings).
12. G. Milton, (in these proceedings).
13. P. N. Sen, Geophysics (to be published).
14. K. S. Mendelson and M. H. Cohen, Geophysics *47*, 257 (1982).
15. P. Baker, J. P. Banavar, W. Kenyon, P. N. Sen, (private communication).
16. W. J. Kenyon, J. Appl. Phys. (to be published).
17. S. Feng and P. N. Sen, (private communication).
18. P. N. Sen, *NATO Advanced Study Institute*, Ed. M. F. Thorpe (Plenum, N.Y., 1981), p.647.
19. D. Wilkinson, J. Langer, P. N. Sen, Phys. Rev. B*28*, 1081 (1983).
20. D. Wilkinson, (private communication).
21. D. M. Grannan, J. C. Garland, and D. B. Tanner, Phys. Rev. Lett. *46,* 375 (1981).
22. A. Weinrib and B. I. Halperin, Phys. Rev. B*26,* 1352; ibid *26*, 1362 (1982).
23. S. Feng and B. I. Halperin, (private communication).
24. R. G. Larson, L. E. Scriven and H. T. Davis, Chem. Eng. Sci. *36*, 57 (1981);
   R. Chandler, J. Koplik, K. Lerman and J. Willemsen, J. Fluid Mech. *119,* 249 (1982);
   D. Wilkinson and J. Willemsen, J. Phys. A (to be published);
   J. Koplik, D. Wilkinson and J. Willemsen, *Proceedings of the Workshop on the Mathematics and Physics of Disordered Media,* University of Minnesota, February 1983 (to be published).
25. M. Fixman, J. Chem. Phys., *78*, 1483 (1983).
26. E. H. B. Delacey and L. R. White, J. Chem. Soc., Faraday Trans. II, *77*, 2007 (1981).

27. A. B. O'Brien and L. R. White, J. Chem. Soc., Faraday Trans. II, *74*, 1607 (1978).
28. S. S. Dukhin and V. N. Shilov, *Dielectric Phenomena and the Double Layer in Disperse Systems and Polyelectrolytes* (Wiley, New York, 1974).
29. M. Fixman, J. Chem. Phys., *72*, 5177, (1981); Macromolecules, *13*, 711 (1981).
30. J. Hinch, J. Sherwood, W. C. Chew and P. N. Sen, J. Fluid Mech. (to be published).
31. W. C. Chew, J. Chem. Phys. (submitted).
32. W. C. Chew and P. N. Sen, J. Chem. Phys. *77*, 2042 (1982).
33. H. P. Schwan, G. Schwarz, J. Maczuk and H. Pauly, J. Phys. Chem., *66*, 2626 (1962).

CORRELATION OF THE ELECTROMAGNETIC AND ELASTIC PROPERTIES
OF COMPOSITES AND MICROGEOMETRIES CORRESPONDING WITH
EFFECTIVE MEDIUM APPROXIMATIONS

G. W. Milton
Baker Laboratory, Cornell University, Ithaca, N.Y. 14853

ABSTRACT

Relationships between the effective conductivity and bulk and
shear moduli of two-component composites are presented and discussed. Some new identities amongst the geometric parameters which
link together these effective properties are given. It turns out
that the effective medium approximation is consistent with all the
new results. This is because the approximation is exact, after certain limits have been taken, for a family of hierarchical models
which are described here.

INTRODUCTION

Various effective properties of statistically homogeneous and
isotropic two-component composites are closely related. For instance it has long been recognized[1] that finding the effective dielectric constant, thermal conductivity, magnetic permeability or
diffusivity is mathematically analogous to finding the effective
conductivity, σ_e in terms of the geometry and the conductivities of
the components. Furthermore, bounds have been developed[2-4] which
interlink these effective properties.

Here correlations between σ_e and the effective bulk and shear
moduli, κ_e and μ_e, are studied. In other words, we focus on finding
what can be said about the effective elastic constants from measurements of the effective conductivity. It is assumed the properties
of the components are known: their conductivities, σ_1 and σ_2, bulk
moduli, κ_1 and κ_2, and shear moduli, μ_1 and μ_2, being given. The
geometry or structure of the composite, as represented by the
characteristic function

$$\Omega(\vec{x}) = \begin{cases} 1, & \text{if x is in component 1} \\ 0, & \text{otherwise,} \end{cases}$$

(1)

need not be completely known. Note that the volume fractions f_1 and
f_2 of the components are related to the average value of $\Omega(\vec{x})$
through the identity

$$f_1 = 1 - f_2 = \langle \Omega(\vec{x}) \rangle .$$

(2)

0094-243X/84/1070066-12 $3.00 Copyright 1984 American Institute of Physics

Here, as elsewhere, the angular brackets denote volume averages rather than ensemble averages.

The paper proceeds as follows. First we discuss perturbation solutions which apply when the properties of the two components are very similar. At this level σ_e, κ_e and μ_e are correlated through common geometric parameters which just depend on the structure of the material. Some relationships between the geometric parameters are studied. Next bounds which interlink σ_e, κ_e and μ_e are considered both for the case where the two components are moderately dissimilar and for the extreme case where the components have drastically different properties.

It is found that the effective medium approximation[5-8], which gives estimates of σ_e, κ_e and μ_e for granular aggregates, is in accord with all the new results. There is a good reason for this. A detailed analysis shows that the approximation is exact for a class of models, described here, once appropriate limits have been taken.

As Schulgasser[9] remarks, the effective medium approximation always seems to produce possible solutions. The reason for this has been somewhat of a mystery, but we now see it is because the approximation produces the solution for a class of model composites.

PERTURBATION SOLUTIONS

Let us suppose the components have approximately similar properties so that $\delta_\sigma = \sigma_1 - \sigma_2$, $\delta_\kappa = \kappa_1 - \kappa_2$ and $\delta_\mu = \mu_1 - \mu_2$ are small. Furthermore consider the composite to be periodic so that $\Omega(\vec{x})$ can be expressed as a Fourier series,

$$\Omega(\vec{x}) = f_1 + \sum_{\vec{k}} \omega(\vec{k})e^{i\vec{k}\cdot\vec{x}} \tag{3}$$

where $\omega(0) = 0$ and the sum extends over all points in the reciprocal space. This approach, first suggested by Brown[10] and developed in detail by Phan-Thien and myself[11,12] is perfectly general so long as the periodicity is much larger than the typical size of inhomogeneities. Note that since $\Omega(\vec{x})$ only takes the values 0 or 1 we have

$$[2\Omega(\vec{x}) - 1]^2 = 1 , \tag{4}$$

which implies that

$$\sum_{\vec{k}} \omega(\vec{k})\omega(-\vec{k}) = f_1 f_2 , \tag{5}$$

and

$$\sum_{\vec{m}} \omega(\vec{m})\omega(\vec{k}-\vec{m}) = (f_2-f_1)\omega(\vec{k}) \ . \tag{6}$$

The field equations can be mapped into Fourier space and solved by recursion to obtain series expansions for σ_e, κ_e and μ_e. To fourth order (i.e. discarding terms of order δ_σ^5, δ_κ^5, $\delta_\kappa^4\delta_\mu$ and so on) one finds that σ_e, κ_e and μ_e just depend on f_1 and the geometrical parameters

$$G_a = \sum_{\vec{k},\vec{m}} \frac{(\vec{k}\cdot\vec{m})^a}{k^a m^a} \ \omega(\vec{k})\omega(\vec{m}-\vec{k})\omega(-\vec{m}), \tag{7}$$

$$H_{abc} = \sum_{\vec{k},\vec{m},\vec{n}} \frac{(\vec{k}\cdot\vec{m})^a (\vec{m}\cdot\vec{n})^b (\vec{n}\cdot\vec{k})^c}{k^{c+a} m^{a+b} n^{b+c}} \ \omega(\vec{k})\omega(\vec{m}-\vec{k})\omega(\vec{n}-\vec{m})\omega(-\vec{n}), \tag{8}$$

where the summations do not include points where $\vec{k}=0$, $\vec{m}=0$ or $\vec{n}=0$. Specifically, σ_e depends on two of the parameters,

$$\sigma_e \cong \sigma(G_2, H_{111}), \tag{9}$$

while κ_e depends on three of them and μ_e on eight,

$$\kappa_e \cong \kappa(G_2, H_{111}, H_{220}), \tag{10}$$

$$\mu_e \cong \mu(G_2, G_4, H_{111}, H_{220}, H_{022}, 2H_{311} + H_{113}, H_{222}). \tag{11}$$

Detailed expressions for these functions have been presented elsewhere[11,12] for the case d=3, where d denotes the dimensionality. Results which apply for arbitrary d are given in the appendix.

It is very difficult to directly calculate the parameters G_a and H_{abc}. Our assumption that the periodicity is much larger than the microstructure means that the high frequency components of $\Omega(\vec{x})$ are very important. This is accentuated by the discontinuous nature of $\Omega(\vec{x})$. So any evaluation based on (7) or (8) requires the summation of an immense number of terms. The parameters can, however, be recast in terms of three and four point correlation functions of $\Omega'(\vec{x}) = \Omega(\vec{x}) - f_1$. For example, when d=3 one finds[11] that

$$G_2 = \frac{1}{(4\pi)^2} \iint \frac{d^3\vec{r} \ d^3\vec{s}}{rs} \ (\frac{\partial^2}{\partial\vec{r}\cdot\partial\vec{s}})^2 \ <\Omega'(\vec{s})\Omega'(\vec{r})\Omega'(0)>, \tag{12}$$

where the integrals extend over all space excluding infinitesimal spheres around $\vec{r}=0$ and $\vec{s}=0$.

Although some of the geometric parameters such as G_2 and G_4 (or their equivalents) have been calculated for a number of geometries[13-16], the point I want to emphasize is that the expressions (9)-(11) are still useful even if the structure of the material is unknown. This follows because G_2 and H_{111} occur in all three expressions. Thus measurements of σ_e lead to information about G_2 and H_{111} which in turn imply something about κ_e and μ_e.

The perturbation solutions can also be used to check the consistency of the effective medium approximation (EMA). For example consider the two dimensional EMA for an aggregate of circular grains. By comparing the approximation for μ_e with (41) one can make the identifications

$$G_2 = 4G_4/3 = -f_1 f_2 (f_1 - f_2)/2, \tag{13}$$

$$H_{111} = H_{022} = f_1 f_2 (1 - 3f_1 f_2)/4, \tag{14}$$

$$H_{220} = f_1 f_2 (2 - 7f_1 f_2)/8, \tag{15}$$

$$2H_{311} + H_{113} = f_1 f_2 (9 - 25f_1 f_2)/16, \tag{16}$$

$$H_{222} = f_1 f_2 (5 - 13f_1 f_2)/32. \tag{17}$$

It turns out that the approximation for σ_e (or κ_e) leads to precisely the same expressions for G_2 and H_{111} (and H_{220}). So in this respect the EMA is self-consistent.

RELATIONS AMONGST THE GEOMETRICAL PARAMETERS

In two dimensions the eight geometrical parameters are not all independent. Consider any three coplanar vectors $\vec{k}$, $\vec{m}$ and $\vec{n}$. It is easy to check that

$$2(\vec{k} \cdot \vec{m})(\vec{m} \cdot \vec{n})(\vec{n} \cdot \vec{k}) = k^2(\vec{m} \cdot \vec{n})^2 + m^2(\vec{n} \cdot \vec{k})^2 + n^2(\vec{k} \cdot \vec{m})^2 - k^2 m^2 n^2. \tag{18}$$

This cyclic combination of scalar products appears in the expression (8) for H_{abc} whenever a, b and c are positive integers. Consequently (7), (8) and (18) together with (5) and (6) lead to the identities

$$4H_{111} = 6(f_2 - f_1)G_2 + f_1 f_2 (9f_1 f_2 - 2), \tag{19}$$

$$2H_{311} = (f_2 - f_1)(G_4 - G_2) + H_{220} + H_{022}, \tag{20}$$

$$2H_{113} = (f_2-f_1)(G_4-G_2) + 2H_{022} + f_1^2 f_2^2/8, \tag{21}$$

$$4H_{222} = 3(f_2-f_1)(G_4-2G_2) + 2H_{220} + 4H_{022} + f_1 f_2 - 35f_1^2 f_2^2/8, \tag{22}$$

which hold for any two dimensional composite. The first identity can alternatively be derived[4] from a well known duality property of σ_e when the two components are interchanged[17,18]. The other relations are new and essentially halve the number of geometric parameters needed to calculate σ_e, κ_e and μ_e to fourth order in perturbation. One can check that the values of the geometric parameters given by the EMA, as in (13)-(17) are consistent with all these identities.

In three dimensions there is no similarly useful identity between the scalar products and consequently there are no identities amongst any of the eight geometrical parameters. Nevertheless one can deduce inequalities such as

$$9H_{111} \lesseqgtr 12(f_2-f_1)G_2 + f_1 f_2(16f_1 f_2 - 3). \tag{23}$$

This relation is proved by considering the field

$$\Gamma(\vec{x}) = \sum_{\vec{k},\vec{m}} \gamma_{abcd} \frac{k_a k_b m_c m_d}{k^2 m^2} \omega(\vec{k}-\vec{m})\omega(\vec{m})e^{i\vec{k}\cdot\vec{x}}, \tag{24}$$

where the Einstein summation convention is used and the summation over $\vec{k} = (k_1,k_2,k_3)$ and $\vec{m} = (m_1,m_2,m_3)$ excludes the points where $\vec{k}=0$ or $\vec{m}=0$. By appropriately choosing the tensor γ_{abcd}, the positivity of $<[\Gamma(\vec{x})]^2>$ then implies (23).

BOUNDS

If δ_σ, δ_μ and δ_κ are not small then the perturbation solutions are clearly unsuitable. One alternative approach is to derive rigorous bounds on σ_e, κ_e and μ_e using variational principles. An appealing choice for the trial fields is to take perturbation solutions for the actual fields and truncate them at some fixed order and then vary the coefficients of the remaining terms to obtain the best bound. Using this method one obtains a sequence of bounds[19]. The nth order bounds depend on the geometrical parameters entering the nth order perturbation solution[4,11,15]. So the geometrical parameters are still useful even if δ_σ, δ_μ and δ_κ are moderately large.

The relationships amongst the geometrical parameters can be used to improve some of the bounds. For example, in three dimensions the fourth order lower bound[4,12] on σ_e (which depends on G_2 and H_{111}) when combined with the inequality (23) gives

$$\sigma_e \geq \sigma_1 \left[\frac{(\sigma_1+2\sigma_2)(\sigma_2+2<\sigma>) - 2f_1\zeta_2\delta_\sigma^2}{(\sigma_1+2\sigma_2)(2\sigma_1+<\tilde{\sigma}>) - 2f_1\zeta_2\delta_\sigma^2} \right] , \qquad (25)$$

for all $\sigma_2 \geq \sigma_1$, where

$$\zeta_2 = (3f_2^2f_1 - 3G_2 - f_1^2f_2)/2f_1f_2 , \qquad (26)$$

and the tilde in $\tilde{\sigma}$ denotes the operation of interchanging the sub-
scripts 1 and 2 on σ, so that

$$<\tilde{\sigma}> = f_2\sigma_1 + f_1\sigma_2. \qquad (27)$$

This rigorous bound, which had previously been conjectured[4], is an
improvement of one of the third order bounds derived by Beran[19,20]
and incorporates the same information about the composite--namely
the geometric parameter G_2. The new bound is in fact attainable for
all possible values of G_2. The composites which realize the bound
are assemblages of doubly coated spheres[4].

One of the most striking examples of the utility of the third
order bounds[19-22] is that they show σ_e and κ_e are highly correlated
when either σ_e or κ_e is close to one of the Hashin-Shtrikman (HS)
bounds[23,24]. In the extreme case when say σ_e coincides with one of
the HS bounds, ζ_2 must be exactly 0 or 1 which then implies that κ_e
must coincide with the corresponding HS bound. This property does
not extend to μ_e since the third order bounds on μ_e depend on G_4
as well as G_2 (or alternatively ζ_2).

When δ_σ, δ_κ and δ_μ are very large the low-order bounds are
seldom narrow enough for practical purposes. This reflects the fact
that σ_e, κ_e and μ_e are very sensitive to details of the geometry.
One can however, deduce some simple relationships between σ_e, κ_e
and μ_e which are useful even when one component is superconducting,
insulating, rigid or void. For example, if $\sigma_e(\sigma_1,\sigma_2)$ denotes the
effective conductivity as a function of σ_1 and σ_2, then the
relation

$$\kappa_e \leq \sigma_e(\kappa_1,\kappa_2) \qquad (28)$$

must hold whenever the Lamé constants λ_1 and λ_2 of the components are both positive.

The basic idea in the proof is to use electric potentials as components of trial displacement fields. Suppose d=3, $\sigma_1 = \kappa_1$ and $\sigma_2 = \kappa_2$ and let $V_1(\vec{x})$, $V_2(\vec{x})$, $V_3(\vec{x})$ denote the local electric potentials such that

$$\langle V_{i,j} \rangle = \delta_{ij}, \tag{29}$$

where the comma in $V_{i,j}$ denotes differentiation of V_i with respect to x_j. The effective conductivity is then

$$\sigma_e(\kappa_1, \kappa_2) = \langle \kappa V_{i,j} V_{i,j} \rangle / 3. \tag{30}$$

Using $\vec{u}^T = (V_1, V_2, V_3)$ as a trial displacement field in the standard variational principle gives

$$9\kappa_e \le \langle \lambda \varepsilon_{ii}^T \varepsilon_{jj}^T + 2\mu \varepsilon_{ij}^T \varepsilon_{ij}^T \rangle, \tag{31}$$

where

$$\varepsilon_{ij}^T = (V_{i,j} + V_{j,i})/2. \tag{32}$$

The chain of inequalities

$$\varepsilon_{ii}^T \varepsilon_{jj}^T \le 3\varepsilon_{ij}^T \varepsilon_{ij}^T \le 3 V_{i,j} V_{i,j} \tag{33}$$

then implies that (28) holds provided λ_1 and λ_2 are positive. The proof extends to other values of d.

As an application, consider a two-component aggregate of spheres where component 1 is a rigid superconductor and component 2 is compressible with finite conductivity and with $\lambda_2 > 0$. Then (28) implies that the composite cannot be rigid with finite conductivity. It does not forbid a composite which is compressible and superconducting. Interestingly the EMA predicts a compressible superconducting composite for f_1 between 1/3 and 1/2, but it does not predict a composite which is rigid with finite conductivity.

MICROGEOMETRIES CORRESPONDING TO THE EMA

The examples already presented add considerable support to the effective medium approximation, also known as the self-consistent scheme. As applied to an aggregate of grains the basis of the approximation is that each grain can be treated as if it is embedded in a homogeneous "effective medium" with conductivity σ_e, bulk modulus κ_e and shear modulus μ_e. One can then find the ratio of the field in the grain to the field in the effective medium and thereby obtain estimates, let us call them σ_*, κ_* and μ_*, for the effective properties[5-8]. For spherical grains one finds

$$f_1/(\sigma_*-\sigma_2) + f_2/(\sigma_*-\sigma_1) = 1/3\sigma_*, \qquad (34)$$

$$f_1/(\kappa_*-\kappa_2) + f_2/(\kappa_*-\kappa_1) = 3/(3\kappa_*+4\mu_*), \qquad (35)$$

$$f_1/(\mu_*-\mu_1) + f_2/(\mu_*-\mu_2) = 6(\kappa_*+2\mu_*)/5\mu_*(3\kappa_*+4\mu_*). \qquad (36)$$

Recently, on the basis of a mild assumption, I have proved that the EMA gives an "exact" solution for σ_e, κ_e and μ_e for a class of granular aggregates such that grains of comparable size are well separated. The models bear a very close resemblance to self-similar models for sedimentary rocks proposed by Sen, Scala and Cohen[25]. They are constructed according to a hierarchical scheme, as described below.

Briefly, one starts with a matrix material "0" with effective properties of $\sigma_m^{(0)}$, $\kappa_m^{(0)}$ and $\mu_m^{(0)}$, composed of the two components compacted together with some characteristic size of inhomogeneities, say h (Fig. 1c). Next, a set of large grains, size αh, of both components is embedded as a dilute suspension, occupying a volume fraction ε_1 in the matrix material "0" to form a new matrix material

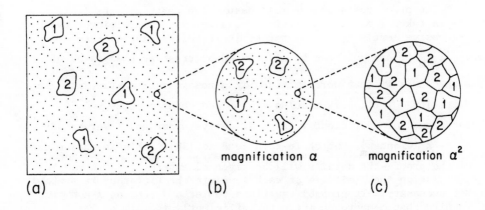

magnification α magnification α^2

(a)   (b)   (c)

Fig. 1. The first stages in the construction of the hierarchical models, as described in the text.

"1" with effective properties $\sigma_m^{(1)}$, $\kappa_m^{(1)}$ and $\mu_m^{(1)}$ (Fig. 1b). The original set of large grains is duplicated and the copies are scaled up in size by a factor α. These even larger grains, of typical size $\alpha^2 h$, are embedded as a dilute suspension, occupying a volume fraction ε_2, in the matrix material "1" to form the next matrix material "2" (Fig. 1a). This procedure is repeated. At the Jth stage a set of grains of size $\alpha^J h$ is embedded as a dilute suspension in the matrix material "J-1" to form a new matrix material "J" with effective properties $\sigma_m^{(J)}$, $\kappa_m^{(J)}$ and $\mu_m^{(J)}$. These largest grains occupy a volume fraction ε_J of the matrix material "J." The grains of components 1 and 2 in this set each occupy volume fractions $f_1 \varepsilon_J$ and $f_2 \varepsilon_J$.

One chooses ε_J such that

$$\lim_{J \to \infty} J\varepsilon_J > \lim_{J \to \infty} \varepsilon_J = 0, \tag{37}$$

which ensures, as $J \to \infty$, that the starting matrix material "0" occupies an infinitesimal portion of matrix material "J" and that the coupling between fields surrounding grains of size $\alpha^J h$ is vanishingly small. Then, if the conductivities, bulk and shear moduli of the components are finite and non-zero the fundamental result is that

$$\lim_{J \to \infty} [\lim_{\alpha \to \infty} (\sigma_m^{(J)}, \kappa_m^{(J)}, \mu_m^{(J)})] = (\sigma_*, \kappa_*, \mu_*) . \tag{38}$$

The proof rests on the mild assumption that once the limit $\alpha \to \infty$ is taken (so that the ratio of scales of inhomogeneity between successive levels in the hierarchy is infinitely large) then $\sigma_m^{(J)}$, $\kappa_m^{(J)}$, and $\mu_m^{(J)}$ can be calculated by treating the grains of size $\alpha^J h$ as if they were embedded in a homogeneous matrix with conductivity $\sigma_m^{(J-1)}$, bulk modulus $\kappa_m^{(J-1)}$ and shear modulus $\mu_m^{(J-1)}$. One can then, for sufficiently large J, derive upper and lower bounds on $\sigma_m^{(J)}$, $\kappa_m^{(J)}$ and $\mu_m^{(J)}$ which in turn lead to (38). This is the essence of the proof--the details will be given elsewhere.

Taking the limit $\alpha \to \infty$ at each level in the hierarchy is probably not necessary. It probably suffices to let α depend on J and just require that α approach infinity sufficiently rapidly as $J \to \infty$.

The EMA has sparked a lot of controversy[8] which still continues. The correspondence (38) between the EMA and the hierarchical models places the approximation on a sounder basis. Furthermore the EMA can now be used as a benchmark for testing new theories and conjectures. In particular it can be used to explore what relationships between σ_e, κ_e and μ_e are possible.

ACKNOWLEDGMENTS

N. Phan-Thien made major contributions towards the work[11,12] which links the effective properties to the geometric parameters and R. C. McPhedran helped establish the connection between the EMA and the hierarchical models. I have also profited from many discussions with M. E. Fisher. The award of a University of Sydney Travelling Scholarship and a Sage Fellowship from Cornell University together with ancillary support from the National Science Foundation, in part through the Material Science Center at Cornell University are gratefully acknowledged.

APPENDIX: THE PERTURBATION EXPANSIONS

By extending the results developed by Phan-Thien and myself[11,12] to arbitrary dimensionality d, one obtains the fourth order perturbation expansions,

$$\sigma_e \cong \langle\sigma\rangle - (f_1 f_2 \bar{\delta}_\sigma - G_2 \bar{\delta}_\sigma^2 + H_{111} \bar{\delta}_\sigma^3)\delta_\sigma/d, \tag{39}$$

$$\kappa_e \cong \langle\kappa\rangle - [f_1 f_2 \hat{\delta}_\kappa - f_1 f_2 (f_2 - f_1)\hat{\delta}_\kappa \hat{\delta}_\lambda - 2G_2 \hat{\delta}_\kappa \hat{\delta}_\mu$$

$$+ f_1 f_2 (f_2 - f_1)^2 \hat{\delta}_\kappa \hat{\delta}_\lambda^2 + 4(f_2 - f_1)G_2 \hat{\delta}_\kappa \hat{\delta}_\lambda \hat{\delta}_\mu$$

$$+ 4(H_{111} - \gamma H_{220})\hat{\delta}_\kappa \hat{\delta}_\mu \bar{\delta}_\mu]\delta_\kappa, \tag{40}$$

$$\mu_e \cong \langle\mu\rangle - \{2f_1 f_2 (d-1)(d+2-2\gamma)\bar{\delta}_\mu + 4[f_1 f_2 (f_2-f_1) - dG_2]\hat{\delta}_\mu \hat{\delta}_\lambda$$

$$- 2[df_1 f_2 (f_2-f_1) + d(d+2-8\gamma)G_2 + 4d\gamma^2 G_4 - 4(1-\gamma)^2 G_2]\bar{\delta}_\mu^2$$

$$+ 4[d(f_2-f_1)G_2 + (d-1)f_1^2 f_2^2 - f_1 f_2 (f_2-f_1)^2]\hat{\delta}_\mu \hat{\delta}_\lambda^2$$

$$+ 16[dH_{111} - d\gamma H_{022} - (f_2-f_1)(1-\gamma)G_2]\hat{\delta}_\mu \bar{\delta}_\mu \hat{\delta}_\lambda$$

$$+ 2[d(d+4-12\gamma)H_{111} - 8(1-\gamma)^2 H_{111} - 4d\gamma(2H_{022} + H_{220})$$

$$+ 8\gamma(1-\gamma)^2 H_{220} + 8d\gamma^2(2H_{311} + H_{113}) - 8d\gamma^3 H_{222}$$

$$+ 3d(f_2-f_1)G_2 + (d-1)f_1^2 f_2^2]\bar{\delta}_\mu^3\}\delta_\mu/d(d-1)(d-2), \tag{41}$$

where λ_1 and λ_2 are the Lamé constants,

$$\lambda_i = \kappa_i - 2\mu_i/d \tag{42}$$

for $i = 1$ or 2, and

$$\bar{\delta}_\sigma = \delta_\sigma/\langle\sigma\rangle, \tag{43}$$

$$\bar{\delta}_\mu = \delta_\mu/\langle\mu\rangle, \tag{44}$$

$$\hat{\delta}_\kappa = \delta_\kappa/\langle\lambda+2\mu\rangle, \tag{45}$$

$$\hat{\delta}_\lambda = \delta_\lambda/\langle\lambda+2\mu\rangle = (\lambda_1-\lambda_2)/\langle\lambda+2\mu\rangle, \tag{46}$$

$$\hat{\delta}_\mu = \delta_\mu/\langle\lambda+2\mu\rangle, \tag{47}$$

$$\gamma = \langle\lambda+\mu\rangle/\langle\lambda+2\mu\rangle. \tag{48}$$

The right hand sides of (39), (40) and (41) should be identified with the functions in (9), (10) and (11).

REFERENCES

1. G. K. Batchelor, Ann. Rev. Fluid Mech. 6, 227 (1974).
2. S. Prager, J. Chem. Phys. 50, 4305 (1969).
3. D. J. Bergman, Phys. Rep. 43C, 377 (1978).
4. G. W. Milton, J. Appl. Phys. 52, 5294 (1981).
5. D. A. G. Bruggeman, Ann. Physik. (Leipzig) 24, 636 (1935).
6. R. Landauer, in Electrical Transport and Optical Properties of Inhomogeneous Media, ed. by J. C. Garland and D. B. Tanner (A.I.P., N.Y., 1978), pp. 2-43.
7. B. Budianski, J. Mech. Phys. Solids, 13, 223 (1965).
8. J. G. Berryman, J. Acoust. Soc. Am. 68, 1809 (1980).
9. K. Schulgasser, J. Phys. C10, 407 (1977).
10. W. F. Brown, Trans. Soc. Rheol. 9, 357 (1965).
11. G. W. Milton and N. Phan-Thien, Proc. R. Soc. Lond., A380, 305 (1982).
12. N. Phan-Thien and G. W. Milton, Proc. R. Soc. Lond., A380, 333 (1982).
13. M. N. Miller, J. Math. Phys. 10, 1988 (1969).
14. N. Silnutzer, Ph.D. Thesis (University of Pennsylvania, Philadelphia, 1972).
15. R. C. McPhedran and G. W. Milton, Appl. Phys. A26, 207 (1981).
16. S. Torquato and G. Stell, J. Chem. Phys. 79, 1505 (1983).
17. J. B. Keller, J. Math. Phys. 5, 548 (1964).
18. A. M. Dykhne, Zh. Eksp. Teor. Fiz 59, 110 (1970).
19. M. Beran, Nuovo Cim. 38, 771 (1965).
20. G. W. Milton, Phys. Rev. Lett. 46, 542 (1981).
21. M. Beran and J. Molyneux, Q. Appl. Math. 24, 107 (1965).
22. J. J. McCoy, in Recent Advances in Engineering Sciences (Gordon and Breach, N.Y., 1970), Vol. 5, pp. 235-254.
23. Z. Hashin and S. Shtrikman, J. Appl. Phys. 33, 3125 (1962).
24. Z. Hashin and S. Shtrikman, J. Mech. Phys. Solids 11, 127 (1963).
25. P. N. Sen, C. Scala and M. H. Cohen, Geophysics 46, 781 (1981).

CONNECTION BETWEEN STRUCTURE AND STRENGTH OF POROUS SOLIDS

K. Kendall
ICI New Science Group, PO Box 8 The Heath, Runcorn UK

ABSTRACT

Two distinct theories of the strength of porous solids may be
found in the literature, one claiming that the volume of pores
dictates strength, the other that the longest pores are crucial
because they initiate cracks. Various empirical attempts have
previously been made to reconcile these apparently conflicting
arguments. This paper shows from first principles, using an energy
balance method, that strength must depend on both pore volume and on
maximum pore length. The theory was verified by measurements on an
ideal porous glass, and was also shown to be useful in describing
the behaviour of complex porous materials such as hydraulic cement.

INTRODUCTION

The controversy around the strength of porous solids stretches
back into antiquity. Should strength be determined by pore volume or
by pore length ? Lucretius [1], in the first century BC,had observed
water seeping through rocks and had associated the weakness of such
materials with their volume porosity,'The more vacuum a thing contains
within it, the more readily it yields'. By contrast, Vitruvius [2] (c.10
AD) thought that long pores dictated the strength of porous building
products,'Cracks make...bricks weak'. In recent times these separate
schools of thought have persisted, despite their conflicting nature;
a long crack may represent only a small pore volume but might have an
enormous weakening effect.

Here, the objective is to produce a theory [3] which reconciles
these two opposing arguments, showing from first principles that both
volume and length of pores influence the strength of a porous body.
This theory is then verified by experiments on a 'model' porous solid
and is also shown to be applicable to practical materials such as
cement.

VOLUME ARGUMENT

There is no doubt that, other things being equal, solids become
weaker as they are made to contain a greater volume of pores. This is
true of compressive strength, tensile and bending strength. It is also
valid for a wide range of substances made by different methods. Some
results are shown in figure 1 for natural rocks and firebrick [4],
alumina and zirconia [5], iron [6], cement [7], plaster of paris [8], and ice [9].
The observed drop in strength is remarkably similar for different
pore sizes and shapes and this suggests some fundamental cause of
this behaviour.

Theoretical attempts to explain these results have largely been
based on the idea that porosity reduces the average cross-sectional
area of the solid body. A typical equation used to describe such

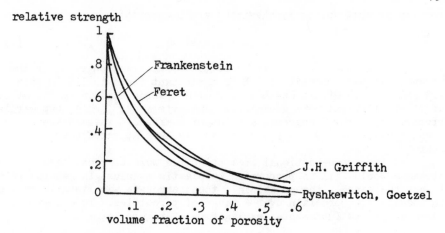

Fig. 1. Relative strength results for various materials as a function of volume porosity

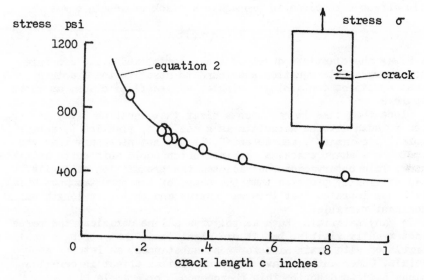

Fig. 2. A.A. Griffith's results for fracture of glass containing a crack of length c for comparison with his theoretical equation derived from the principle of energy conservation.

results is that due to Ryshkewitch[5] and Duckworth[10]

$$\sigma = \sigma_0 \exp(-bp) \qquad (1)$$

in which σ is the strength at porosity volume fraction p, σ_0 is the strength at zero porosity and b is a constant found to lie between 1.3 and 9. Much effort has been directed towards explaining the value of b for different pore geometries. Eudier's model[11] which was earlier proposed by Tabor[12] suggests a value of b around 3 whereas Knudsen's[13] gives a value near 9. Many similar models have appeared over the years[14-17].

If the cross-sectional area principle were correct, then strength would fall in proportion to elastic modulus. In general this is not the case[18], though Kalnin[19] found strength was linearly related to modulus for porcelain over a range of porosities. To summarise, there is yet no fundamental explanation of figure 1.

PORE LENGTH ARGUMENT

The powerful influence of long pores or cracks on the tensile strength of brittle materials was first explained by A.A. Griffith[3], who used the principle of energy conservation to show that the tensile stress σ required to propagate a crack of length c was

$$\sigma = (ER/\pi c)^{\frac{1}{2}} \qquad (2)$$

where E was the elastic modulus of the material and R its fracture surface energy. This equation was found to describe the fracture of glass specimens containing a single, well-defined crack, as shown in figure 2.

Since that time it has become clear that equation 2 may be applied to such diverse materials as glass[20-25], plastics[26], rubber[27], [28], metal[29], ceramic[30], and cement[31]. It was not necessary that the long pore be a sharp crack; a machined notch would suffice to initiate cracking. This observation contradicted the presumption of Inglis[32] who had originally proposed that the shape of the pore was most vital. Griffith demonstrated that this was untrue and that pore length was the dominant variable.

In many materials, such as polycrystalline ceramics, the pores were not readily visible, but it was significant that strength could be correlated with grain size for most substances, as Petch[33] showed for metals. Other authors have observed similar effect in ceramics[34-36]. Equations used to describe this phenomenon, for example

$$\sigma = Kd^{-\frac{1}{2}} \qquad (3)$$

(where d is the grain size, and K a constant) are sufficiently similar to equation 2 to suggest that flaws or cracks exist at grain boundaries, related in length to the grains themselves.

In summary, there seems to be no exception to the rule that one long pore causes predictable weakness in a brittle material. However, this idea has not been extended to bodies containing many pores.

THE PROBLEM

The need is to produce a theory which encompasses these two well-known effects:- the influence of porosity volume in degrading strength, and the influence of long pores or cracks. Knudsen[13] first produced an empirical combination of equations 1 and 3

$$\sigma = Kd^{-a}\exp(-bp) \qquad (4)$$

to explain the combined effect of grain size d and porosity volume p using experimentally determined constants K, a and b. Numerous variants of this equation have been offered pragmatically since then[37-41]. But it has not been made clear whether grain size d is related to the length of large pores. Nor is it certain why the two variables can be separated in this manner. Equation 4 demands a fundamental explanation.

Previous theories have been based on stress arguments, with the exponential term in equation 4 arising from the reduction in cross-sectional area by porosity volume, and the d term stemming from stress concentration effects due to pore size, shape, and distribution[39,42-44]. This paper, in contrast, denies these stress arguments. Instead, the energy approach[3] is used to explain the behaviour of equation 4 from first principles. This theory is then verified by experiments on porous silica glass.

THEORY

The model of an ideal porous solid is shown in figure 3. A sheet of material contains many small pores of total volume fraction p, each pore being too short to initiate cracking, but the total porosity being such that the elastic modulus and fracture energy of the body are significantly reduced. Failure stems from a single long 'crack-like' pore which is of length 2c but of insignificant volume. In practice there may be several such long pores in the body but, in total, these have an insignificant influence on elastic modulus and fracture energy. Thus, we imagine two independent types of pore; those myriads of pores having volume but no length, and a few failure initiating pores having length but insignificant volume.

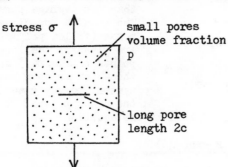

Fig. 3. Model of an ideal porous solid

To produce such a body experimentally is simple. One takes a porous material and cuts a thin notch in it with a diamond impregnated wheel, ensuring that the length of this notch far exceeds the size of the natural pores in the material, while being sufficiently short compared with the dimensions of the sample that the stiffness of the body remains essentially unaltered.

This model allows separation of the volume and length variables, the crack of length 2c propagating as though through a continuum whose elastic modulus and fracture energy vary with porosity volume in the manner described below.

As Coble and Kingery[45] pointed out, there are two limiting cases of porosity, one in which the solid structure is continuous and whose pores are closed, and the other with interpenetrating networks of solid and pores. Closed pore alumina gave the upper curve in figure 4 closely approximating the modulus prediction of Mackenzie[46], described approximately by

$$E = E_o(1-1.9p+0.9p^2) \tag{5}$$

Open pore materials, such as the porous silica described later, are known to give a greater fall in modulus, approximating empirically to

$$E = E_o(1-p)^3 \tag{6}$$

an equation mentioned in the cement literature[47,48] and also closely comparable with results for iron compacts[49].

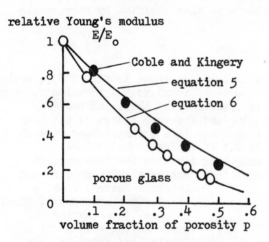

relative Young's modulus E/E_o

Fig. 4. Variation of modulus with porosity for sintered alumina (●) and porous silica glass (○)

The dependence of fracture energy on porosity is less well documented[50,51]. It has been suggested that pores have little effect on fracture energy of alumina. However, it was demonstrated by tearing filled polymers[52] that fracture energy should fall with porosity volume fraction and because the crack can select the weakest path, will fall more rapidly than the average porosity. The results for closed pores (filled polymer) are given in the lower points of figure 5 and those for an open pore system (porous glass) in the upper points. The results could be reasonably well fitted by the equation

$$R = R_o\exp(-dp) \tag{7}$$

where R_o was the fracture energy of dense material and d was a constant. Figure 5 also shows the range of values of d predicted for simple pore shapes[53] (dotted lines).

Knowing the variation in E and R for a porous material from equations 6 and 7, it was possible to work out the condition for propagation of a long 'crack-like' pore of length 2c. The energy U

relative fracture energy R/R_o

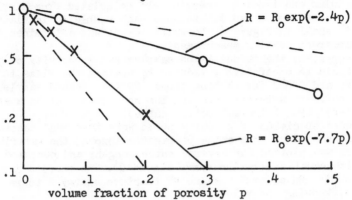

Fig. 5. Variation of fracture energy with porosity for porous glass
(O) and filled polymer (X).

associated with the 'crack-like' pore of length 2c in an infinite
sheet under a tensile stress σ was calculated and the condition for
energy conservation applied (for example see reference 54).

$$\frac{dU}{dc} = 0 \tag{8}$$

giving the criterion for extension of the 'crack-like' pore in porous
glass

$$\sigma = \left[\frac{E_o R_o (1-p)^3 \exp(-dp)}{\pi c}\right]^{\frac{1}{2}} \tag{9}$$

For closed pore materials , a slightly different equation would result
from the use of equation 5 to describe the modulus variation rather
than equation 6.

EXPERIMENTAL

The object of the experiments was to test this equation, which
predicts that 1) porous materials should give Griffith behaviour, the
strength diminishing with (critical pore length)$^{-\frac{1}{2}}$,
but with a separate Griffith curve for each porosity
volume,
and 2) there is no unique curve relating strength to volume
porosity, equation 9 representing a family of strength
-porosity curves, one for each value of critical pore
length c.
In other words, strength is a function of two independent variables p
and c.

Samples of porous silica glass, made by leaching sodium borate
from phase-separated sodium borosilicate glass rods[55,56], were kindly
supplied by Dr C. Howard of Pilkington Brothers plc, Lathom ,Ormskirk.

   Mechanical testing was carried out in three point bending.
Young's modulus and bending strength were calculated from simple beam
theory. A central notch was cut through each sample to initiate
cracking as shown in figure 6. Porosity volume was determined from
true and apparent density measurements.

   As supplied, the porous glass samples had a porosity of p=.48
but this could be controllably reduced by heating the glass to
between 800 and 900°C for various times. By this method samples of
different porosity were obtained and the modulus variation measured
to be $70(1-p)^3$ GPa   (figure 4 bottom curve).

   Notched specimens of porosity p=.48 were then bend tested to
find the stress at which a crack propagated through the material.
This stress was plotted for several notch lengths and compared with
the Griffith equation (bottom curve figure 6). The results gave a
reasonable fit and allowed a value of fracture energy R to be
calculated, knowing the value of E.

   This process was repeated for samples of porosity p=.29 and
also for dense silica. Again the results matched the Griffith curve
but with higher values of fracture energy and modulus, the denser
the material. The fracture energy variation is shown in figure 5
(open circles). The conclusion was that equation 9 described the
results satisfactorily.

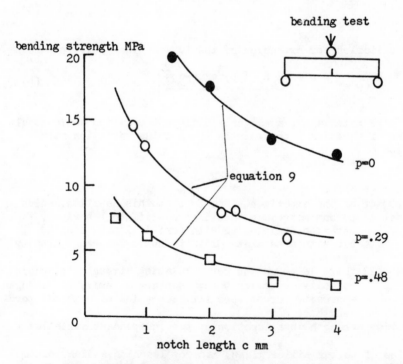

Fig. 6. Results for bending strength of porous silica glass
       compared with the predictions of equation 9.

bending strength MPa

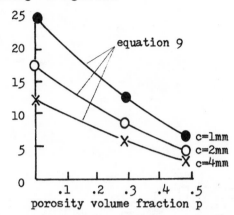

Fig. 7. Variation of bending strength
with volume porosity for
porous silica glass.

Plotting the strength
against porosity volume,
keeping the notch depth
constant, gave the behaviour
of figure 7. There was a
different curve for each
separate notch depth.
Thus, there was no unique
plot of strength against
porosity volume. Equation 9
provided a reasonable
fit to the results.

These ideas explain
much confusion in previous
reports. In the first place
it becomes clear why strength
is not merely a function of
the reduction in material
cross-section due to pores,
the usual explanation of
figure 1. Strength depends
on the reduction of both

elastic modulus and fracture energy with volume porosity. Secondly,
the model explains why introducing pores into a material may give
unpredictable effects on strength, since both the length and the
volume of pores have an influence[39,43].

PRACTICAL APPLICATION

To test these principles in a practical case, experiments were
performed on hydraulic cement[57,58], a notoriously weak and porous
material. Bending tests on notched samples of ordinary cement gave
the results shown in figure 8 (bottom line). These points fitted
equation 9 for long notches, but deviated from the theory for notches
less than 1mm in length. The inference was that natural pores existed
in the cement, around 1 mm long, and that these long pores were
limiting the strength to low values. Microscopic examination of
polished and decorated cement surfaces proved the existence of these
long pores.

Many previous investigators have attempted to improve the
strength of cement by reducing the volume of porosity from its high
level (about $p=.25$) through impregnation or by pressure compaction.
However, inspection of equation 9 reveals that complete densification
of the cement can only double the strength, whereas the removal of
the longest pores, from 1 mm down to .01 mm, can raise the strength
by an order of magnitude.

A new method of mixing cement slurries[59,60] was found to remove
these long pores and the bending strength was raised from 10 MPa to
66 MPa (figure 8 middle curve). During this process, the volume
porosity was also somewhat diminished, and in consequence the elastic
modulus and fracture energy of the material were improved slightly.

bending strength MPa

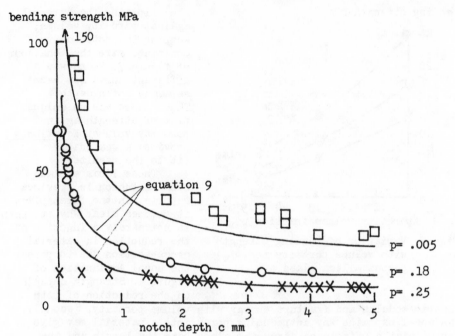

Fig. 8. Bending strength of notched beams of cement for three
different porosities compared with equation 9.

Further reduction in the volume porosity, keeping the pore
length constant, gave the results in the upper curve of figure 8.
Here the modulus was raised to 50 GPa, and the fracture energy to
150 Jm^{-2}, in reasonable accord with equations 6 and 7, the bending
strength of the cement rising to 150 MPa.
At each value of porosity volume, the strength figures fitted
the Griffith behaviour, the overall picture giving a pleasing fit to
the predictions of equation 9. This suggests that the theoretical
model applies not only to ideal materials such as porous silica
but also to practical, complex situations like cement which contain
several phases and a wide distribution of pore sizes.

CONCLUSIONS

A theory explaining the strength of porous solids in terms of
both volume porosity and critical pore length has been deduced using
the energy approach devised by Griffith. The theory has been verified
through experiments on porous silica glass in which the fine pores
provided the volume porosity which was shown to reduce the modulus
and fracture energy of the material, while a machined notch acted as
a long pore which initiated fracture. Results on cements of different
porosities indicated that the theory was useful in describing the
strength of practical and complicated porous solids.

REFERENCES

1. Lucretius, On The Nature of The Universe (translated by R. Lathom) (Penguin, London,1951), p. 43.
2. Vitruvius, The Ten Books of Architecture (translated by M.H. Morgan) (Dover,N.Y., 1960), p.43.
3. A.A. Griffith, Phil. Trans. R. Soc. Lond. A221, 163 (1920).
4. J.H. Griffith, Ceram. Abstr. 18, 35 (1939).
5. E. Ryshkewitch, J. Amer. Ceram. Soc. 36, 65 (1953).
6. C.G. Goetzel, Iron Age 150,82 (1942).
7. R. Feret, Bull.Soc.Encouragement Indust. Nat.II, 1604 (1897).
8. C.M. Lambe & J.S. Offutt, Bull. Am. Ceram. Soc. 33, 272 (1954).
9. G. Frankenstein, US Army Cold Regions Res. & Eng. Lab. Tech. Rep. No.172, 1-36 (1968).
10. W. Duckworth, J. Amer. Ceram. Soc. 36, 68 (1953).
11. M. Eudier, Powder Met. 9, 278 (1962).
12. D. Tabor, Mechanical Properties of Non Metallic Brittle Materials (ed. H. Walton)(Butterworths, London,1958),p. 48.
13. F.P. Knudsen, J. Amer. Ceram. Soc. 42, 376 (1959).
14. K.K. Schiller, Mechanical Properties of Non Metallic Brittle Materials,(ed. H. Walton)(Butterworths, London, 1958), p.35.
15. A. Assur, Natl. Acad. Sci.-Natl. Res. Council US Publ. 598,106(1958).
16. D.L. Anderson & W.F. Weeks, Trans. Amer. Geophys. Union 39,632(1958).
17. T.C. Powers,Proc. 4th Int. Symp. Chemistry of Cement, Nat. Bur. Stds. Monograph No. 43 VolII, Washington DC (1960) p.577.
18. R.L. Coble & N.M. Parikh, Fracture Vol.VII, (ed. H. Liebowitz) (Academic Press, London, 1972) P.243.
19. I.L. Kalnin, J. Amer. Ceram. Soc. 46, 1174 (1967).
20. J.P.A. Tillet, Proc. Phys. Soc. Lond. 69B, 47 (1956).
21. R.J. Charles, J. Appl. Phys. 29, 1554 (1958).
22. W.C. Levengrod, J. Appl. Phys. 29, 820 (1958).
23. R.E. Mould & R.D. Southwick, J. Am. Ceram. Soc. 42, 542 (1959).
24. E.B. Shand, J. Am. Ceram. Soc. 44, 21 (1961).
25. R.E. Mould, Fundamental Phenomena in the Material Sciences Vol.4, (Plenum, New York, 1967)
26. J.P. Berry, J. Polymer Sci. 50, 107, 313 (1961).
27. R.S. Rivlin & A.G. Thomas, J. Polymer Sci. 10, 291 (1953).
28. A.G. Thomas, J. Appl. Polymer Sci. 3, 168 (1960).
29. D.K. Felbeck & E. Orowan, Welding J.(NY) Res. Suppl. 34,510 (1955).
30. R.W. Davidge & G. Tappin, J. Mater. Sci. 3, 165 (1968).
31. J.D. Birchall, A.J. Howard & K. Kendall, Nature 289, 388 (1981).
32. C.E. Inglis, Trans. Inst. Naval Architects 55, 219 (1913).
33. N.J. Petch, J. Iron Steel Inst. Lond. 173, 25 (1953).
34. S.C. Carniglia, Mater. Sci. Res. 3, 425 (1966).
35. R.M. Spriggs, J.B. Mitchell & T. Vasilos, J. Amer. Ceram. Soc. 47, 323 (1964).
36. G.G. Bentle & R.M. Kniefel, J. Am. Ceram. Soc. 48, 570 (1965).
37. M.E. Kassem, Bull. Fac. Eng. Assiut Univ. 9, 125 (1981).
38. M. Beauvy, Rev. Int. Hautes Temp. Refract. 19, 301 (1982).
39. D.P.H. Hasselman & R.M. Fulrath, J. Am. Ceram. Soc. 46, 52 (1964), 49, 68 (1966).
40. R.M. Spriggs, J. Am. Ceram. Soc. 44, 628 (1961); 45, 454 (1962).
41. S.C. Carniglia, J. Am. Ceram. Soc. 55, 610 (1972).
42. R. Haynes, Powder Met. 14, 64 (1971).
43. R.L. Bertolotti & R.M. Fulrath, J. Am. Ceram. Soc. 50, 558 (1967).

88

44. D.R. Biswas & R.M. Fulrath,Fracture Mechanics of Ceramics,(ed.Bradt, Hasselman & Lange)(Plenum, New York,1978) p.933, Vol.4.
45. R.L. Coble & W.D. Kingery, J. Am. Ceram. Soc. 39, 377 (1956).
46. J.K. Mackenzie, Proc. Phys. Soc. Lond. 63B, 2 (1950).
47. T.C. Hansen, J. Am. Concrete Inst. 62, 193 (1965).
48. R.A. Helmuth & D.A. Turk, Symp.on Struct. of Portland Cement Paste & Concrete, (Highway Res. Board, Washington No.90 1966)p.135.
49. G.D. McAdam, J. Iron & Steel Inst. Lond. 168, 346 (1951).
50. J.A. Coppola & R.C. Bradt, J. Am. Ceram. Soc. 56, 392 (1973).
51. L.A. Simpson, J.Am. Ceram. Soc. 56, 7 (1973).
52. K. Kendall, Brit. Polymer J. 10, 35 (1978).
53. R.W. Rice, S.W. Freiman, R.C. Pohanka, J.J. Mecholsky & C.C. Wu, Fracture Mechanics of Ceramics Vol.4 (ed. Bradt, Hasselman & Lange) (Plenum, New York, 1978) p. 849.
54. B.R. Lawn & T.R. Wilshaw, Fracture of Brittle Solids, (University Press, Cambridge, 1975) chapter 1.
55. H.P. Hood & M.E. Nordberg, U.S. Pat. 2,106,704, 1938.
56. M.E. Nordberg, J. Am. Ceram. Soc. 27, 299 (1944).
57. J.D. Birchall, A.J. Howard & K. Kendall, Proc. Brit. Ceram. Soc. 32, 25 (1982).
58. K. Kendall, A.J. Howard & J.D. Birchall, Phil. Trans. R. Soc. Lond., in press (1983).
59. J.D. Birchall, A.J. Howard & K. Kendall, European Patent Publication No. 0021682, 1981, U.S. Pat. 4,353,749.
60. J.D. Birchall, A.J. Howard, K. Kendall & J. H. Raistrick, European Patent Publication No. 0055035, 1982.

ACOUSTIC PROPERTIES OF POROUS SYSTEMS:
I. PHENOMENOLOGICAL DESCRIPTION

T. J. Plona and David Linton Johnson

Schlumberger-Doll Research
P. O. Box 307, Ridgefield, CT 06877

ABSTRACT

Various aspects of acoustic propagation in macroscopically disordered, fluid-saturated porous media are discussed. By treating the oscillatory displacements of the two constituents separately and on an equal footing one is able to describe the attenuation and dispersion of sound due to the relative motion that can occur between the fluid and solid parts. Because there are two degrees of freedom in the formulation, the phenomenological theory predicts two longitudinal modes. The diffusive mode in polymer gels, 4th sound in HeII, the diffusion of a fluid pressure pulse through a porous medium, and the recent observation of a slow compressional propagatory wave in water saturated fused glass beads, are all shown to be special cases of this additional mode. We show that it is possible to independently measure all the necessary input parameters of the theory, at least in the high frequency limit, and predict all the bulk modes that can propagate in fluid-saturated porous systems. The predictions are in excellent agreement with our measured values.

INTRODUCTION

We consider the acoustic properties of fluid saturated porous media which have the unusual property that they support two distinct longitudinal acoustic modes.[1] The class of porous materials being considered is characterized by the unique topological property that the fluid and solid components each forms its own percolating, infinite cluster. Examples of such systems, which have immense practical importance as regards the search for energy sources, are porous sedimentary rocks. These may be idealized as a collection of individual grains, typically 1-100 μm in size, which are fused/cemented together in some random fashion; the spaces in between the grains (the pores) are saturated with some fluid, usually water but sometimes oil or gas or a combination thereof. The theoretical development which describes this longitudinal double mode behavior, while preserving the unique topology of the system, is due to Biot.[2-4] The Biot theory has been successfully applied to various problems including fourth sound in a superfluid/superleak system,[5] pressure diffusion through porous media,[6] slow waves and the consolidation transition[7] and the elastodynamics of gels.[8] In addition there have been attempts to describe the acoustic properties of other porous media, typically sediments and sedimentary rocks,[9] but in these cases the most crucial aspect of the theory, the existence of a second "slow" compressional mode, was not observed experimentally. In this paper we review most of the key results in this area.

THEORY

Consider then, the acoustic properties of a homogeneous isotropic disordered medium consisting of two different constituents with densities ρ_i, bulk modulus K_i, and shear modulus N_i where $i=1,2$ labels the 2 constituents. One expects the composite to support a longitudinal and transverse wave in the long wavelength limit. Were that all there was to it, one would have the complicated, tedious task of calculating only two numbers - the longitudinal and transverse speeds. If one of the components is a viscous liquid, then there is the possibility that the fluid and solid parts can oscillate relative to each other, to a degree which is very much frequency dependent. In fact it is generally recognized that an important aspect of acoustic attenuation and dispersion in porous fluid- saturated media is due to the relative motion that can occur between these two constituents. Therefore, it is important to develop a theory in which the displacements of the two components are followed separately and on an equal footing.

In a series of papers,[2-4] Biot proposed a simple phenomenological theory of acoustic propagation in porous, fluid filled, macroscopically homogeneous and isotropic media. It is assumed that there exist volumes large compared to pore/grain sizes but small compared to a wavelength and that each volume element is describable by the average displacement of the fluid $\vec{U}(\vec{r},t)$ and of the solid parts $\vec{u}(\vec{r},t)$. The equations of motion, including viscous damping, are

$$\rho_{11}\frac{\partial^2\vec{u}}{\partial t^2}+\rho_{12}\frac{\partial^2\vec{U}}{\partial t^2} = P\nabla(\nabla\cdot\vec{u})+Q\nabla(\nabla\cdot\vec{U})-N\nabla\times\nabla\times\vec{u}$$

$$+bF(\omega)\left|\frac{\partial\vec{U}}{\partial t} - \frac{\partial\vec{u}}{\partial t}\right|, \qquad (1a)$$

$$\rho_{22}\frac{\partial^2\vec{U}}{\partial t^2} + \rho_{12}\frac{\partial^2\vec{u}}{\partial t^2} = R\nabla(\nabla\cdot\vec{U}) + Q\nabla(\nabla\cdot\vec{u})$$

$$-bF(\omega)\left[\frac{\partial\vec{U}}{\partial t} - \frac{\partial\vec{u}}{\partial t}\right]. \tag{1b}$$

Here we have used the notation of ref. 2 as it is simpler than (although equivalent to) that of the later articles. P, Q, R are generalized elastic coefficients which can be related[4] to the bulk modulus of fluid K_f, the bulk modulus of solid K_s, the bulk modulus K_b of the skeletal frame ("jacketed and drained") and to N which is the shear modulus of both the skeletal frame and of the composite:

$$P = \frac{(1-\phi)\left[1-\phi-\dfrac{K_b}{K_s}\right]K_s+\phi\dfrac{K_s}{K_f}K_b}{1-\phi-\dfrac{K_b}{K_s}+\phi\dfrac{K_s}{K_f}}+\frac{4}{3}N \quad, \tag{2a}$$

$$Q = \frac{\left[1-\phi-\dfrac{K_b}{K_s}\right]\phi K_s}{1-\phi-\dfrac{K_b}{K_s}+\phi\dfrac{K_s}{K_f}} \quad, \tag{2b}$$

$$R = \frac{\phi^2 K_s}{1-\phi-\dfrac{K_b}{K_s}+\phi\dfrac{K_s}{K_f}}. \tag{2c}$$

ϕ is the porosity (fluid volume fraction). In the so-called "jacketed and drained" gedanken test[4] the sample is stressed but the fluid is allowed to escape as needed in order to remain at ambient pressure. Therefore, K_b and N are the elastic constants of the bare skeletal frame and, in the absence of an electrochemical interfacial effect between fluid and solid, they are independent of what fluid is in the pores, including vacuum; we will make this assumption throughout the paper.[10] Equations (2) are equivalent to those given in e.g., Stoll[9] or Geertsma and Smit.[11] The density terms ρ_{ij}, are related to the density of solid, ρ_s, and fluid, ρ_f, by

$$\rho_{11} + \rho_{12} = (1-\phi)\rho_s \quad, \tag{3a}$$

$$\rho_{22} + \rho_{12} = \phi\,\rho_f \quad. \tag{3b}$$

The term ρ_{12} describes the inertial (as opposed to viscous) drag that the fluid exerts on the solid as the latter is accelerated relative to the former and vice-versa. The equation of motion of the solid part, for example, equation (1a), may be rewritten using (3a):

$$(1-\phi)\rho_s\frac{\partial^2\vec{u}}{\partial t^2} = -\rho_{12}\left[\frac{\partial^2\vec{U}}{\partial t^2} - \frac{\partial^2\vec{u}}{\partial t^2}\right]$$

$$+ bF(\omega)\left[\frac{\partial\vec{U}}{\partial t} - \frac{\partial\vec{u}}{\partial t}\right] + \text{(spatial derivative terms)}. \qquad (1a')$$

That is, even for a non-viscous pore fluid ($bF(\omega)\equiv0$), there is a reactive force per unit volume on the solid [whose mass is $(1-\phi)\rho_s$] whenever one component is accelerated relative to the other. The proportionality constant, ρ_{12}, represents the induced mass tensor[12] per unit volume, assumed to be diagonal in the coordinate indices for a homogeneous isotropic system; it is always negative and is always proportional to the fluid density:

$$\rho_{12} = -(\alpha-1)\,\phi\,\rho_f \qquad (3c)$$

where $\alpha>1$ is a purely geometrical quantity independent of solid or fluid densities. Berryman[13] has considered the case of isolated spherical solid particles in the fluid to derive $\alpha=(1/2)[\phi^{-1}+1]$, for example. The remaining parameters, b and $F(\omega)$, govern attenuation. $b=\eta\phi^2/k$ where η is the fluid viscosity and k is the permeability. The permeability is a kind of normalized fluid flow conductance and has the dimensions of area; for a collection of circularly cylindrical tubes of radius R, $k=\phi R^2/8$. $F(\omega)$ allows from the fact that the effective damping changes when the viscous skin depth ($\sqrt{2\eta/\rho_f\omega}$) becomes smaller than the pore size as the frequency ω increases.[14] It is worth noting that ρ_{12} and $bF(\omega)$ *always* appear together in the combination $\rho_{12}-\dfrac{ibF(\omega)}{\omega}$. i.e., equation (1a') can be rewritten

$$(1-\phi)\rho_s\frac{\partial^2\vec{u}}{\partial t^2} = -\tilde{\rho}_{12}(\omega)\left[\frac{\partial^2\vec{U}}{\partial t} - \frac{\partial^2\vec{u}}{\partial t^2}\right] + \text{(spatial derivative terms)} \quad (1a'')$$

where

$$\tilde{\rho}_{12}(\omega) = \rho_{12} - \frac{ibF(\omega)}{\omega}$$

and similarly for equation (1b).

Although the linear term in the Taylors series expansion of $F(\omega)$ mimics the effects of ρ_{12} (i.e., both terms describe an ω^2 dependence of the force on the relative displacement), they are of different physical origin and it is not valid to put $\alpha=1$ (i.e., $\rho_{12}=0$) as has been done.[15] Equivalently, one could define $\tilde{\alpha}(\omega)$ by analogy with equation (3c), viz: $\tilde{\rho}_{12}(\omega) = -[\tilde{\alpha}(\omega)-1]\phi\,\rho_f$. Therefore,

$$\tilde{\alpha}(\omega) = \alpha + \frac{ibF(\omega)}{\omega\phi\rho_f}. \qquad (3c')$$

The crossover between the high-frequency and low-frequency behavior of $F(\omega)$ occurs when the viscous skin depth is approximately equal to the pore size, a:

$$\omega_c = \frac{2\eta}{\rho_f a^2} \quad .$$

If $\omega \gg \omega_c$, the attenuation mechanism has little effect on the velocities of the normal modes which are derived from Eqs. (1); one has[3] $\lim_{\omega \to \infty} F(\omega) \alpha \, \omega^{1/2}$ and therefore $\lim_{\omega \to \infty} \tilde{\rho}_{12}(\omega) = \rho_{12}$ (a constant *not* equal to zero), and $\lim_{\omega \to \infty} \tilde{\alpha}(\omega) = \alpha$ (a constant *not* equal to 1). (As was shown previously,[5] the constant α is the crucial parameter for the slow wave in systems having a very stiff frame; see Equations (8a,b) below also.)

In this high frequency limit, the non-dispersive velocities of the normal modes are

$$V^2(\text{SHEAR}) = \frac{N}{(1-\phi)\rho_s + (1-\alpha^{-1})\phi\rho_f} \quad , \tag{4a}$$

$$V^2(\text{FAST, SLOW}) = \frac{\Delta \pm \sqrt{\Delta^2 - 4(\rho_{11}\rho_{22} - \rho_{12}^2)(PR-Q^2)}}{2(\rho_{11}\rho_{22} - \rho_{12}^2)} \quad , \tag{4b}$$

where

$$\Delta = P\rho_{22} + R\rho_{11} - 2\rho_{12}Q \quad .$$

That is, there is one shear wave, a fast compressional wave corresponding to solid and fluid moving in phase, and a slow compressional wave corresponding to solid and fluid moving out of phase. Note that these equations depend on α either explicitly or through Eq. (3c) but not on $bF(\omega)$. Indeed, using various literature approximations to $F(\omega)$ and measured values of $k(\sim 10^{-8}\text{cm}^2)$, we have verified[16] that Eqs. (4a,b) are accurate to better than 1%. (In the ultrasonics experiments considered in this article,[1,17] the viscous skin depth in water is less than 1 μm at 500 kHz whereas the pore sizes are larger than 20 μm. Thus, these experiments were made in the high frequency limit of the theory.)

LOW FREQUENCY LIMIT

First, though, we consider the opposite limit, $\omega \ll \omega_c$; the fast and shear waves are still propagatory but the slow wave is described by a diffusion equation,

$$C_D \nabla^2 \vec{\xi} = \frac{\partial \vec{\xi}}{\partial t} \quad , \tag{5a}$$

where $\vec{\xi}$ is a normal mode coordinate and C_D is given by

$$C_D \equiv \frac{kK_f}{\eta\phi}\left[1+\frac{K_f}{\phi\left(K_b+\frac{4}{3}N\right)}\right.$$

$$\cdot\left.\left\{1+\frac{1}{K_s}\left[\frac{4}{3}N\left(1-\frac{K_b}{K_s}\right)-K_b-\phi\left(K_b+\frac{4}{3}N\right)\right]\right\}\right]^{-1} \qquad (5b)$$

In ref. 6 it was shown that Eqs.(5a,b) provide the most general description of quasi-static flow in permeable media and that they subsume other theories as special cases (well-to-well pressure pulse testing in the petroleum industry, diffusion in dilute polymer gels). Two cases of special interest (in the low frequency limit) are:

1) Very stiff frame, $K_b, N \gg K_f$. In this case Equation 5b simplifies greatly:

$$\lim_{K_b, N \gg K_f} C_D = \frac{kK_f}{\eta\phi}. \qquad (5c)$$

Chandler[6] has measured the diffusivity of porous water saturated media (fused glass bead samples and a Berea sandstone). He found that tne permeability deduced from the approximate Equation (5c) differs from the statically measured permeability by factors of 2-3 whereas if one accounts for the finite compressibility of the frame (i.e. Equation 5b) agreement is much improved. In Fig. 1, $G = N$, the open symbols refer to permeability deduced from Eq. (5c) and the closed symbols refer to permeability deduced from the full theory, Eq. (5b). (The abscissa is the statically measured permeability whereas the ordinate is that deduced from either Eq. (5b) or (5c). One "darcy" is $10^{-8} cm^2$.) Although one is nearly in the stiff frame limit here, it is not valid to neglect the finite compressibility of the solid matrix.

2) A cross-linked polymer gel in an aqueous solution corresponds to a fluid-solid system in the *weak* frame limit, $K_b, N, \ll K_f, K_s$. Since the pores are considerably less than a micron in size, one is essentially always in the low frequency limit where the slow wave is diffusive. Indeed, light scattering experiments clearly indicate a diffusive mode in addition to the usual propagatory mode.[18] Upon gelation, the individual molecules cross link, thus taking the system from the "sol" phase to the "gel" phase, and so the skeletal frame moduli grow from zero in the former to some small value in the latter. In this weak frame limit the diffusivity Equation 5b simplifies greatly[6,8]:

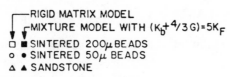

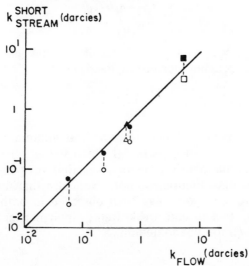

Fig. 1. **Permeability deduced from diffusivity vs. static permeability (from Ref. 6).**

$$\lim_{K_b, N \ll K_f, K_s} C_D = \frac{k}{\eta} (K_b + \frac{4}{3} N).$$ (5d)

This is to be compared with an expression derived independently by Tanaka et al[18] and DeGennes[19] which is, in the present notation:

$$C_D = \frac{k}{\eta \phi^2} (K_b + \frac{4}{3} N)$$ (5e)

Since (5e) was derived under the assumption of a dilute concentration of molecules ($\phi \approx 1$), it is essentially the same as (5d). We may confidently conclude that the slow wave has been observed in gels. The speed and attenuation of the fast wave (ordinary sound) also change upon gelation. It is straightforward to show from Equation (4b) that the speed in the gel phase is[8]

$$V(\text{FAST}) = V_0 [1 + \zeta_1 K_b + \zeta_2 N]$$ (6a)

where V_0 is the speed in the sol phase and $\{\zeta_i\}$ are complicated functions of ϕ, ρ_f, ρ_s, K_f, K_s. This is to be compared with an expression derived by Bacri, et al.[20] which involved several simplifying assumptions:

$$V(FAST) = V_o[1+(K_b+\frac{4}{3}N)/(2K_f)].$$ (6b)

Similarly, the attenuation of the ordinary sound (fast wave) in the weak frame limit is

$$\alpha = \frac{1}{2} \frac{(\rho_T-\rho_f)^2}{V_o\rho_T} \frac{k}{\eta} \omega^2$$ (7a)

where $\rho_T = (1-\phi)\rho_s+\phi\rho_f$ is the total density of the gel. This is to be compared witth an expression derived by Bacri, et al[20]

$$\alpha = \frac{1}{2} \frac{(1-\phi)^2\rho_s^2}{V_o\rho_T} \frac{k}{\eta} \omega^2$$ (7b)

which is the same as (7a) *if* one neglects the volume occupied by the polymer molecules, $\rho_T = \rho_f+(1-\phi)\rho_s$. Note that the general Biot theory, equations (1a,b) simultaneously provide a description of the 2 longitudinal modes, which these other theories do not. Note also that the low frequency limit of the diffusive slow wave has been observed in both the stiff frame (fused glass beads, rocks) and weak frame (polymer gels) limit. It is obviously a fairly common phenomenon.

HIGH FREQUENCY LIMIT

What happens when the frequency is increased to, say, the point where the viscous skin depth is much less than the pore size? According to the theory $\tilde{\alpha}(\omega) \approx \alpha$, a real constant (Equation 3c') and all 3 modes fast, slow, and shear, are propagatory with speeds given by Equations (4a,b). (It should be emphasized that all modes are dispersionless in this limit. There is no "optic branch" with a finite frequency cutoff at long wavelength because it has been assumed in Eqs. (1) that there is no restoring force in Eqs. (1a,b) due to uniform relative displacement, proportional to $(\vec{u}-\vec{U})$.) The slow wave had never been observed as a propagatory mode until we observed it in water saturated fused glass beads and in other porous solids (typically water filter materials). The experimental procedures are contained in Ref. 1 and basically involve using an ultrasonic immersion technique to generate the bulk modes in a fluid-saturated solid based on the concept of mode conversion and refraction at liquid-solid interfaces. Some of our data are reproduced in Table I.[17] Note that the slow wave speed is always less than that of water (which is 1.5 km/sec). The theoretical velocities of the modes in the high frequency limit depend on three microgeometric parameters α, K_b, N (in adddition to bulk properties ρ_s, K_s etc.). It is particularly informative to consider the speeds as a continuous function of the frame moduli K_b, N keeping α (and all the other parameters) fixed. For

example, an unconsolidated (loose) sample of glass beads corresponds to
vanishing frame moduli ($K_b = N = 0$) whereas a light sintering of the beads

	SINTERED GLASS BEADS 1	2	3M	MOTT: STEEL	COORS: CERAMIC
PORE SIZE (μm)	60	40	55	20	55
POROSITY	28.3	18.5	34.5	48.0	41.5
PERMEABILITY (μm^2)	9.1	1.5	8.8	5.9	8.9
VELOCITY: FAST COMPRESSIONAL (km/sec)	4.05	4.84	2.76	2.74	3.95
VELOCITY: SLOW COMPRESSIONAL (km/sec)	1.04	0.82	0.91	0.92	0.96

Table I. Acoustic speeds of fast and slow waves and related parameters for four different porous materials (from Ref. 17).

obviously "stiffen up" the skeletal frame without changing the porosity ϕ or
the inertial drag parameter α measurably. A comparison of the calculated
speeds as a function of the longitudinal modulus of the skeletal frame
$K_b+\frac{4}{3}N$ are shown in Fig. 2, keeping K_b/N a constant.[7]

We have also plotted the experimental points corresponding to a lightly
fused frame ($K_b,N\neq0$) and to a non-fused, loose collection of water
saturated glass beads ($K_b = N = 0$). We see that in this latter limit both
theoretically and experimentally there is only a fast compressional wave
whose speeds are in good agreement with each other. We hope eventually
to fill in a substantial portion of these curves by controlling the frame
moduli; one might, for example, apply an overburden pressure to compress
the beads together and thus continuously increase the value of the slow
wave speed from zero.

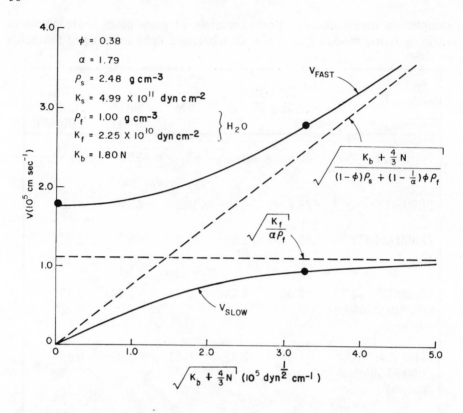

Fig. 2. Fast and slow speeds as a function of frame moduli (from Ref. 7).

Notice from Fig. 2 that the complicated expressions for the compressional velocities in the high frequency limit, Equation 4a, simplify greatly if the skeletal frame is very stiff; $K_b, N >> K_f$. In this limit the speeds are[5]:

$$V(FAST) = \sqrt{\frac{K_b + (4/3)N}{(1-\phi)\rho_s + (1-\alpha^{-1})\phi\rho_f}} \qquad (8a)$$

$$V(SLOW) = \frac{V_f}{\sqrt{\alpha}} \qquad (8b)$$

The fast wave corresponds now to oscillation of the skeletal frame in which some, but not all, of the fluid is dragged along. The slow wave, on the other hand, corresponds to oscillation of the fluid only; the speed is renormalized down from V_f (speed of sound in fluid) because of the tortuous nature of the pore space. We see from Fig. 2 that the light fusing used to make the consolidated frame already puts us in the stiff frame limit.

		Sample 1	Sample 2	Sample 3
	ϕ	0.283	0.258	0.185
	$\alpha = n^2$	1.81	1.94	3.00
Fast-compressional	full theory	4.06	4.18	4.89
speed(km s^{-1})	$\left(\dfrac{K_b + \frac{4}{3}N}{(1 - \phi)\rho_s + (1 - 1/\alpha)\phi\rho_f} \right)^{1/2}$	4.06	4.18	4.89
Shear speed (km s^{-1})	full theory	2.44	2.57	3.00
Slow wave/	full theory	173.514	170.797	137.357
fourth-sound speed (m s^{-1})	$\left(\dfrac{K_f}{\alpha\rho_f} \right)^{1/2} = \dfrac{C_4^0(T=0)}{n}$	173.554	170.839	137.381

Table II. Theoretical wave speeds for the samples of fused glass beads under the condition of saturation with superfluid ^{4}He (from Ref. 5).

Suppose one puts superfluid ^{4}He in the pore space. Since the viscosity of the superfluid fraction is identically zero, we are always in the "high frequency" limit of the theory. Let us compare the prediction of the full theory, Equations (4a,b), with the approximate formulae, Equations (8a,b). The results, for three of our glass bead samples, are presented in Table II.[5] Since the speeds of the slow wave are very accurately given by $V_f/\sqrt{\alpha}$, we conclude that in this limit the slow wave is identical to the phenomenon known as 4th sound.[21,22] In 4th sound, the normal fluid component (if any) is assumed to be locked relative to the porous superleak by its viscosity and only the superfluid fraction can oscillate; from the 2 fluid equations of motion one can calculate the theoretical speed of 4th sound as a function of temperature, $C_4^0(T)$. The tortuous pore geometry renormalizes the speed so that the experimentally observed speed, $C_4^E(T)$, is considerably less than the theoretical one. The ratio of the two is the index of refraction, n, of 4th sound:

$$C_4^E(T) = \frac{C_4^0(T)}{n} \qquad (9)$$

This equation is identical to Equation (8b) which we have derived from the Biot theory, with $n^2 = \alpha$. Therefore 1) 4th sound, which has been observed since 1965,[22] is an ideal example of the propagatory Biot slow wave. 2) Any porous and permeable solid will exhibit a propagatory slow wave if it is saturated with superfluid ^{4}He. 3) Observations of the slow wave under condition of water saturation have enabled us to make predictions of 4th sound velocities. Conversely, 4th sound speeds very directly give us the key parameter (α) for the high frequency speed of the slow wave when other fluids are in the pore space. (Note that in these Proceedings, Rudnick[27] addresses the interesting problem of porous media partially saturated with superfluid. The effective modulus of the fluid-cum-vapor bubbles, K_f, is now greatly reduced. On classical grounds, from Fig. 2, one expects the slow wave speed to be greatly reduced. Quantum mechanically, 4th sound is renormalized to 5th sound.)

It is clear that the parameter α, or more generally $\tilde{\alpha}(\omega)$, Equation (3c'), is the key parameter for the slow wave, at least in the theory presented so far. It turns out that α is also simply related to the electrical conductivity of the pore space because both are determined by the solution of Poisson's equation with the same boundary condition.[23] If the (non conducting) matrix is saturated with a conducting fluid of conductivity σ_f, the sample conductivity, σ, is simply $\sigma = \dfrac{1}{F}\sigma_f$, where the quantity F is a geometrical factor independent of pore fluid conductivity and is related to the acoustic parameter α by $\alpha = F\phi$. We have plotted the values of α (acoustical and electrical) against the porosities of these samples in Fig. 3. We see that

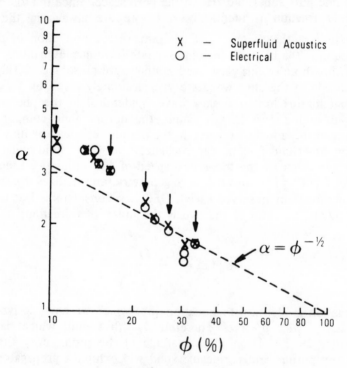

Figure 3. Values of the tortuosity of fused glass bead samples deduced acoustically with superfluid ^{4}He and deduced electrically using saline water (from Ref. 25).

there is excellent agreement between these two measurements of this one parameter. This experimental verification of the rigorous theorem has apparently never been done before. The power of this equivalence is that one now has two complementary techniques for measuring the same microgeometric parameter: Obviously, electrical measurements are useless if the solid is itself a conductor. An effective medium theory described by Sen[24] in this conference, predicts $F = \phi^{-m}$ where m depends on the aspect ratio of the grains. This theoretical result is also plotted in Fig. 3 to show its agreement with the theory.

Porosity ϕ (%)	Tortuosity α	Slow		Fast		Shear	
		Theo.	Exp.	Theo.	Exp.	Theo.	Exp.
33.5	1.75	1.01 [1.13]	0.99	3.23 (3.10)	3.19	1.75 (1.82)	1.68
26.6	2.00	0.97 [1.06]	0.94	3.89 (3.83)	3.98	2.20 (2.28)	2.21
21.9	2.40	0.89 [0.97]	0.88	4.35 (4.32)	4.60	2.57 (2.65)	2.57
16.2	3.02	0.81 [0.86]	0.70	4.82 (4.84)	4.83	2.74 (2.81)	2.68
10.5	3.84	0.71 [0.77]	0.58	5.17 (5.16)	5.15	3.04 (3.09)	2.97

Table III. **Comparison of theoretically calculated speeds of sound for water saturated fused glass bead samples with the experimentally measured values. The input data are the dry speeds, listed in ( ) parentheses and the tortuosity α, deduced from the superfluid ^{4}He saturated data. For comparison, the theoretical result for an infinitely rigid frame, $V_{slow}=V_f/\sqrt{\alpha}$ is given in [ ] parentheses. All speeds are in km/sec (from Ref. 25).**

In the high frequency limit of the theory there are, then, three nontrivial parameters reflecting the microscopic structure of the system. The parameter α describes properties of the pore space and is amenable to calculation, as has been shown. The two frame moduli of the skeleton, K_b and N, are descriptive of the grain space. As is clear from Fig. 2, they are very much dependent on grain-grain contacts and any theory of the frame moduli must include this explicitly, as is discussed by L. Schwartz in these Proceedings[26]. The values of K_b and N can be determined from measurements of the dry acoustic speeds using Eqs. 8a and 4a. We can thus make a successful comparison between theory and experiment which is meaningful only because all the modes predicted by the theory are measured experimentally. With the measured values of α, K_b and N, we calculate, with no adjustable parameters, the speeds of the fast longitudinal, slow longitudinal, and transverse waves in a set of water saturated samples. The comparison of theory vs. experiment is presented in Table III; the agreement is seen to be excellent thus giving the first direct experimental evidence for the validity of the Biot theory[25].

SLOW WAVES

	WEAK FRAME	STIFF FRAME
LOW FREQUENCY (DIFFUSIVE)	POLYMER GELS	ROCKS, FUSED GLASS BEADS. (e.g. PRESSURE PULSE TESTING)
HIGH FREQUENCY (PROPAGATORY)	UNCONSOLIDATED BEADS UNDER CONFINING PRESSURE (?)	4TH SOUND IN He II FUSED GLASS BEADS & OTHER ARTIFICIAL MEDIA

Table IV. Systems in which the slow wave has been observed.

CONCLUSIONS

We have seen that the slow compressional wave predicted by the theory is a much more commonly observed phenomenon than previously thought. Table IV summarizes the systems in which the slow wave has been observed in one form or another. As yet, a propagatory slow wave in an unconsolidated saturated system (under confining pressure) has <u>not</u> been observed but we expect that it will be. We have experimentally demonstrated the equivalence of acoustic and electrical means of measuring the tortuosity, α, of a porous solid, thus making them complimentary techniques. Since bulk superfluid ^{4}He is so well understood, it can now be used as a probe of the physics of disorder of porous media. In addition, measurements of the dry speeds and of the tortuosity have enabled us to accurately predict the water-saturated speeds with no adjustable parameters. Thus, the Biot theory is seen to effectively cut in half the problem of understanding acoustic propagation in porous media. It now becomes possible to focus on theories of the individual parameters; we have done this for the tortuosity, α, in the present article and Schwartz[26] will discuss K_b and N elsewhere in these Proceedings.

REFERENCES

1. T. J. Plona, App. Phys. Lett. *36*, 259 (1980).

2. M. A. Biot, J. Acoust. Soc. Am. *28*, 168 (1956); *28*, 179 (1956).

3. M. A. Biot, J. Appl. Phys. *33*, 1482 (1962); J. Acoust. Soc. Am. *34*, 1254 (1962).

4. M. A. Biot and D. G. Willis, J. Appl. Mech. *24*, 594 (1957).

5. D. L. Johnson, Appl. Phys. Lett. *37*, 1065 (1980); ibid *38*, 827 (1980) (E).

6. R. N. Chandler and D. L. Johnson, J. Appl. Phys. *52*, 3391 (1981); R. N. Chandler, J. Acoust. Soc. Am. *70*, 116 (1981).

7. D. L. Johnson and T. J. Plona, J. Acoust. Soc. Am. *72*, 556 (1982).

8. D. L. Johnson, J. Chem. Phys. *77*, 1531 (1982).

9. R. D. Stoll in *Physics of Sound in Marine Sediments,* edited by L. Hampton (Plenum, NY, 1974).

10. This assumption may very well break down when the pore fluid is water and the matrix is a rock [M. R. J. Wyllie, G. H. F. Gardner, and A. R. Gregory, Geophysics *27*, 569 (1962)].

11. J. Geertsma and D. C. Smit, Geophysics *26*, 169 (1961).

12. L. D. Landau and E. M. Lifshitz, *Fluid Mechanics,* (Pergamon, NY, 1959) p. 31ff.

13. J. G. Berryman, Appl. Phys. Lett. *37*, 382 (1980).

14. Ref. 9, p. 88 ff.

15. C. H. Yew and P. N. Jogi, Exp. Mech. *18*, 167 (1978); H. D. McNiven and Y. Mengi, J. Acoust. Soc. Am. *61*, 972 (1977).

16. R. Johnson and D. Johnson (private communication).

17. T. J. Plona and D. L. Johnson in *1980 Ultrasonic Symposium Proceedings,* edited by J. deKlerk and B. R. McAvoy (IEEE, NY, NY 1980), pp.868.

18. T. Tanaka, L. O. Hocker, and G. B. Benedek, J. Chem. Phys. *59,* 5151 (1973).

19. P. G. DeGennes, Macromolecule *9,* 587 (1976).

20. J. C. Bacri, J. M. Courdille, J. Dumas and R. Rajaonarison, J. Physique *41,* L-369 (1980); J. C. Bacri and R. Rajaonarison, J. Physique *40,* L-5 (1979).

21. I. Rudnick, *New Directions in Physical Acoustics,* Proceedings of the Enrico Fermi Summer School, Course LXIII (Academic, NY, 1976), p. 112.

22. K. A. Shapiro and I. Rudnick, Phys. Rev. *137,* A1383 (1965).

23. R. J. S. Brown, Geophysics *45,* 1269 (1980).

24. P. N. Sen, C. Scala and M. H. Cohen, Geophysics *46,* 781 (1981).

25. D. L. Johnson, T. J. Plona, C. Scala, F. Pasierb and H. Kojima, Phys. Rev. Lett. *49,* 1840 (1982).

26. L. Schwartz, in these Proceedings.

27. I. Rudnick, in these Proceedings.

ACOUSTIC PROPERTIES OF POROUS SYSTEMS: II. MICROSCOPIC DESCRIPTION

Lawrence M. Schwartz

Schlumberger-Doll Research
P. O. Box 307, Ridgefield, CT 06877

ABSTRACT

We present a microscopic model for the dynamics of granular systems based on the Hertz-Mindlin theory of inter-grain contact forces. We argue that the requirement of rotational invariance implies that both the *translational* and *rotational* motion of the individual grains must be taken into account. The new rotational degrees of freedom give rise to additional modes whose behavior is studied in ordered and disordered packings. In the limit of long wavelengths our normal mode calculations reproduce the earlier results of Mindlin (ordered packings) and Digby (disordered packings). We discuss experimental results on compressional and shear wave speeds in systems where the contact forces are generated by (hydrostatic and uniaxial) pressure.

INTRODUCTION

We are concerned with the vibrational properties of porous and dry composites. In these systems the mass is spread in a roughly uniform way over grains which interact via forces exerted at their points of contact. The simplest example of such a system is a dense packing of spherical beads under external confining pressure.[1] In related systems the inter-granular forces are generated by cementing or sintering the contact points between adjacent particles.[2] Model systems of this kind are a useful starting point in the description of ocean sediments and sedimentary rocks.[3] In a related article in these Proceedings, Plona and Johnson[4] consider the effects of saturating such composites with a fluid; in the language of Ref. 4, one of the issues with which we will be concerned is a microscopic calculation of the (dry) frame moduli.

The static properties of granular composites are usually treated[5,6] in terms of the description of two interacting grains developed by Hertz[7] and Mindlin.[8] The central idea is that each contact point can be characterized in

0094-243X/84/1070105-14 $3.00 Copyright 1984 American Institute of Physics

terms of longitudinal and transverse force constants which we denote as $D_{\parallel}$ and $D_{\perp}$. In the case of *pressure generated* contact forces, Mindlin derived the following expressions for these parameters:

$$D_{\parallel} = \frac{2\mu a}{1-\nu}\,, \qquad D_{\perp} = \frac{4\mu a}{2-\nu}\,. \tag{1}$$

Here μ and ν denote, respectively, the shear modulus and Poisson ratio of the constituent grain material and a is the radius of the (circular) contact area (see Fig. 1). [In deriving Eqs. (1), it is assumed that there is no slipping between adjacent grains, i.e. that the confining pressure is high enough that *static* friction prevails in the contact region[8].] It might be thought that the dynamics of the system could be described by a model in which the grains are represented by *point masses* interacting via the force matrix:

$$D(\vec{R}_{ij}) \equiv D(\vec{R}_i - \vec{R}_j) = D_{\parallel}\hat{R}_{ij}\hat{R}_{ij} + D_{\perp}(1-\hat{R}_{ij}\hat{R}_{ij})\,, \tag{2a}$$

$$D(\vec{R}_{ii}) = -\sum_{j(\neq i)} D(\vec{R}_{ij})\cdot \tag{2b}$$

In this model the force $\vec{F}_i$ on the ith grain due to a displacement $\delta\vec{u}_j$ of the jth grain from it's equilibrium position $\vec{R}_j$ would be

$$\vec{F}_i = D(\vec{R}_{ij})\cdot\delta\vec{u}_j\,, \tag{3}$$

and the second of Eqs. (2) guarantees *translational* invariance of the theory. It is known, however, that this procedure leads to results that are unphysical because the implied potential energy

$$V = \frac{1}{4}\sum_{ij} \{\delta\vec{u}_i-\delta\vec{u}_j\}\cdot D(\vec{R}_{ij})\cdot\{\delta\vec{u}_i-\delta\vec{u}_j\}\,, \tag{4}$$

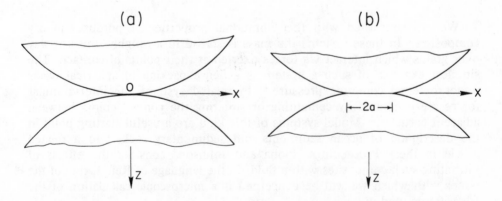

Fig. 1. Elastic Spheres in contact. (a) unstressed state, (b) pressed together under normal force applied along the z axis to form circular area of contact with radius a.

is not *rotationally* invariant.[9,10] [The essential point is that the transverse component of $D(\vec{R}_{ij})$ (i.e. the part proportional to $D_{\perp}$) gives rise to a net change in energy when the entire system undergoes an infinitesimal rotation (see footnote 9).]

MICROSCOPIC MODEL

In our view a satisfactory description of the dynamics of granular systems should take account of the most important new degrees of freedom associated with the finite size of the particles. Since the elastic deformations at the contact points extend over only a small fraction of the grain's volume, it seems reasonable to treat the grains as essentially *rigid bodies* subjected to external forces and torques exerted at each contact point. Accordingly, the principal new degrees of freedom are those associated with the rotations of the individual grains. Our aim, then, is to treat systems where, in addition to a mass M and an infinitesimal displacement $\delta\vec{u}$, we associate with each "particle" a moment of inertia I and an infinitesimal rotation $\delta\vec{\theta}$.[11,12]

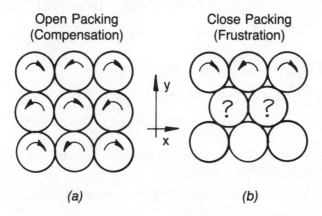

(a)   (b)

Fig. 2. Schematic illustration of pure rotational motion [i.e. $\delta\vec{u}\equiv0$] in open and closed ordered packings.

To illustrate the new features of the normal mode spectrum, let us begin by looking at *ordered* systems and by setting all of the displacements $\delta\vec{u}_i\equiv0$. In Fig. 2 we show that there are important effects associated with the local geometry of the lattice. In open structures it is possible to set up counter-rotating modes in which, to first order, there is no relative motion of the contact regions on adjacent grains and, therefore, no cost in elastic energy. By contrast, in systems with closed paths containing an odd number of grains, such zero frequency modes are eliminated by frustration. Although we are principally interested in close-packed systems, one surprising feature of the spectrum in open structures is worth commenting on. It might be thought that the fully compensated mode illustrated in Fig. 2a could only be formed at the corner of the Brillouin zone. It turns out, however, that coupling to the translational degrees of freedom can, in fact, *enhance* the occurrence of compensation phenomena. This effect is especially dramatic in the case of one dimension. In a single horizontal row on the left side of Fig. 2, displacements along the chain do not interact with the coupled rotations and transverse motion. We assume that the inter-grain force is proportional (with force constant $D_\perp$) to the relative displacement of adjacent contact points. Taking δu_i along the y axis and counterclockwise $\delta\theta_i$ as positive, the positions of the left and right hand contact points for the ith grain are $P_i^{(l)} = \delta u_i - R\delta\theta_i$ and $P_i^{(r)} = \delta u_i + R\delta\theta_i$, and the net force on this grain is simply $F_i = D_\perp[\{P_{i+1}^{(l)} - P_i^{(r)}\} + \{P_{i-1}^{(r)} - P_i^{(l)}\}]$. The equations describing the coupled transverse motion are then:[11]

$$M\frac{d^2\delta u_i}{dt^2} = D_\perp[(\delta u_{i-1} - \delta u_i) + (\delta u_{i+1} - \delta u_i)$$

$$+ R\{(\delta\theta_{i-1} + \delta\theta_i) - (\delta\theta_{i+1} + \delta\theta_i)\}] , \tag{5a}$$

and

$$I\frac{d^2\delta\theta_i}{dt^2} = RD_\perp[-R\{(\delta\theta_{i-1} + \delta\theta_i) + (\delta\theta_{i+1} + \delta\theta_i)\}$$

$$- (\delta u_{i-1} - \delta u_i) + (\delta u_{i+1} - \delta u_i)] , \tag{5b}$$

where R is the grain radius. Invoking Bloch's theorem, the secular equation corresponding to Eqs. (5) reduces to

$$0 = \omega^2[\omega^2 - \omega_0^2\{\sin^2(ka/2) + \alpha\cos^2(ka/2)\}] , \tag{6}$$

where $\omega_0^2 = 4D_\perp/M$ and $\alpha = MR^2/I$. Clearly, one solution of (6) is $\omega(k) \equiv 0$. [Physically, for each k, there is a *balance* between displacement and rotation such that no relative motion of the contact points is involved.]

In two and three dimensional systems, the relative displacement of adjacent contact points must be treated as a vector. Following Mindlin, we describe the dynamics of the composite in terms of a microscopic model in which the inter-grain forces are generated by either longitudinal or transverse deformations of the contact region. The essential point is that we are now treating the forces associated with $D_\parallel$ and $D_\perp$ as acting at the *surface of a rigid body* rather than between point masses. Our model for the potential energy of the granular composite is then:

$$V = \frac{1}{4}\sum_{ij}\left\{D_{\perp}[\{\delta\vec{u}_i-\delta\vec{u}_j\} - (1/2)\{\delta\vec{\theta}_i+\delta\vec{\theta}_j\} \times \vec{R}_{ij}]^2\right.$$

$$\left. + (D_{\parallel}-D_{\perp}) [\{\delta\vec{u}_i-\delta\vec{u}_j\}\cdot\hat{R}_{ij}]^2\right\} . \tag{7}$$

Introducing the variables $\vec{U}_i \equiv \sqrt{M}\,\delta\vec{u}_i$ and $\vec{\Theta}_i \equiv \sqrt{I}\,\delta\vec{\theta}_i$ (which have the same dimensions), the equations of motion for the ith grain are:

$$\frac{d^2V_i(\alpha)}{dt^2} = \sum_{j\beta} \Gamma_{ij}(\alpha|\beta)\, V_j(\beta) , \tag{8}$$

were $V_i(\alpha)$ denotes the composite vector $[\vec{U}_i, \vec{\Theta}_i]$ and the operator $\Gamma_{ij}(\alpha|\beta)$ is defined as follows:

$$\Gamma_{ij}(U|U) = M^{-1}D_{\parallel}\hat{R}_{ij}\hat{R}_{ij} + M^{-1}D_{\perp}[1-\hat{R}_{ij}\hat{R}_{ij}] , \tag{9a}$$

$$\Gamma_{ij}(\Theta|\Theta) = - (4I)^{-1}D_{\perp}|R_{ij}^2|[1-\hat{R}_{ij}\hat{R}_{ij}] , \tag{9b}$$

$$\Gamma_{ii}(U|U) = - \sum_{j(\neq i)} \Gamma_{ij}(U|U) , \qquad \Gamma_{ii}(\Theta|\Theta) = \sum_{j(\neq i)} \Gamma_{ij}(\Theta|\Theta) , \tag{9c}$$

$$\Gamma_{ij}(\Theta|U) = \tfrac{1}{2}(M\,I)^{-\frac{1}{2}} D_{\perp}\vec{R}_{ij} \times = \Gamma_{ij}(U|\Theta) , \tag{9d}$$

$$\Gamma_{ii}(U|\Theta) = \sum_{j(\neq i)} \Gamma_{ij}(U|\Theta) = -\Gamma_{ii}(\Theta|U) \cdot \tag{9e}$$

[Here the symbol $\times$ indicates the usual vector cross product.]

In ordered systems, the normal mode spectrum can be evaluated from the secular equation

$$\| \omega^2 1 + \Gamma_{\vec{k}}(\alpha|\beta) \| = 0 , \tag{10}$$

where the form of $\Gamma_{\vec{k}}(\alpha|\beta)$ follows from Bloch's theorem:

$$\Gamma_{\vec{k}}(\alpha|\beta) = \sum_j \Gamma_{ij}(\alpha|\beta)\, e^{i\vec{k}\cdot\vec{R}_{ij}} . \tag{11}$$

In the case of disordered packings, approximate dispersion relations can be computed from an equation of the form (10) by using the pair distribution function, $g(|\vec{R}_{ij}|)$, to construct the matrix $\Gamma_{\vec{k}}(\alpha|\beta)$:

$$\Gamma_{\vec{k}}(U|U) = \int d\vec{R}_{ij}\, g(|\vec{R}_{ij}|)\, [e^{i\vec{k}\cdot\vec{R}_{ij}}-1]\, \Gamma_{ij}(U|U) , \tag{12a}$$

$$\Gamma_{\vec{k}}(\Theta|\Theta) = \int d\vec{R}_{ij}\, g(|\vec{R}_{ij}|)\, [e^{i\vec{k}\cdot\vec{R}_{ij}}+1]\, \Gamma_{ij}(\Theta|\Theta) , \tag{12b}$$

$$\Gamma_{\vec{k}}(\Theta|U) = \int d\vec{R}_{ij}\, g(|\vec{R}_{ij}|)\, [e^{i\vec{k}\cdot\vec{R}_{ij}}-1]\, \Gamma_{ij}(\Theta|U) , \tag{12c}$$

$$\Gamma_{\vec{k}}(U|\Theta) = \int d\vec{R}_{ij} g(|\vec{R}_{ij}|) [e^{i\vec{k}\cdot\vec{R}_{ij}}+1] \Gamma_{ij}(U|\Theta) \cdot \qquad (12d)$$

[In an earlier paper,[13] we showed that this approximation reproduces the essential features of the spectrum in systems with purely longitudinal coupling between point particles.[14]] Calculations based on Eqs.(11) and (12) are shown in Figs. 3 and 4. In Fig.4 calculations are compared with the results of machine simulations based on the application of the equation of motion method to a close packed 500 site amorphous structure.[15] The general agreement between these two sets of calculations (for the disordered case) indicates that the averaged dynamical matrix again yields a reasonable picture of the average spectrum. In both Figs. 3 and 4 the upper and lower longitudinal modes correspond, respectively, to pure rotational and translational motion, while (as in the one-dimensional case) the two effects are coupled in the transverse modes.

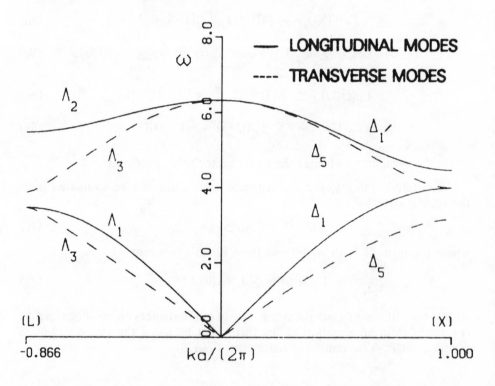

Fig. 3. Coupled rotational and translational mode spectrum in an fcc crystal. Here $D_\perp = D_\parallel$, $I = (2/5)MR^2$, and $2\sqrt{2}R = a$ (the cube edge). The frequency scale is in units of ω_0 where $\omega_0^2 = 4D_\parallel/M$.

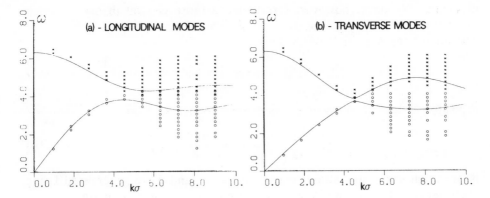

Fig. 4. Longitudinal (a) and transverse (b) dispersion relations in a disordered packing. The solid curves are calculated using Eqs. (12).[11,13] [The average coordination number and center to center grain separation are taken as $Z=12$ and $\sigma=2R$.] The crosses and circles indicate the half widths of the upper and lower peaks in the numerically computed spectral density functions.[11]

ELASTIC THEORY

In the long wavelength limit, the dispersion relations shown in Figs. 3 and 4 can be related to expressions for static elastic coefficients obtained by previous workers. In the ordered case, the sound speeds along various symmetry directions lead to relations between the macroscopic elastic constants C_{ij} and the microscopic force constants $D_{\parallel}$ and $D_{\perp}$:

$$C_{11} = \frac{1}{\sqrt{2}R}[D_{\parallel}+D_{\perp}] = 2C_{44} , \quad C_{12} = \frac{1}{2\sqrt{2}R}[D_{\parallel}-D_{\perp}] , \qquad (13)$$

obtained by Duffy and Mindlin.[5] In the disordered case we find for the ratio of the longitudinal to the transverse sound speeds:

$$\left\{\frac{V_L}{V_T}\right\}^2 = 3\frac{[1+(2D_{\perp}/3D_{\parallel})]}{[1+(3D_{\perp}/2D_{\parallel})]} \leq 3 , \qquad (14)$$

which is equivalent to the results for the effective Lame moduli derived by Digby.[6]

We emphasize that, because of problems related to rotational invariance, Eqs.(13) and (14) cannot be derived from the conventional theory of elasticity. We have, however, formulated a more general theory in which one allows for two continuously varying vector fields $\delta\vec{u}(\vec{r})$ and $\delta\vec{\theta}(\vec{r})$.[11,16] The underlying potential energy density

$$U(\vec{r}) = \frac{1}{2}\left\{\sum_{ij}[\lambda\epsilon_{ii}\epsilon_{jj} + 2\mu\epsilon_{ij}\epsilon_{ij}] + \nu|\delta\vec{\theta}-\tfrac{1}{2}\nabla\times\delta\vec{u}|^2\right\}, \qquad (15)$$

is positive definite and invariant under rigid rotations. Here

$$\epsilon_{ij}(\vec{r}) = \frac{1}{2}\left\{\frac{\partial u_i(\vec{r})}{\partial x_j} + \frac{\partial u_j(\vec{r})}{\partial x_i}\right\}, \qquad (16)$$

is the usual symmetric strain tensor, and λ, μ, and ν are generalized Lame coefficients. The relevant long wavelength equations of motion are:

$$\rho_I\omega^2\delta\vec{\theta} = \nu[\delta\vec{\theta}-\tfrac{1}{2}\nabla\times\delta\vec{u}], \qquad (17a)$$

and

$$\rho_M\omega^2\delta\vec{u} = -(\lambda+2\mu)\nabla(\nabla\cdot\delta\vec{u}) + \mu\nabla\times(\nabla\times\delta\vec{u})$$

$$- (\nu/2)\nabla\times[\delta\vec{\theta}-\tfrac{1}{2}\nabla\times\delta\vec{u}], \qquad (17b)$$

where ρ_M and ρ_I are the mass and moment of inertia densities. [For the specific microscopic model defined by Eqs.(7)→(9), $\{\lambda,\mu,\nu\}$ are simply related[16] to $\{D_\|, D_\perp\}$. Note that as $\omega\to0$, Eq.(17a) leads to the condition $\delta\vec{\theta}-\tfrac{1}{2}\nabla\times\delta\vec{u}=0$. [In the low frequency transverse mode, rotation and translation couple so as to guarantee, not that $\delta\vec{\theta}\equiv0$, but that the local torque vanishes.] The fact that the parameter ν does not appear explicitly in the $\omega\to0$ shear wave speed is related to a surprising feature of the coupled translational and rotational motion.[16] In terms of the microscopic model considered earlier, the requirement $\delta\vec{\theta}-\tfrac{1}{2}\nabla\times\delta\vec{u}=0$ implies that the transverse sound speed will be *independent* of the moments of inertia of the individual grains. Thus the rotational coupling changes the value of V_T [from the value corresponding to the condition $\delta\vec{\theta}\equiv0$] in a way that does not vary with $\alpha\equiv MR^2/I$. This point is illustrated in Fig. 5.

DISCUSSION OF EXPERIMENTAL RESULTS

For systems comprised of unconsolidated spherical grains under hydrostatic pressure, Eqs.(1) give the dependence of the parameters $D_\|$ and $D_\perp$ on (1) the radius, a, of the contact area (which increases with pressure) and (2) the elastic properties of the grain material (which are roughly independent of pressure). Since both $D_\|$ and $D_\perp$ are proportional to a, their ratio is independent of a and, therefore, of the confining pressure. It follows from Eq.(14) that $(V_L/V_T)^2$ should be *independent of pressure* and

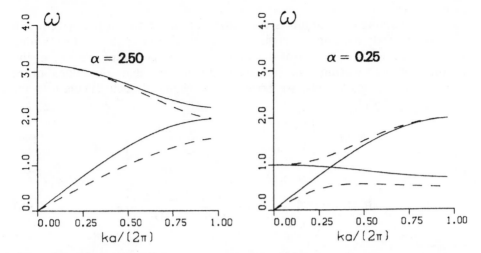

Fig. 5. Longitudinal (solid) and transverse (dashed) modes in an fcc crystal along the [100] direction. Results for two values of α are shown; all other parameters are as in Fig. 3. Note that the lower longitudinal mode (all k) and the k→0 slope of the lower transverse mode are independent of α.

should have a value between 2.44 and 2.0 [assuming that $(D_\perp/D_\parallel)$ has a value between 0.33 and 1.0]. Experiments by Domenico[1] on disordered packings of spherical glass grains indicate that $(V_L/V_T)^2$ is essentially constant (≈ 2.43) as the (hydrostatic) confining pressure is increased from 2.7 to 34.0 MPa. While the value 2.43 is somewhat high, the fact that the measured ratio does not vary with pressure, is consistent with our Eq.(14) and Mindlin's argument that $D_\parallel$ and $D_\perp$ are both proportional to a *single* contact area.[17] Eqs.(1) also indicate that, in the weak contact regime, the ratio $(D_\perp/D_\parallel)$ should be rather insensitive to the elastic properties of the material from which the individual grains are made. Further measurements on systems in which the composite geometries are similar, but the elastic properties of the grains vary greatly, would be useful in testing this prediction.

A second class of experiments of interest here are measurements on granular composites under *uniaxial* rather than *hydrostatic* pressure. This technique is widely used to measure the properties of both synthetic materials and sedimentary rocks.[18,19] Within the present context, the effects of a uniaxial environment can be modeled by allowing the force constants $D_\parallel$ and $D_\perp$ to vary as a function of the angle ψ between the normal to the contact plane and the pressure axis:

$$D_\parallel(\psi) = D_\parallel[1+\delta\cos^2\psi] \qquad (18a)$$

$$D_\perp(\psi) = D_\perp[1+\delta\cos^2\psi] \cdot \qquad (18b)$$

Here, the parameter δ monitors the degree of anisotropy in the system and reflects the fact that contact areas will vary with the angle ψ. Combining Eqs.(18) with the formalism developed in the preceding Sections, the normal mode spectrum can be calculated for a range of values of δ. Without giving any details, we present the results of such calculations for the ratio (V_L/V_T):

$$R(\delta) \equiv \left\{\frac{V_L(\delta)}{V_T(\delta)}\right\}^2 = R(0)\cdot\frac{F_L[\delta,D_\perp,D_\parallel]}{F_T[\delta,D_\perp,D_\parallel]} , \qquad (19a)$$

where

$$F_L[\delta,D_\perp,D_\parallel] = 1 + \left\{\frac{(5/7)D_\parallel + (2/7)D_\perp}{D_\parallel + (2/3)D_\perp}\right\}\delta , \qquad (19b)$$

and

$$F_T[\delta,D_\perp,D_\parallel] = 1 + \left\{\frac{(3/7)D_\parallel + (4/7)D_\perp}{D_\parallel + (3/2)D_\perp}\right\}\delta$$

$$- \left\{\frac{(D_\perp/10)}{[D_\parallel + (3/2)D_\perp][1 + (2\delta/5)]}\right\}\delta^2 . \qquad (19c)$$

Since $R(0)$, given by Eq.(14), is a function of only the ratio $(D_\perp/D_\parallel)$, which is *unchanged* by Eqs.(18), it might have been guessed that (V_L/V_T) would also be independent of δ. It turns out, however, that the coefficient multiplying $R(0)$ in Eq.(19a) is always *positive* over the range of δ and $(D_\perp/D_\parallel)$ of physical interest. [Typically, $0 < \delta < 1.0$ and $0.3 < (D_\perp/D_\parallel) < 1.0$.] For example, taking $(D_\perp/D_\parallel) = 0.35$ [which corresponds to $R(0) = 2.43$] and $\delta = 1.0$, this coefficient takes the value 1.19; we would then predict $R(\delta=1) \approx 2.89$ which is remarkably close to the values measured under uniaxial conditions.[19] More generally, this simple calculation indicates that uniaxial measurements are expected to yield higher values for (V_L/V_T) than their hydrostatic counterparts.[18] It should also be noted that (V_L/V_T) values determined by uniaxial techniques tend to show more pressure dependence than the corresponding hydrostatic data.[19] At low pressures ($\leq 2.5\,\text{MPa}$) uniaxial and hydrostatic results are roughly equal. However, as the pressure is raised, the uniaxial (V_L/V_T) ratios tend to increase from roughly 1.55 to 1.75, while the hydrostatic (V_L/V_T) values remain essentially constant. If the anisotropy can really be modeled as in Eqs.(18), this would indicate that the parameter δ must be viewed as a function of pressure.

To conclude, we note that there is at least one granular system whose behavior does not appear to be consistent with Eq.(14). If the contacts in a spherical grain pack are generated by sintering (i.e. fusing), the measured[2]

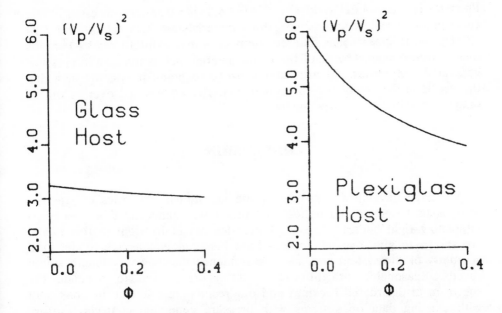

Fig. 6. $(V_L/V_T)^2$ calculated from Eqs. (20) for two host materials.

value of $(V_L/V_T)^2 \approx 3.1$; a value that is obviously difficult to reconcile with Eq. (14). While the porosity ($\phi \approx 0.38$) of the pressurized and fused samples are essentially identical, the absolute strengths of the contacts are much greater in the latter case.[2] [Typical values for the compressional and shear sound speeds in sintered composites are 2.63 and 1.48 (km/sec), respectively, whereas the corresponding values in pressure generated composites are 1.37 and 0.89 (km/sec).] Indeed, it may well be that the sintered contacts represent such strong bonds that the present model is not really applicable. If instead, this system is modeled as a solid with a volume fraction 0.38 of voids, then the value of $(V_L/V_T)^2$ can be calculated from the results of multiple scattering theory:[20]

$$\frac{(K-K^*)}{(3K^*+4\mu)} = \phi\frac{K}{4\mu} , \quad \frac{(\mu-\mu^*)}{(\mu^*+F)} = \phi\frac{\mu}{F} , \qquad (20a)$$

where

$$F = \frac{\mu(9K+8\mu)}{6(K+2\mu)} . \qquad (20b)$$

Here K and μ are the bulk and shear moduli of the solid matrix and K^* and μ^* are the corresponding effective moduli for the solid/void composite. Calculations based on these equations for two materials with rather different elastic properties are shown in Fig. 6. If the parameters for glass are used [$(K/\mu)=1.60$], we find $(V_L/V_T)^2 \approx 3.1$; by comparison, parameters for

116

Plexiglas $[(K/\mu)=4.62]$ yield $(V_L/V_T)^2\approx4.2$. $[\phi=0.38$ in both cases.] The corresponding values for the pure host materials are 3.25 (glass) and 5.94 (Plexiglas). It appears that sintered composites may exhibit $(V_L/V_T)^2$ ratios that are more characteristic of the grain material than is the case in pressure generated composites. Measurements on fused granular systems in which the elastic properties of the constituent material were varied over as wide a range as possible are clearly needed.

CONCLUSION

We have developed a picture of the vibrational properties of granular composites based on the notion that individual grains must be treated as interacting rigid bodies. The additional degrees of freedom in this model are shown to give rise to modes whose behavior is sensitive to the local geometry of the system and, also, to influence the long wavelength sound speeds. Reasonably straightforward methods are used to calculate the spectrum in disordered packings and our results are found to be consistent with existing data on systems with pressure generated contacts. Further experiments, which would be useful in determining the range of parameters for which our model is valid, are suggested.

ACKNOWLEDGEMENT

The work described in this review has been carried out in collaboration with David Johnson and Shechao Feng. In developing our understanding of these problems, we have benefited from several discussions with P. N. Sen. Conversations with W. Murphy, K. Winkler, and B. Halperin are also acknowledged. R. Alben and J. Rehr provided copies of various programs and helpful advice.

REFERENCES

1. S. N. Domenico, Geophysics 42, 1339 (1977).
2. D. L. Johnson, and T. J. Plona, J. Acous. Soc. Am. 72, 556 (1982).
3. P. N. Sen, C. Scala and M. H. Cohen, Geophysics 46, 781 (1981).
4. T. J. Plona and D. L. Johnson, (These Proceedings).

117

5. J. Duffy and R. D. Mindlin, Journal of Applied Mechanics *24*, 585 (1957).

6. P. J. Digby, Journal of Applied Mechanics *48*, 803 (1981).

7. S. P. Timoshenko and J. N. Goodier, *Theory of Elasticity*, Third Edition (McGraw-Hill Inc., New York, 1970). See Section 140 for a discussion of Hertz's original solution of the two-sphere problem.

8. R. D. Mindlin, Journal of Applied Mechanics *16*, 259 (1949).

9. P. N. Keating, Phys. Rev. *145*, 637 (1966).

10. Perhaps the simplest way to see the problem is to note that the long wavelength limit of the normal mode spectrum and the classical theory of elasticity can lead to *different* results for the longitudinal and transverse sound speeds when Eq.(2) is applied to an ordered solid. For example, following Aschroft and Mermin [*Solid State Physics*, Holt, Rinehart and Winston, New York, 1976], we find that the results of problem 5, page 449, are not consistent with the sound speeds derived from the elastic constants C_{ij} calculated via their Eqs.(22.78) and (22.79). The origin of this contradiction is the fact that (22.78) and (22.79) *assume* that the underlying Hamiltonian is rotationally invariant. Indeed, if their earlier equations (22.72) and (22.73) are used to compute the sound speeds, one obtains agreement with the results of Problem 5.

11. L. Schwartz, D. L. Johnson, and S. Feng, Physical Review Letters (submitted).

12. Related issues arise in the calculation of librational spectra in molecular solids. See A. B. Harris and A. J. Berlinsky, Phys Rev. B*16*, 3791 (1977) and F. G. Mertens and W. Beim, Z. Phys. *250*, 273 (1972).

13. Lawrence M. Schwartz, Physical Review Letters *50*, 140 (1983).

14. G. S. Grest, S. R. Nagel, and A. Rahman, Physical Review Letters *49*, 1271 (1982).

15. J. J. Rehr and R. Alben, Phys. Rev. B*16*, 2400 (1977).

16. L. Schwartz, D. L. Johnson, and S. Feng, (private communication)

17. While our Eq.(14) is equivalent to Eq.(33) and (34) of Ref. 6, there is a significant point regarding the interpretation of $D_{||}$ and $D_{\perp}$ on which we differ with Digby. Although he claims to be using Mindlin's results, Digby assumes that $D_{||}$ and $D_{\perp}$ depend on *different* effective contact radii [$a_{||}=a$ and $a_{\perp}=b$] only one of which, $a_{||}$, varies with pressure. Accordingly, his calculations indicate that $(V_L/V_T)^2$ should increase with pressure to the value 3.0 as the ratio $d_{||}/d_{\perp}$ increases. This prediction is *not* consistent with the data presented in Ref. 1.

118

18. K. W. Winkler, J. Geophysical Res. (private communication), K. W. Winkler and W. M. Murphy, J. Acous. Soc. Am. (submitted).

19. W. M. Murphy, Ph.D thesis, Stanford University Department of Geophysics (unpublished); J. Acous. Soc. Am. (submitted).

20. J. Berryman, J. Acoust. Soc. Am. *68,* 1809 (1980); see Eqs.(13),(15), and (16).

ACOUSTIC PROPERTIES OF SUPERLEAKS
PARTIALLY SATURATED WITH SUPERFLUID

S. Baker, J. Marcus, G.A. Williams, and I. Rudnick
Department of Physics
University of California, Los Angeles, CA 90024

ABSTRACT

The index of refraction, n, has been measured for the sound
mode which propagates in a superleak partially filled with liquid
He II so that the liquid forms a film on the powder grains.
Motivated by a model which treats the scattering from the powder
grains independently from the scattering from the vapor spaces, we
find that for filling fractions f>0.4 the data are well described
by $n^2 = P^{-\beta_1} f^{-\beta_2}$ with $\beta_1 = 0.67$ and $\beta_2 = 1.29$ and where f is the fraction
of the pore volume occupied with liquid He II and P is the fraction
of the volume occupied by both liquid and vapor He. Unusual
behavior is observed for low filling fractions. Below f=0.4 n
rises with decreasing f to a peak value of nearly 10 before
dropping precipitously to a constant value of 3.7 in the limit of
very thin films.

INTRODUCTION

Acoustics plays a very important role in studying the
superfluid state of liquid helium.[1] Above T_λ the only propagating
sound mode is ordinary sound. Below T_λ there is a galaxy of sound
modes. In addition to 1st and 2nd sound, there are 3rd, 4th and
5th sound. Although liquid helium was first produced 75 years ago,
it was only four years ago that the last of these sounds was
experimentally demonstrated to exist.

Fig. 1 lists these modes and their characteristics. It
should be noted that the values of c_3 and c_4 listed are the
isothermal values. The adiabatic values are given by

$$c_{3ad}^2 = c_3^2 + c_5^2, \quad c_{4ad}^2 = c_4^2 + c_5^2$$

In first sound the normal and superfluid components oscillate
together. There are pressure and density oscillations, but little
or no temperature or entropy oscillations. In 2nd sound the
situation is reversed. The two components oscillate out of phase
in such a way that the center of mass undergoes little or no
motion. There are temperature and entropy oscillations and little
or no density or pressure oscillations. This mode was first
predicted by Tisza in 1938.[2] Its velocity was accurately given by
Landau in 1941,[3] and was measured by Peshkov in 1946.[4] It is the
only known propagating entropy wave. All other entropy waves
diffuse.

Third sound: when a small amount of gas is introduced into an
otherwise empty container at temperatures well below T_λ the helium

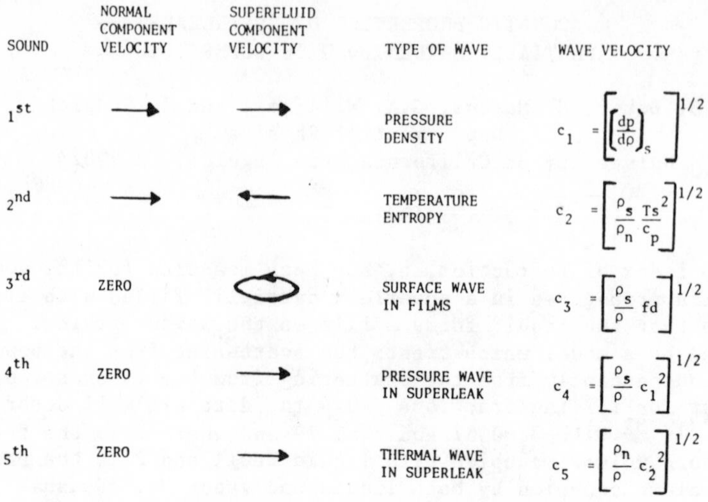

SOUND	NORMAL COMPONENT VELOCITY	SUPERFLUID COMPONENT VELOCITY	TYPE OF WAVE	WAVE VELOCITY
1st	→	→	PRESSURE DENSITY	$c_1 = \left[\left[\dfrac{dp}{d\rho}\right]_s\right]^{1/2}$
2nd	→	←	TEMPERATURE ENTROPY	$c_2 = \left[\dfrac{\rho_s}{\rho_n}\dfrac{Ts^2}{c_p}\right]^{1/2}$
3rd	ZERO	⬭	SURFACE WAVE IN FILMS	$c_3 = \left[\dfrac{\rho_s}{\rho}fd\right]^{1/2}$
4th	ZERO	→	PRESSURE WAVE IN SUPERLEAK	$c_4 = \left[\dfrac{\rho_s}{\rho}c_1^2\right]^{1/2}$
5th	ZERO	→	THERMAL WAVE IN SUPERLEAK	$c_5 = \left[\dfrac{\rho_n}{\rho}c_2^2\right]^{1/2}$

Fig. 1 Schematic of the kinds of normal modes that can occur in ^{4}He for temperatures below T_λ. First and second sound occur in the bulk; third, fourth, and fifth sound occur in restricted geometries only.

film of thickness d which is adsorbed on the inner surface of the container is superfluid. One can have surface waves in it similar to shallow water gravity waves. The body force is the Van der Waals force of attraction, f, of the solid substrate. The normal component does not move--it is locked by the viscous force. These two facts account for the appearance of f, and the ρ_s/ρ term in c_3. This wave's existence was first pointed out by Atkins in 1959[5] and verified experimentally a couple of years later in his laboratory.[6]

Fourth sound is what 1st sound becomes if the normal component is locked by a superleak. The square of its velocity is $(\rho_s/\rho)c_1^2$. Its existence was pointed out by John Pellam in 1948.[7] Atkins described it again in his 1959 paper. Its velocity was experimentally measured shortly thereafter.[8]

Finally 5th sound is what one gets if one immobilizes the normal component in 2nd sound and at the same time takes measures to insure that there are no pressure swings, for instance by supplying pressure release boundary conditions:

$$c_5^2 = \frac{\rho_n}{\rho}c_2^2 = \frac{\rho_s}{\rho}\frac{s^2}{\left(\frac{\partial s}{\partial T}\right)_p}$$

ρ_s/ρ appears here for the same reason it appears in the expressions for c_4^2 and c_3^2. It's existence was predicted[9] and experimentally demonstrated[10,11] in 1979. Fig. 2 is a plot of the velocities of

these modes, except for c_3, as a function of T at the vapor
pressure. c_3 is not included because its value is also a function
of film thickness. The velocity has a range of tens of centimeters
per sec to 10^4 cm/sec.

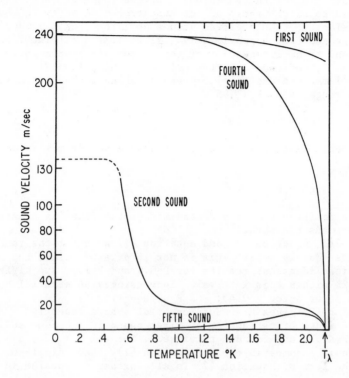

Fig. 2 The sound velocities of the various modes described in
        figure 1 as a function of temperature. The speed of third
        sound is not plotted because it is a function of film
        thickness and substrate properties. The speeds of fourth and
        fifth sound are typically scaled down by a temperature
        independent index of refraction, n, which is a function of
        the restricted geometry, as described in the text.

The excellent description of these modes by the Landau two-
fluid theory now makes it possible to extract information about the
complex flow of the fluid in the random matrix of the porous
superleak material. Also, recent advances in multiple scattering
theory,[12,13] and the identification of fourth sound with Biot's
slow wave,[14] now make it possible to compare the results of
superfluid helium experiments with theories of the behavior of
classical fluids in porous materials.

In a typical fourth sound cell the volume occupied by the
porous superleak is about equal to the volume occupied by the
superfluid helium in which the sound signal propagates. It came,

then, as no surprise in early experiments that the measured
velocity of the fourth-sound wave was significantly less than that
for an ideal superleak (one which locks the normal component yet
has negligible volume). It was recognized that this must be due to
multiple scattering by the superleak. If the index of refraction,
n, is defined to be the ratio of the unscattered velocity to the
scattered velocity, then observed values of n for packed powder
superleaks ranged from approximately 1.01 to 1.27.[15,16] The value
of n was found to be independent of temperature, depending only on
the porosity, P, defined to be the volume of the helium divided by
the total volume. An empirical expression which worked reasonably
well in the range .45 < P < .95 was

$$n^2 = 2-P \quad . \tag{1}$$

However, recent theoretical studies based on a self-similar model[17]
yield

$$n^2 = P^{-\beta} \quad , \tag{2}$$

where β is a positive geometry dependent constant that is greater
the more tortuous the path.[18]
    With $\beta=2/3$, equation (2) and equation (1) both fit the fourth
sound results equally well. This is not surprising, since the two
equations yield identical results for P=0.6 and P=1.0, and differ
by at most 2% within this interval. Increasingly substantial
differences occur below P=0.45: as P$\to$0, equation (1) gives n$\to$2
where equation (2) gives n$\to\infty$. Johnson et al[19] have recently
measured the index of refraction of first sound in a porous solid
where .1 < P < .34 and found n to exceed 2 for all P < .27, a
result which is incompatible with equation (1). Accordingly we
shall use the form of equation (2) in all further discussion in
this paper.
    If, instead of completely saturating the superleak with He II,
only a fraction of that which is needed to fill the pores is
admitted, then a well dispersed yet highly connected film
everywhere coats the superleak particles. The liquid is
distributed uniformly over the height of the superleak because the
force of gravity here is dominated by capillary and Van der Waals
forces. Surface waves can propagate in this film as demonstrated
by Williams, Rosenbaum, and Rudnick (hereafter WRR),[20] and
Rosenbaum et al.[21]
    We shall show in this paper that in these partially filled
geometries the index of refraction becomes quite large as the
filling fraction decreases. We will argue that this is associated
with the fact that the wave is scattered not only by the solid but
also by the vapor and that the large values of n occur because the
surfaces defined by the vapor spaces are more tortuous than those
defined by the solid particles. This is done within the framework
of the results for the Biot theory[22] and the self-similar
model.[17,18] This is the first such application of the results of
the self-similar model to a surface wave as opposed to a
compressional wave.

VELOCITY OF SURFACE WAVES

One can write for the velocity, c, of surface waves in a packed powder superleak:

$$n^2c^2 = c_3^2 + c_\sigma^2 + c_5^2 \qquad (3)$$

where $c_3^2 = (\rho_s/\rho)3\alpha/d^3$ is the third sound velocity, $c_\sigma^2 = (\rho_s/\rho)g(\sigma,f)$ is the velocity of a surface tension wave and $c_5^2 = (\rho_n/\rho)c_2^2$ is the fifth sound velocity. In these expressions ρ_s/ρ and ρ_n/ρ are the[23] fractional densities of superfluid and normalfluid, respectively, α is the Van der Waals constant for the substrate, d is the film thickness, σ is the surface tension, $g(\sigma,f)$ is a function of σ and f, and c_2 is the velocity of second sound. In the expressions for c_3 and c_σ, the only temperature dependent quantity is ρ_s/ρ (for our temperature range we can neglect the weak temperature dependence of σ). c_5 is a pure thermal wave and consequently has a strong temperature dependence. Figure 3, from WRR, shows the wave speed

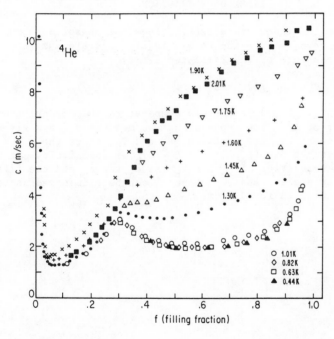

Fig. 3 The speed of sound as a function of filling fraction, f, for a 1 μm diameter packed powder superleak at various temperatures. The total porosity is P=0.75 (from Ref. 20).

as a function of filling fraction for a (1 micron diameter) packed powder superleak. As a function of filling fraction f, four distinct regions can be seen. The precipitous drop in wave speed for increasing f near f=0 is characteristic[21] of the very thin film region where Van der Waals forces dominate. Here the wave is

essentially adiabatic third sound. Above a critical filling
fraction (.02 for this superleak) Van der Waals forces have
weakened to the point where capillary condensation can occur in
those places where the curvature of the film is very high, such as
where two powder particles touch. This region is marked by an
increasing wave speed with filling fraction at all temperatures.
There is very little separation of curves with temperature here,
indicating the dominance of c_σ. Above a certain filling fraction
(about .3 here) the wave speed abruptly decreases with increasing f
for the lowest temperatures. In this region it is believed that
individual pores are filling in, reducing the effects of surface
tension on the wave speed. The effects of thermal restoring forces
(c_5), which increase with increasing temperature, remain
unaffected. Hence curves taken at different temperatures are well
separated in this region. As the filling fraction approaches 1 the
wave speed at a given temperature increases more and more sharply,
approaching the value of fourth sound for that temperature (on the
order of two hundred meters per second below 2K).

INDEX OF REFRACTION

To extract the index of refraction from the measured sound
speed data, we rewrite Eq. (3) to explicitly separate out the
temperature dependence of the first two terms,

$$n^2 c^2 = (\rho_s/\rho)c_0^2 + c_5^2 \quad , \qquad (4)$$

where $c_0^2 = 3\alpha/d^3 + g(\sigma,f)$ is largely temperature independent (but
not independent of f). Now suppose that we measure c for a given
filling fraction at two temperatures, T_a and T_b, where the
superfluid fractions are $(\rho_s/\rho)_a$ and $(\rho_s/\rho)_b$, respectively. If the
measured sound velocities at T_a and T_b are c_a and c_b and the fifth
sound velocities are c_{5a} and c_{5b}, then c_0^2 can be eliminated and the
index of refraction is found from

$$n^2 = \frac{c_{5b}^2 \left(\frac{\rho}{\rho_s}\right)_b - c_{5a}^2 \left(\frac{\rho}{\rho_s}\right)_a}{c_b^2 \left(\frac{\rho}{\rho_s}\right)_b - c_a^2 \left(\frac{\rho}{\rho_s}\right)_a} \quad . \qquad (5)$$

In the WRR experiment the velocity was determined by measuring
the resonant frequencies of an annular cavity packed with aluminum
oxide powder particles of nominal diameter 1 micron and having a
porosity equal to 0.75. The channel had a mean circumference of
11.4 cm and was 1.1 cm deep. Thermal transducers were used to
generate and detect the resonant frequencies, which occurred when
the circumference of the annulus was an integral number of
wavelengths.

In applying equation (5) to the ^{4}He data, T_a was taken to be less than 0.8K and T_b to be 1.45K and 1.75K. Then $(\rho/\rho_s)_a = 1$, $c_{5_a}^2 \ll c_{5_b}^2$, and

$$n^2 = c_{5_b}^2 \left/ \left[c_b^2 - \left(\frac{\rho_s}{\rho}\right)_b c_a^2 \right] \right. . \qquad (6)$$

Measurements were also made in the same superleak with a 2% (molar) mixture of ^{3}He in ^{4}He. Equation (6) was also used for the ^{3}He-^{4}He mixture data at T_b=1.55K with c_a taken to be the same as for pure ^{4}He below 0.8K, scaled by the factor $(\sigma_{34}/\sigma_4)^{1/2}$, where σ_{34} and σ_4 are the surface tensions for the mixture and for ^{4}He, respectively.[22]

More recently, in an experiment on the nature of persistent currents in a similar helium film resonator, Marcus[24] measured the wave velocity at six different temperatures between 1.216K and 1.678K in ^{4}He. The mean circumference was 19.85 cm, the depth 1.0 cm, and the porosity 0.79. Equation (5) was used to extract n.

Figure 4 contains the results of these two sets of measurements in a log-log plot. The points represent the average

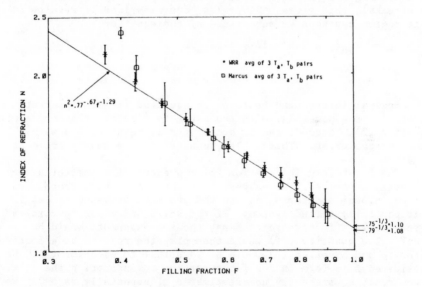

Fig. 4 The index of refraction of fifth sound as a function of filling fraction for two nearly identical superleaks (Ref. 20, 24). The method by which n is extracted from the data is described in the text as is the theoretical curve.

of n extracted from three different T_a, T_b pairs in equation (5) and the bars are the standard deviations for the three determinations. The arrows at f=1 indicate the expected fourth sound values of n for each superleak: $(.75)^{-1/3}$ and $(.79)^{-1/3}$.

The line is a least squares fit of the combined data for filling fractions above f=0.45 to a power law of n vs f.[25] The standard deviations are greatest for small and large values of f; in the former case because c_a and c_b become small and approach each other in magnitude as f decreases, and in the latter case because as f→1 the signals deteriorate (until f reaches 1), and moreover because the velocities become very strong functions of f so that small uncertainties in f produce large uncertainties in velocity. The standard deviations at intermediate values of f are quite small and are clear evidence that n is relatively independent of temperature.

We return to Figure 4 and emphasize the two quantitative experimental results: (1) the asympototic limit of n(f) as f approaches 1 is very accurately the index of refraction of fourth sound, and (2) the variation of n as a function of f in the range .4<f<1 is a power law,

$$n = af^{-b} \qquad (7)$$

The intercept and the slope determine a and b respectively. We find a=1.09 ±.03 and b=0.64±.03. Since a is just the value of n in the fourth sound limit (f=1), we identify a^2 with $P^{-\beta}$ in equation (2). Taking P equal to 0.77 (the average porosity of the two superleaks), this gives β=0.67±.12. Our experimental results in this region can thus be summarized by the equation

$$n^2 = P^{-0.67\pm.12} f^{-1.29\pm.07} \qquad (8)$$

DISCUSSION

Several interesting features of equation (8) are apparent. First, it is a power law with two parameters rather than one as in equation (2). Second, the exponent of P is equal to 2/3 within experimental error. Third, the exponent of f is nearly twice as great.

The first term in equation (8) represents the scattering by the solid superleak. We suggest that the second term represents the additional scattering due to the presence of vapor spaces in this partially filled system. If the solid and vapor "particles" were equally effective scatterers, the two exponents would be equal. The quantity (Pf) would then play the role of an effective porosity and equation (8) would be identical to equation (2). We considered this form in our first attempt to understand the data. However, it consistently underestimates n, especially as f→0. We believe that this can be understood by the following argument. Recall that in the self-similar model the exponent β is indicative of the tortuosity of the microscopic geometry.[18] Now the shape (and hence the tortuosity) of the fluid-solid boundary is the same for a partially filled superleak as when it is completely filled. Then it is reasonable that the first exponent in equation (8) is equal to 2/3. On the other hand, the shape of the fluid-vapor boundary depends on how the film coats the solid and how many pores have filled completely, and may not resemble the shape of the fluid-solid boundary. Hence we should not expect the two exponents in

equation (8) to be equal. A more negative exponent for the second
term in equation (8) means that a given volume of vapor scatters
the surface wave more effectively than would the same volume of
solid. The experimental results summarized by Eq. (8) suggest
that the fluid-vapor boundary is more tortuous than the fluid-solid
boundary.[26]

It should be emphasized that Eq. (8) describes only the data
in the region 0.4<f<1.0, where the fifth sound component is
significant. It becomes more difficult to extract n at the lower
values of f, where the lack of separation of the sound speed curves
with temperature makes the determination less reliable. We have
attempted rough estimates of n for f<0.4, and the results are shown
in Figs. 5 and 6 (figure 6 is a log-log plot of figure 5). The

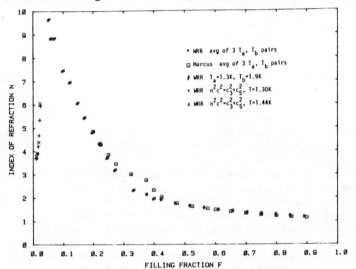

Fig. 5 Similar to figure 4 but showing the dependence of the index
on filling fraction over essentially the entire range of the
latter.

points above f=0.4 are repeated from Figure 4. The points down to
f=0.05 were determined from the WRR data using Eq. (5) with
T_a=1.3K and T_b=1.9K, as these sound speed curves have the greatest
separation at low values of f (see Fig. 2). We estimate the
uncertainty in this determination to be of the order of 10 to 20
percent. The points below f=0.025 were determined by comparing the
observed wave speed to the speed of adiabatic third sound on a flat
(Al_2O_3) substrate: $n=c_{3ad}/c_{obs}$. Shown are the values of n
determined from unpublished data of Williams and Rosenbaum at
T=1.30K and 1.44K[27] taken in the course of the original WRR
measurements.

The picture of n versus f that has emerged displays strikingly
unusual features at low filling fractions. We find that n
increases with decreasing f below f=0.3 more sharply than above
f=0.4, rising to almost 10 near f=0.05. The data very near the
peak value of n are too uncertain to conclude whether a plateau
decreasing the contribution of surface tension to the wave

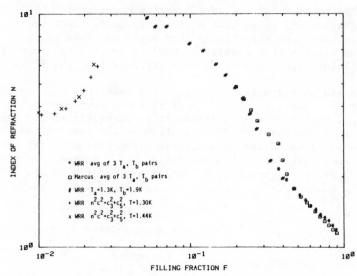

Fig. 6 Same data as in figure 5, plotted on a log-log scale. The regions where the mode is dominated by third sound, surface tension sound, and then fifth sound as f is progressively increased from 10^{-2} to unity are apparent, as described in the text.

region exists. For the lowest values of f there is a precipitous drop in the value of n from its peak value, leveling off to a nearly constant value of 3.7 below f=0.01 (film thickness of about 4 atomic layers).[28] This is most easily seen in Fig. 6.

As in the sound velocity data, the distinctly different behavior of the index of refraction in different regions of filling fraction is associated with the details of how additional fluid distributes itself within the superleak. The constant index of refraction for the thinnest films marks the third sound region where the Van der Waals force predominates. Here changing the volume of fluid changes only the film thickness and does not affect the microscopic tortuosity. This is in marked contrast to the behavior above f=0.05, where slight changes in fluid volume change both film thickness and tortuosity (indeed, a tortuosity change with filling is a necessary ingredient for any self-similar model to successfully describe the behavior of n vs f, as it appears to do in the region f>0.4). The index of refraction rises sharply with the addition of fluid above f=0.02 as the Van der Waals force weakens and capillary condensation sets in. In the region where surface tension forces dominate the sound speed, 0.05<f< 0.3 or 0.4, the index of refraction drops fairly rapidly with increasing f. Finally we observe there is a transition at about f=0.3 or 0.4, above which the index of refraction decreases more slowly with filling fraction. This is the region where the pores are filling in, speed, hence the large spread in speeds with temperature--a sign that the speed of fifth sound is a significant contribution here. This is also the region where we find the power law relation between n and f.

ACKNOWLEDGEMENTS

This work is supported in part by the ONR, and in part by the
NSF, Contract No. DMR 81-00218. We thank R. Rosenbaum and V.
Kotsubo for the use of unpublished data.

REFERENCES

1.   For an introduction to superfluid helium see for example S.J.
     Putterman, Superfluid Hydrodynamics (North Holland/Elsevier,
     New York, 1974).
2.   L. Tisza, C.R. Acad. Sci. Paris 207, 1035 (1938).
3.   L. Landau, J. Phys. USSR 5, 77 (1941).
4.   See Ref. 7. Additional references (elementary and advanced)
     on the general subject of liquid helium are: K.R. Atkins,
     Liquid Helium (Cambridge U.P., Cambridge, 1959), Vol. II; F.
     London, Superfluids (Dover, New York, 1954); K. Mendelssohn,
     The Quest for Absolute Zero (Halsted, New York, 1977) 2nd ed.;
     W.E. Keller, Helium 3 and Helium 4 (Plenum, New York, 1969);
     D.K.C. MacDonald, Near Zero (Doubleday, New York, 1961); J.
     Wilks, Liquid and Solid Helium (Clarendon Press, England,
     1967).
5.   K.R. Atkins, Phys. Rev. 113, 962 (1959).
6.   C.W.F. Everett, K.R. Atkins, and A. Denenstein, Phys. Rev.
     136, A1494 (1964).
7.   J.R. Pellam, Phys. Rev. 73, 608 (1948).
8.   I. Rudnick and K.A. Shapiro, Phys. Rev. Lett. 9, 191
     (1962); Phys. Rev. 137, A1383 (1965).
9.   Isadore Rudnick, Jay Maynard, Gary Williams and Seth
     Putterman, Phys. Rev. B20, 1934 (1979).
10. G.A. Williams, R. Rosenbaum, and I. Rudnick, Phys. Rev.
     Lett. 42, 1282 (1979).
11. G.J. Jelatis, J.A. Roth, and J.D. Maynard, Phys. Rev.
     Lett. 42, 1285 (1979).
12. P.L. Chow, W.E. Kohler, G.C. Papanicolaou, eds., Multiple
     Scattering and Waves in Random Media, Proceedings of the U.S.
     Army Workshop, 24-26 March 1980, Blacksburg, Virginia (North
     Holland, 1981).
13. Akira Ishimaru, Wave Propagation and Scattering in Random
     Media, (Academic Press, 1978).
14. David Linton Johnson, Appl. Phys. Lett. 37, 1065 (1980).
15. K.A. Shapiro and I. Rudnick, Phys. Rev. 137, A1383 (1965).
16. M. Kriss and I. Rudnick, J. Low. Temp. Phys. 3, 339
     (1970).
17. P.N. Sen, C. Scala, and M.H. Cohen, Geophysics 46, 781
     (1981).
18. D.L. Johnson and P.N. Sen, Phys. Rev. B24, 2486 (1981).
19. D.L. Johnson, T.J. Plona, C. Scala, F. Pasierb, and H.
     Kojima, Phys. Rev. Lett. 49, 1840 (1982). This paper
     contains a concise summary of recent work on the propagation
     of acoustic waves in a fluid-saturated porous medium with up-

130

to-date references. Note that ϕ and α in this reference
correspond to P and n^2, respectively, in the present work.

20. G.A. Williams, R. Rosenbaum, and I. Rudnick, Phys. Rev.
     Lett. 42, 1282 (1979).

21. R. Rosenbaum, G.A. Williams, D. Heckerman, J. Marcus, D.
     Scholler, J. Maynard, and I. Rudnick, J. Low Temp. Phys.
     37, 663 (1979).

22. M.A. Biot, J. Acous. Soc. Am. 28, 168 (1956); 28, 179
     (1956); J. Appl. Phys 33, 1482 (1962); J. Acous. Soc. Am.
     34, 1254 (1962); M.A. Biot and D.G. Willis, J. Appl. Mech.
     24, 594 (1957).

23. Actually we should write $\bar{\rho}_s/\rho$ here, where $\bar{\rho}_s$ is the superfluid
     density averaged over the film thickness, taking into account
     the depression of superfluid density due to the solid helium
     layer and the finite superfluid healing length at the fluid-
     solid interface. Where it is important to distinguish between
     $\bar{\rho}_s$ and ρ_s in further development of Eq. (3) the proper
     average will be understood.

24. J. Marcus, thesis (1982).

25. Because the experimental precision of n is at best a few
     percent, the difference between these two superleaks is not
     significant and the data was combined for numerical analysis.

26. Power law dependence of n vs f has also tentatively been
     observed in the 25 micron powder data from WRR, with an
     exponent whose magnitude is about 15% less than that for the 1
     micron powder. The reliability of this estimate is not
     comparable to the 1 micron results however, as it is
     determined from only a single application of equation (6)
     between 1.30K and 0.55K. Equation (5) cannot be used to
     analyze the sound velocity data in 500Å powder from WRR
     because in order to quantitatively extract n we require that
     the c_5 term in equation (3) not be overwhelmed by the c_σ term,
     a criterion which the 500Å powder data fails to meet.

27. G.A. Williams and R. Rosenbaum (unpublished).

28. A constant value for n in the thin film limit has also been
     observed in 500Å powder, V. Kotsubo and G.A. Williams, Phys.
     Rev. B28, 440 (1983). More recent preliminary data in 1
     micron powder show the same sort of behavior at low f as in
     Fig. 5, with a limiting value of n equal to 2.9: V. Kotsubo
     and G.A. Williams, to be published.

DISSIPATION OF ELASTIC WAVES IN FLUID SATURATED ROCKS

B.R. Tittmann, J.R. Bulau, M. Abdel-Gawad
Rockwell International Science Center, Thousand Oaks, CA 91360

ABSTRACT

Experimental results are presented on the dissipation of elastic waves in porous rock. These results show the combined effects of frequency, pressure, temperature, and fluid viscosity on attenuation and modulus in fluid-saturated sandstones. An attenuation peak and an associated modulus defect have been mapped. The data are consistent with a linear relaxation mechanism involving the flow of a viscous intergranular fluid, with a characteristic relaxation time proporational to fluid viscosity.

INTRODUCTION

In the last several years, considerable progress has been made in understanding the mechanisms responsible for the dissipation of elastic wave energy in rock. Until recently, the intrinsic attenuation of elastic waves in rock under near-surface conditions has been attributed to frictional dissipation. This process has been perceived as the rubbing of internal crack surfaces past one another in response to elastic wave stresses, resulting in the conversion of elastic energy to heat through friction. The original reason for widespread acceptance of this mechanism was the observation, based primarily on measurements on "room dry" rocks, that attenuation is essentially independent of frequency (Born, 1941). Classical friction was the only viable mechanism known to be rate independent. Until recently, friction was still regarded as the primary mechanism for attenuation in 'dry' rocks and a major contribution to attenuation in fluid-bearing rocks. Gordon and Davis (1968) recognized that attenuation in "room dry" rocks is independent of amplitude at sufficiently low amplitudes ($< 10^{-6}$) with a transition to an amplitude dependent regime at higher strain amplitudes. They argued on theoretical grounds that a dissipation mechanism based upon a Coulomb-type friction law results in both an amplitude and a frequency independent Q. More recently, Mavko (1979) refuted this and demonstrated that a Coulomb friction mechanism is inherently nonlinear, and required that attenuation increase with the first power of strain. He concluded that friction is important only at high strains ($> 10^{-6}$), and that linear mechanisms are required to account for practically all attenuation at low seismic amplitudes in both 'dry' and wet rock. Richardson and Tittmann (1980) recently presented a phenomenological theory to explain the effects of minute amounts of adsorbed water on attenuation in 'dry' rock. Their model assumes a linear thermally activated process with a distribution of activation energies.

Attenuation mechanisms involving the flow of a viscous pore fluid have only recently received considerable attention. The classic work in this area was published by Biot (1956a,b), who considered the "global" flow of fluid from regions of bulk compression to regions of bulk dilatation. Johnston et al (1979) and Mochuziki (1982) evaluated the possible contribution of the Biot-type mechanism to attenuation in fully and partially saturated rocks at seismic and well logging frequencies. They conclude that the Biot-type loss mechanism is not likely to be significant, except perhaps in very permeable and porous rocks at high frequencies.

While the Biot mechanism considers fluid flow on a scale which is much larger than individual pores and cracks, attenuation can also be attributed to fluid flow on a microscopic scale. Several types of microscopic fluid flow mechanisms have been considered. The first was considered initially by Walsh (1968, 1969) and involves the shear of a viscous fluid in very thin cracks. This mechanism was reexamined by O'Connell and Budiansky (1977). Mavko and Nur (1979) considered the special case of fluid shear in partially saturated cracks. Each of these three studies shows attenuation increasing linearly with frequency at low frequencies. O'Connell and Budiansky (1977) and Walsh (1969) both predict a characteristic frequency (maximum attenuation) which is inversely proportional to fluid viscosity. They also conclude that the intercrack fluid shear mechanism is unlikely to contribute significantly to attenuation in water-bearing rocks at low frequencies.

The second type of fluid flow mechanism was proposed initially by Mavko and Nur (1975) and later treated quantitatively by O'Connell and Budiansky (1977). This mechanism, commonly referred to as liquid 'squirt' involves intercrack fluid flow. As elastic waves pass through a material containing cracks, the stresses exerted on any crack plane at any given time can be resolved into normal and shear components. Depending on the crack orientation with respect to the direction of wave propagation, the normal stress component may be either compressional or dilational. Thus, in the case of random crack distribution, some cracks will necessarily be in compression, while others will be in dilation. Responding to pressure gradients, fluid will flow from compressional cracks to dilational cracks. Attenuation will be maximized when $\omega\tau = 1$, where ω is the angular frequency of the wave, and τ is the time required to move fluid into and out of cracks. O'Connell and Budiansky (1977) predict that maximum attenuation will occur when $\omega = (K/\eta)(c/a)^3$, where K is rock bulk modulus, η is fluid viscosity, and c/a is the thickness to length (aspect) ratio of the crack. They also show attenuation increasing linearly with frequency at low frequencies. According to their model, the 'squirt' flow of intergranular water is the only fluid flow mechanism which is likely to be significant at seismic and well-logging frequencies.

Mavko and Nur (1979) describe a fluid flow mechanism which also involves the compression and dilation of intergranular cracks. Their model treats partially saturated cracks containing a very compressible gas phase and a relatively incompressible fluid phase.

From experimental evidence, we now recognize that the dissipation of elastic wave energy in rock under upper crustal conditions depends on many factors, including adsorbed water content (in 'dry' rocks), hydrostatic effective stress, nonhydrostatic stress, fluid saturation, frequency, intergranular fluid viscosity, rock microstructure, vibration amplitude, and certain effects apparently involving the chemical interaction of the rock with either condensed or surface adsorbed fluids. For the purpose of understanding mechanisms, the most important experimental observations are those in which the effects of one variable can be observed, while holding all other factors constant.

In summary, previous studies collectively show that elastic wave attenuation in rock under upper crustal conditions involves at least several different mechanisms. At very high amplitude the attenuation process is nonlinear, and probably involves classical intergranular friction, as described by Walsh[12] and Mavko.[13] At very low amplitudes, characteristic of far-field seismic waves, attenuation is critically dependent on the amount of water in the rock, which may be present as either a surface adsorbed film in 'dry' rocks or as a bulk fluid in partially and fully saturated rocks. At low seismic amplitudes, the attenuation process involving surface adsorbed water appears to be nearly independent of frequency, suggesting a linear mechanism with a broad distribution of relaxation times. When condensed fluid is present in the rock, attenuation is frequency dependent, and apparently related to the relaxation of stresses within the viscous intergranular fluid.

Our recent experimental results show the combined effects of frequency, pressure, temperature, and fluid viscosity on attenuation in fluid saturated sandstones. The experimental techniques are described elsewhere.[14-18] The data shown here are for vibrations described by Young's modulus and consist of both flexural and extensional waves.

EXPERIMENTAL RESULTS

1. Frequency Dependence of Attenuation

One of the objectives was a detailed examination of the dependence of Q on frequency. A series of experiments were made on saturated Berea and Wingate sandstones at ambient pressure, and on Berea sandstone at high confining pressures. The porosities for Berea and Wingate are 20% and 18%, respectively. By varying sample length and inertial end loading, and in some cases by using higher harmonics, it was possible to obtain reliable resonance measurements between 25 Hz and 10 kHz.

Figure 1.1 shows Q^{-1} values vs frequency for saturated and dry Berea sandstone at ambient pressure. The saturated Berea shows strong frequency dependence of Q^{-1} in the entire range from 25 Hz to ~ 7000 Hz, and in particular, at frequencies above 150 Hz. The dry Berea, in contrast, shows no strong frequency dependence over the same range. The minimum measurable Q^{-1} is about 1×10^{-4}.

134

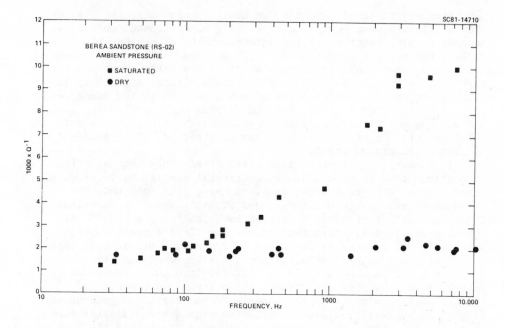

Fig. 1.1 Q^{-1} vs frequency for water saturated Berea sandstone at 1 atm pressure. Losses in the room dry rock
are compared with losses in the saturated rocks.

Q^{-1} vs frequency data comparing Wingate and Berea sandstones
show Wingate, the less indurated of the two sandstones, displays a
stronger dissipation than Berea. These data indicate that at ambient pressure, the saturated sandstones show a dependence of dissipation on frequency and that the more indurated the rock, or the
stronger the bond between grains, the smaller the total
dissipation.

2.   Pressure/Microstructure Dependence

The influence of effective pressure on Q^{-1} in saturated sandstones at 7 kHz and 200 Hz is presented in this section, where
effective pressure is defined as the difference between the hydrostatic confining pressure and the pore fluid pressure. Our results
clearly illustrate two important observations which have impact on
our understanding of wave dissipation mechanisms: a) At kHz frequencies, the dissipation is more strongly pressure-dependent than
at low frequencies. This is indicated by the data on water-saturated Berea and Wingate sandstones, which are shown in Fig. 2.1.

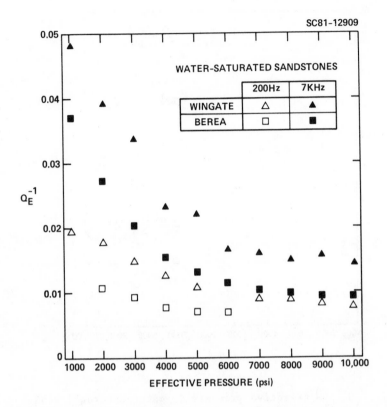

Fig. 2.1 Q^{-1} vs effective pressure in fully saturated Wingate
and Berea sandstone at two different frequencies.

The effective pressure dependence is greatest at low pressures. b)
Petrofabric characteristics of the rock frame play a very important
role in the dissipation of elastic wave energy at both kHz and low
frequencies. Data on the pressure dependence of dissipation in
Boise sandstone at 7000 kHz are compared with Wingate and Berea
data in Fig. 2.2. Boise has a porosity of 22%. Within this group,
Boise is the most indurated and shows only a very small pressure
and frequency dependence, as illustrated in Fig. 2.3. The 200 Hz
data set is qualitatively consistent with the 7 kHz data set.
     Velocities have been calculated to show velocity vs effective
pressure in water-saturated Boise, Berea and Wingate sandstones at
7 kHz. The velocity data shown in Fig. 2.4 clearly indicate significant differences in wave velocities among the three rocks at
low effective pressures. However, wave velocities became nearly
coincident at high effective pressures. By comparing Figs. 2.2 and
2.4, it becomes apparent that significant differences in attenuation among the three rocks continue to exist at high effective
pressures where velocities are nearly identical.

136

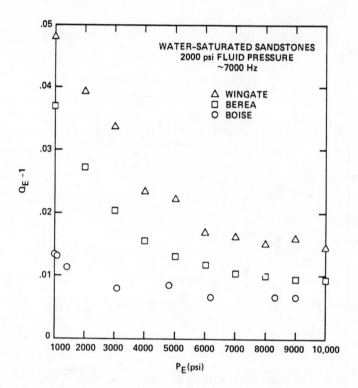

Fig. 2.2 Q^{-1} vs effective pressure in water-saturated sandstone at ~ 7 kHz.

SC81-12710

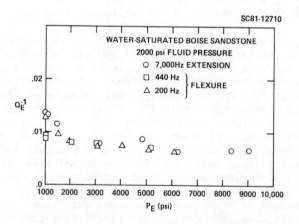

Fig. 2.3 Q^{-1} vs effective pressure in water-saturated Boise
sandstone at 3 different frequencies.

coincident at high effective pressures. By comparing Figs. 2.2 and
2.4, it become apparent that significant differences in attenuation
among the three rocks continue to exist at high effective pressures
where velocities are nearly identical.

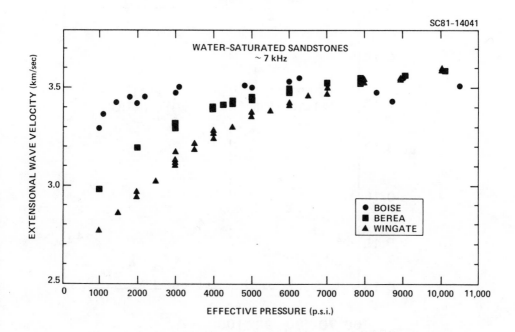

Fig. 2.4 Velocity vs effective pressure for three water-
saturated sandstones at ~ 7 kHz.

3. High Pressure Partial Saturation in Boise Sandstone

The effect of partial water saturation on attenuation in Boise
sandstone has been investigated at an effective pressure of about
P_c = 900 psi and a frequency between 6640 and 6800 Hz.
Attenuation and resonant frequency measurements for both runs
are shown in Fig. 3.1. The following observations are made: a)
Resonant frequency and Q were both fairly uniform for all pore
fluid pressures in excess of a certain critical value (marked by a
vertical dashed line). b) When the pore fluid pressure was decreased below this critical pressure, resonant frequency decreased
sharply and attenuation increased significantly. c) At a somewhat
lower pressure (7-10 psi) below the "critical" pressure, resonant

138

frequency reached a minimum and remained unchanged at even lower pore fluid pressures. d) Attenuation reached a maximum when pore fluid pressure had decreased 5-10 psi below the "critical" pressure.

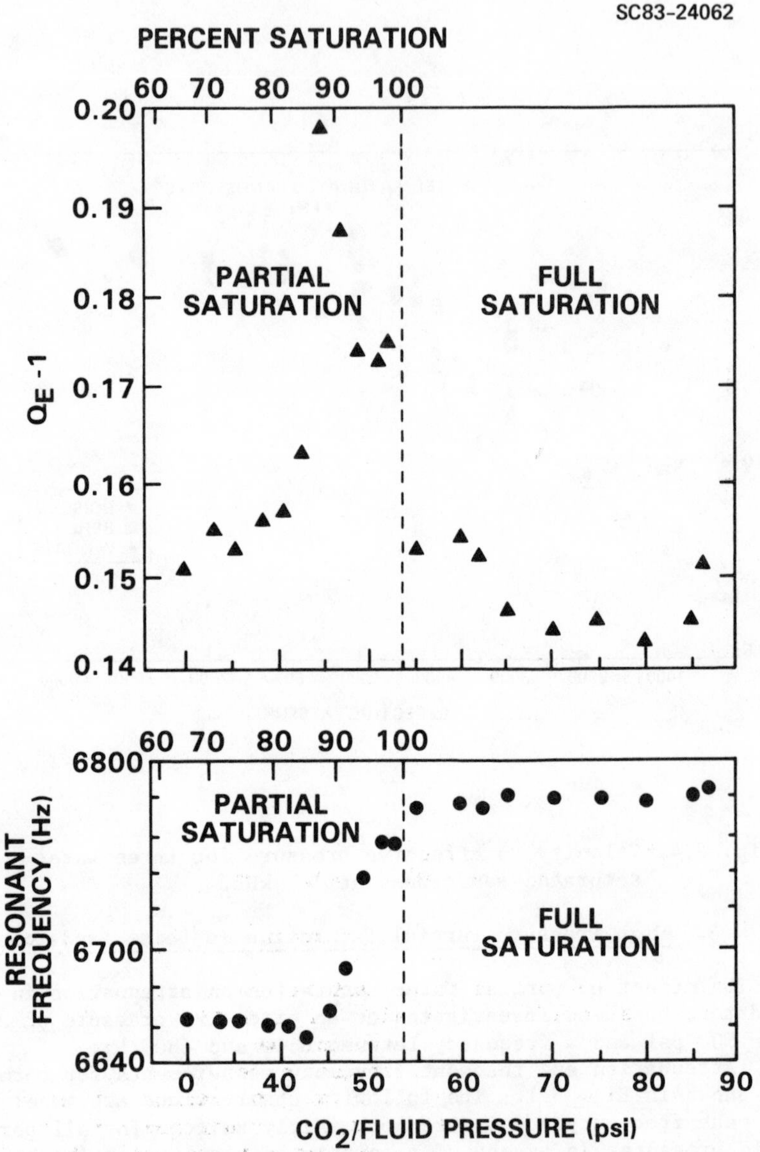

SC83-24062

Fig. 3.1 Sample resonant frequency and Q^{-1} vs percent saturation and pore fluid pressure for Boise sandstone at 900 psi confining pressure.

tion of gas within the rock. This is consistent with the observations of Nur[18] who demonstrated a sharp drop in P-wave velocity
with the formation of steam in a water-saturated Berea sandstone at
high temperatures. The percent saturation is estimated by a calculation which assumes a) ideal gas behavior, b) Henry's solubility
law is obeyed, and c) that the gas/water ratio in the fluid being
expelled from the rock as gas forms is identical to that of the
fluid remaining in the rock (that is, gas and water have the same
effective permeability).

The small attenuation peak, shown here in Boise sandstone at
high partial saturation levels and at moderate effective pressures,
is qualitatively consistent with similar peaks which are observed
with other sandstones at ambient pressure. Presumably, a similar
mechanism involving viscous dissipation is operating in both cases.

4. Fluid Viscosity

Gordon[19] demonstrated the existence of a stress relaxation
peak in glycerin saturated Rhode Island granite by controlling temperature and thus viscosity. Assuming a viscous relaxation mechanism with laminar flow the relaxation time is expected to be proportional to fluid viscosity. The combined effects of frequency
and fluid viscosity can be lumped into a common parameter, the product of frequency and viscosity. This relationship has now been
demonstrated in our laboratory using fluid saturated Coconino sandstone at elevated effective pressures. Attenuation was measured in
flexure as a function of frequency, pressure, and temperature with
both water and glycerin as pore fluids. Young's modulus values
were calculated from the resonant frequencies, taking into consideration the geometry of the sample and the inertial moments of the
apparatus.[20,15] These results are shown in Fig. 4.1. The lines
represent a visual fit of the data to the dispersion relationship
shown in the lower corner. The "peak" is thought to represent the
condition $\omega\tau = 1$, where ω is the angular frequency of the wave and
τ is the characteristic relaxation time of a viscous pore fluid.

It is also useful to consider the functional dependence of
attenuation on frequency. Attenuation models describing the relaxation of a viscous pore fluid[8-10,3] predict that attenuation increases with the first power of frequency at low frequencies. Our
experimental (Fig. 4.2) data show attenuation increasing with frequency to a power significantly less than one, near 1/4. This discrepancy could conceivably be explained by a distribution of pore
shapes and sizes, thus broadening the relaxation time spectrum for
a viscous flow process.

These observations and others lead us to conclude that the
attenuation of elastic waves in fluid saturated Coconino sandstone
in the frequency-viscosity range of this study involves the flow of
a viscous pore fluid, with a characteristic time proportional to
fluid viscosity. The relationship between Q and modulus is consistent with such a linear relaxation mechanism. Of the attenuation
mechanisms proposed to date only the liquid "squirt"-type model

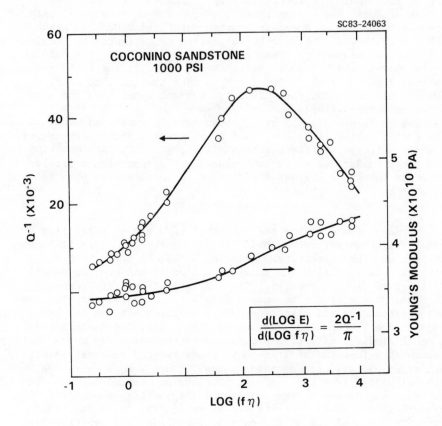

Fig. 4.1   Attenuation and Young's modulus plotted against log
           (frequency x fluid viscosity) in fluid saturated
           Coconino sandstone at 1000 psi effective pressure.
           Lines represent a visual fit of the data to the
           dispersion relationship shown in the lower right
           corner. (Here, frequency has units of Hz and
           viscosity poise.)

of O'Connell and Budiansky[10] satisfactorily predicts a relaxation
peak at the value of frequency-viscosity observed in this study.   A
significant velocity dispersion is associated with the viscous relaxation, and the amount of dispersion at low frequencies is expected to increase with increasing pore fluid viscosity.   The
dependence of velocity on pressure appears to be relatively more
significant at low frequencies than at high frequencies.

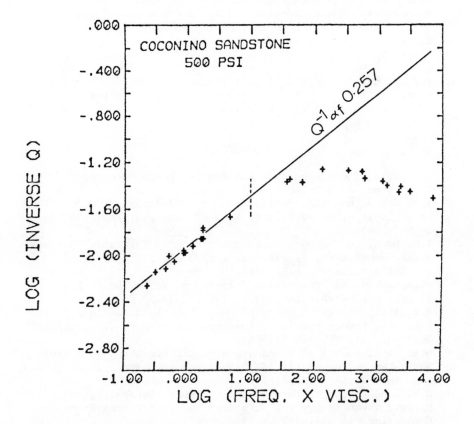

Fig. 4.2 Log attenuation vs log (frequency x viscosity) showing
low frequency power fit. Data for fluid saturated
Coconino sandstone at 1000 psi effective pressure.
The data points to the left of the dashed line were
obtained with water as pore fluid, the data to the
left with glycerine.

CONCLUSIONS

The general observations of studies are summarized below:

1. In general, Q is not constant – Q increases with frequency in
    the seismic band. Velocity dispersion is observed and corre-
    lated with Q.

142

2. Significant differences in Q and velocity are observed among
    the various rocks studied. Differences are related
    qualitatively to microstructures.

3. Bulk modulus and shear modulus should be treated as complex
    quantities. Q and velocity are not independent of each
    other. Low Q (high attenuation) indicates high velocity
    dispersion. High Q (low attenuation) indicates low velocity
    dispersion.

4. For the purpose of modeling, reliable estimates of Q and v are
    needed at the frequency of interest. Ultrasonic and sonic
    measurements are not necessarily representative of seismic
    measurements.

REFERENCES

1. W.T. Born, The Attenuation Constant of Earth Materials,
   Geophysics, 6, 132-148 (1941).
2. R.B. Gordon and L.A. Davis, Velocity and Attenuation of Seismic
   Waves in Imperfectly Elastic Rock, J. Geophys. Res., 73, 3917-
   3935 (1968).
3. F.M. Mavko and A. Nur, Wave Attenuation in Partially Saturated
   Rocks. Geophysics, 44, 161-178 (1979).
4. J.M. Richardson and B.R. Tittmann, Phenomenological Theory of
   Attenuation and Propagation Velocity in Rocks, Proc. Lunar
   Planet. Sci. Conf. 11th, 1837-1846 (1980).
5. M.A. Biot, Theory of Propagation of Elastic Waves in a Fluid-
   Saturated Porous Solid. I. Low-Frequency Range, J. Acoustical
   Soc. Am., 28, 168-178 (1956a).
6. M.A. Biot, Theory of Propagation of Elastic Waves in a Fluid-
   Saturated Porous Solid. II. High-Frequency Range, J. Acoustical
   Soc. Am., 28, 179-191 (1956b).
7. D.H. Johnston, M.N. Toksoz, and A. Timur, Attenuation of
   Seismic Waves in Dry and Saturated Rocks: II. Mechanisms,
   Geophysics, 44, 691-771, 1979.
8. S. Mochuziki, Attenuation in Partially Saturated Rocks, J.
   Geophys. Res., 87, 8598-8604, 1982.
9. J.B. Walsh, Attenuation in a Partially Melted Material, J.
   Geophys. Res., 73, 2209-2216 (1968).
10. J.B. Walsh., New Analysis of Attenuation in Partially Melted
    Rock, J. Geophys. Res., 74, 4333-4337 (1969).
11. R.J. O'Connell and B. Budiansky, Viscoelastic Properties of
    Fluid Saturated Cracked Solids, J. Geophys. Res., 82, 5701-5735
    (1977).
12. G.M. Mavko and A. Nur, Melt Squirt in the Asthenosphere, J.
    Geophys. Res., 80m 1444-1448, 1975.
13. J.B. Walsh, Seismic Wave Attenuation in Rock Due to Friction,
    J. Geophys. Res., 71, 2591-2599 (1966).

14. G.M. Mavko, Frictional Attenuation: An Inherent Amplitude Dependence, J. Geophy. Res., 84, 4769-4775 (1979).
15. B.R. Tittmann, M. Abdel-Gawad, and R.M. Housley, "Elastic Velocity and Q Factor Measurements on Apollo 12, 14, and 15 Rocks, Proc. Third Lunar Sci. Conf., 2565-2575 (1972).
16. B.R. Tittmann and J.M. Curnow, Apparatus for Measuring Internal Friction Q Factors in Brittle Materials, Rev. Sci. Instrum., 47, 1516-1518 (1976).
17. B.R. Tittmann, Lunar Rock Q in 3000-5000 Range Achieved in Laboratory, Phil Trans. R. Soc. Lond. A, 285, 475-479 (1977).
18. B.R. Tittmann, H. Nadler, V.A. Clark, L.A. Ahlberg, and T.W. Spencer, Frequency Dependence of Seismic Dissipation in Saturated Rocks, Geophys. Res. Letters, 8, 36-38 (1981a).
19. A.M. Nur, J.D. Walls, K. Winkler, and J. DeVilbiss, Effects of Fluid Saturation on Waves in Porous Rock and Relation to Hydraulic Permeability, Soc. Petroleum Eng. Jour., 20, 450-458 (1980).
20. B.R. Tittmann, M. Abdel-Gawad, C. Salvado, J. Bulau, L. Ahlberg, and T.W. Spencer, A Brief Note on the Effect of Interface Bonding on Seismic Dissipation, Proc. Lunar Planet. Sci. Conf. 12th, 1737-1745 (1981b).
21. R.B. Gordon, Mechanical Relaxation Spectrum of Crystalline Rock Containing Water, J. Geophys. Res., 79, 2129-2131 (1974).
22. E.P. Papadakis, Balanced Resonator for Infrasonic Measurements of Young's Modulus and Damping in Flexure, J. Testing Evaluation, 1, 126-132 (1973).

CONSISTENT THEORETICAL DESCRIPTION FOR
ELECTRICAL AND ACOUSTIC
PROPERTIES OF SEDIMENTARY ROCKS

Ping Sheng and A.J. Callegari
Exxon Corporate Research Science Laboratories
Clinton Township
Annandale, NJ 08801

ABSTRACT

We present a differential effective medium theory which is
capable of providing a consistent description for both the electrical and acoustic properties of sedimentary rocks. Besides the
correct prediction of dc and finite-frequency electrical behaviors
for sandstones, calculations based on the differential effective
medium picture of rock microstructure are shown to yield sonic
travel times and acoustic attenuation in good agreement with
experimental data. Physical interpretation of the various rock
characteristics within our theoretical framework leads to the
interesting picture of a rock as a fluid-solid composite system
that is in the vicinity of a percolation threshold.

I. INTRODUCTION

Porous rocks are one of the most abundant forms of matter in
nature. However, it was not until the development of oil exploration techniques in modern times that the physical properties of
rocks, such as electrical conductivity, acoustic velocity,
porosity, permeability, etc., became the focus of intensive study.
In 1942, G. E. Archie[1] found that there is a definite correlation
between the electrical conductivity σ and the porosity of fluid-
filled sandstones. The relation $\sigma = \sigma_f \phi^m$, where σ_f is the fluid
conductivity, ϕ is the porosity, and $m \sim 2$ is a constant, has
later become known as Archie's law. Subsequently, similar
correlations between the sonic velocity and porosity in sandstones
led M.R.J. Wyllie[2] to deduce an empirical relation $V^{-1} = \phi\, V_f^{-1} +
(1-\phi)V_s^{-1}$, where V is the acoustic velocity and V_f and V_s are the

fluid and solid acoustic velocities, respectively. Besides their utility in inferring rock porosity from electrical and acoustic logs, these two relations present a set of intriguing clues for the basic underlying structure of rocks. For example, if viewed in the framework of percolation theory, Archie's law would imply that sandstone is an inhomogeneous composite with a structure that yields a percolation threshold $\phi \sim 0$. Recently, additional interest on rocks has been aroused by sonic attenuation experiments[3,4] in which the fluid-saturated sandstones are shown to exhibit a frequency peak in attenuation whose value is up to several orders of magnitude larger than the attenuation of either the fluid or the solid phase alone. It is the purpose of this paper to present a differential effective medium (DEM) theory[5] which is capable of providing a consistent description for both acoustic and electrical properties of sedimentary rocks. Besides the derivation of DEM equations for the elastic moduli, our theoretical results include predictions of acoustic attentuation and resistivity-sonic travel time correlation which are in quantitative agreement with field and laboratory data. In what follows, Section II presents a review of the electromagnetic properties as predicted by the DEM theory and their comparison with observed sandstone characteristics. This is followed by the formulation and derivation of the acoustic DEM theory in Section III. Results of numerical calculations for acoustic properties and a comparison with experiments are shown in Section IV. In Section V we discuss physical implications of the results, the shortcomings of the DEM theory, and direction for possible future research.

II. ELECTRICAL PROPERTIES

In the context of electrical properties, DEM theory was first proposed by Bruggeman[6] to calculate the conductivity of a two-component composite structure formed by successive substitutions. That is, the structure is built up by starting from homogeneous component 1 and using the iterative process as shown in Fig. 1:

146

replace a small amount of the starting component 1 by the second
component, and then regard the resulting "effective" material as
the homogeneous component for the succeeding substitution step.

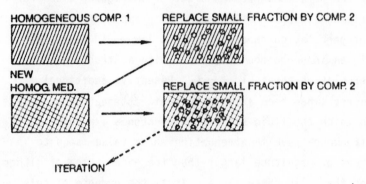

Fig. 1. The basic microstructure build-up process in
the DEM theory.

Mathematically, if we let $\varepsilon = \kappa - i\frac{4\pi\sigma}{\omega}$ (where κ is the dielectric
constant and ω the angular frequency) denote the complex dielectric
constant of the composite mixture after the first replacement step
and $\varepsilon_1, \varepsilon_2$ the two complex dielectric constants of the constituents,
then Bruggeman's self-consistent[6] theory tells us that

$$(1 - \Delta\psi) \frac{\varepsilon - \varepsilon_1}{2\varepsilon + \varepsilon_1} + \Delta\psi \frac{\varepsilon - \varepsilon_2}{2\varepsilon + \varepsilon_2} = 0 , \qquad (1)$$

where $\Delta\psi$ is the amount of component 2 replacing component 1, and
the replacement unit is assumed to be spherical in shape. In terms
of $\Delta\varepsilon \equiv \varepsilon - \varepsilon_1$ the solution for ε to first order in $\Delta\psi$ is given
by

$$\Delta\varepsilon = 3\varepsilon_1 \left(\frac{\varepsilon_2 - \varepsilon_1}{\varepsilon_2 + 2\varepsilon_1} \right) \Delta\psi . \qquad (2)$$

If, instead of replacing $\Delta\psi$ of the homogeneous component 1 by
component 2, one were to replace $\Delta\psi$ of a homogeneous composite
medium (characterized by dielectric constant ε) by component 2,
then Eq. (2) should read

$$\Delta\varepsilon = 3\varepsilon \left(\frac{\varepsilon_2 - \varepsilon}{\varepsilon_2 + 2\varepsilon} \right) \Delta\psi . \qquad (3)$$

However, since $\Delta\psi$ now stands for the amount of the composite replaced by component 1, the actual amount of component 2 added in the replacement step is given by

$$\Delta\psi_{actual} = (1 - \psi_{actual})\,\Delta\psi, \qquad (4)$$

where ψ_{actual} denotes the amount of component 2 in the composite. If now we let ψ denote the ψ_{actual}, then the correct DEM equation is given by

$$\frac{1}{3\varepsilon}\left(\frac{\varepsilon_2 + 2\varepsilon}{\varepsilon_2 - \varepsilon}\right)d\varepsilon = \frac{d\psi}{1 - \psi}. \qquad (5)$$

Direct integration of Eq. (5) yields

$$1 - \psi = \left(\frac{\varepsilon/\varepsilon_1 - \varepsilon_2/\varepsilon_1}{1 - \varepsilon_2/\varepsilon_1}\right)\left(\frac{\varepsilon_1}{\varepsilon}\right)^d, \qquad (6)$$

where d is the depolarization factor of the substituting unit and is equal to 1/3 in the case of spheres. It should be remarked here that although the present derivation starts with Bruggeman's self-consistent theory, the same DEM equation would be obtained by starting with some other effective medium theory, such as the Maxwell Garnett theory[6]. The independence of the final result from the starting version of the effective medium theory is due to the fact that the different theories all agree to first order in the dilute inclusion limit.

For dc conductivity of sedimentary rocks, Eq. (6) has a particularly simple form. If we let component 1 be the fluid and component 2 be the solid, then the assumptions that the imaginary part of the dielectric constants dominates over the real part (valid at dc and low frequencies where $4\pi\sigma/\omega \gg \kappa$) and $\sigma_2=0$, $\sigma_1=\sigma_f$ yield

$$\sigma = \sigma_f\phi^{\frac{1}{1-d}}, \qquad (7)$$

148

where $\phi = 1 - \psi$ is the porosity. Sen et al.[7] has noted that Eq.
(7) has precisely the same general form as Archie's law. They also
pointed out that one possible realization of the DEM model is a
structure which possesses the character of self-similarity as shown
in Fig. 2. Such a structure can be obtained, for example, by considering the size of the substituting units as increasing at every
successive replacement step. In a later work Mendelson and Cohen[8]

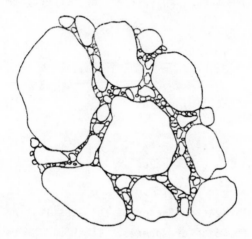

Fig. 2. Schematic picture of a
microstructure with self-similar
characteristics.

generalized Eq. (7) to cases where there is a mixture of shapes for
the substituting units. The exponent m is then the average of a
function (of d) over the shape distribution. Within such a theoretical framework, the value of Archie's law exponent, $m \sim 2$, can
thus be interpreted as arising from the pore structure of the DEM
model arrived at by using a general preponderance of randomly-
oriented, platelet-like solid substitution units.

At finite frequencies, the displacement-current effects can no
longer be neglected. We have numerically solved Eq. (6) for d =
1/2 (consistent with Archie's law), $\varepsilon_2 = \varepsilon_s = \kappa$, and $\varepsilon_1 = \varepsilon_f =
- i4\pi\sigma_f/\omega$. The resulting complex impedance of the composite,
$Z = 1/\sigma = R + iX$, is plotted in Fig. 3 for $\phi = 0.1$. The values of

R and X, expressed in units of $1/\sigma_f$, are calculated as an increasing function of frequency, defined in dimensionless form as $\Omega = \omega\kappa/4\pi\sigma_f$. As seen in the figure, at $\Omega = 0$ we have $X = 0$ and

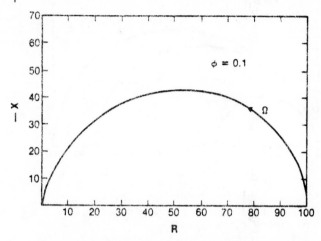

Fig. 3. Complex impedance plot for the DEM theory. The arrow on the curve shows the direction for increasing frequency.

$R = 100 = 1/\phi^2$, consistent with Archie's law. As Ω is increased, the trajectory of the complex impedance plot traces out a near semicircle whose center is below the real axis. Such a form for the frequency dependence of complex impedance is precisely what has been experimentally observed in Berea sandstones by R. Knight.[9]

Sandstones usually contain a certain amount of clay. The modification of the electrical properties due to the presence of clay can be modelled by attributing a finite conductivity σ_s to solid rock grains. That is, $\varepsilon_s = \kappa - i4\pi\sigma_s/\omega$. Provided that $\sigma_s/\sigma_f \ll 1$, and $d = 1/2$, Archie's law (dc conductivity) is modified to read as

$$\sigma = \sigma_f\phi^2 + \sigma_s (1-\phi^2), \qquad (8)$$

which is in the form of the empirical de Witte[10] formula, $\sigma = A + B\sigma_f$, for the conductivity of shaly sands (sandstones containing clay and other minerals). In Fig. 4, we show the frequency dependence of the resulting complex impedance. It is seen that the

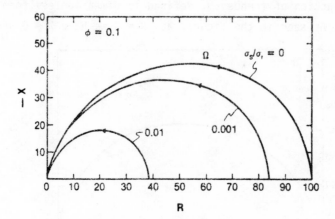

Fig. 4. Complex impedance plot for the
DEM theory in which the solid particles
has finite conductivity.

only effect of a finite σ_s is to decrease the radius of the semicircle. The centers of the semicircles still lie below the real
axis.

Another interesting effect of the DEM model is that it
predicts dielectric constant enhancement at low frequencies. This
effect, on the order of a factor between 1 and 2, is present in our
finite-frequency calculations described above. However, for the
case where the solid particles are conducting (or coated with a
conducting material) and the fluid insulating, the predicted
enhancement is huge. In order to see this, let $\varepsilon_1 = \kappa$ and $\varepsilon_2 =
- i \, 4\pi\sigma_s/\omega$, then Eq. (6) reads

$$\phi = \left(\frac{\varepsilon/\kappa + i4\pi\sigma_s/\kappa\omega}{1 + i \, 4\pi\sigma_s/\kappa\omega} \right) \left(\frac{\kappa}{\varepsilon} \right)^{1/2} \tag{9}$$

for $d = 1/2$. In the limit $\omega \to 0$, it is seen that $\varepsilon/\kappa = \phi^{-2}$. That
implies extremely large values of the dielectric constant at low
porosities. In Fig. 5 the dielectric constant is plotted as a
function of ϕ for various values of the dimensionless frequency

$\Omega' = \dfrac{\kappa\omega}{4\pi\sigma_s}$. It is seen that at finite frequencies the value of

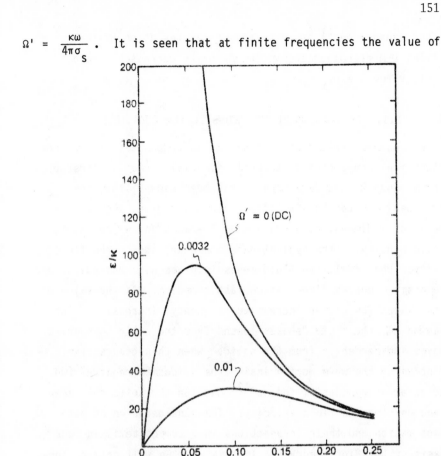

Fig. 5. Dielectric constant as a function of porosity for the system in which the solid particles are conducting and the fluid insulating. Different curves are for different measuring frequencies.

ε/κ has a maximum at some $\phi > 0$. Physically, the enhancement effect arises from the appearance of microcracks between the solid grains at low porosities. When the solid is conducting, these microcracks act as capacitors with large capacitances, thereby giving rise to an increased value of dielectric constant for the composite. Since the existence of microcracks is a general feature of composite microstructure in the vicinity of the percolation threshold,[6] the geometric interpretation of the dielectric constant effect shows that similar to the case of Archie's law, the predicted enhancement[11] is just another manifestation of the underlying DEM microgeometry as the porosity decreases toward the threshold value $\phi = 0$.

III. DERIVATION OF THE ACOUSTIC DEM EQUATIONS

The acoustic properties of fluid-solid composites differ from the electrical properties in several essential aspects. First of all, from general considerations it has been shown[12] that the acoustic behavior can be classified into two regimes according to the value of a dimensionless parameter $\delta = \omega \rho_f h^2/n$, where ρ_f is the fluid density, h the typical pore diameter, and n the fluid viscosity. When $\delta \ll 1$, the fluid moves in phase with the solid, and the composite behaves like a viscoelastic medium. As the value of δ is increased (by either increasing frequency, increasing h, or decreasing n), the fluid "shakes loose" from the solid boundaries and moves independently from the solid. When this occurs, the description of the wave motion inside the composite requires two variables at every spatial "point"[13]: one for the solid displacement and one for the fluid velocity. The consideration of both kinds of motion and their interactions in a composite is in fact the basis of the Biot theory.[14] In this work we will only be concerned with the acoustic properties of the fluid-solid composite in the viscoelastic regime, i.e. $\delta \ll 1$. For water-saturated rocks with pore dimension $h \simeq 1$ μm and viscosity $n=1$ centipoise, this requirement translates into a frequency constraint of $\omega/2\pi = f < 10^5$ Hz.

In the limit where the scales of the inhomogeneities are small compared to the probing wavelength, the propagation of acoustic waves in a viscoelastic composite is specified by three quantities: the two complex Lame constants λ, μ and the density ρ. Differential equations for the determination of these parameters can be derived by considering the mathematical formulation of the iterative replacement steps in the DEM microstructure build-up process shown in Fig. 1. With component 1 as the starting point, the substitution of a fraction $d\psi$ of material 1 by material 2 yields a composite whose elastic constants and density ρ can be determined by the use of an effective medium theory:

$$F(1-\Delta\psi,\ \beta_1,\ \mu_1,\ \Delta\psi,\ \beta_2,\ \mu_2,\ \beta,\mu) = 0 \quad , \tag{10}$$

$$G(1-\Delta\psi,\ \beta_1,\ \mu_1,\ \Delta\psi,\ \beta_2,\ \mu_2,\ \beta,\mu) = 0 \quad , \tag{11}$$

$$\rho = (1-\Delta\psi)\rho_1 + \Delta\psi\rho_2 \ , \tag{12}$$

where $\beta \equiv \lambda + 2\mu$, and F=0, G=0 represent the effective medium conditions for the simultaneous determination of μ,β. The differentation of Eqs. (10) and (11) and the evaluation of the derivatives at $\psi = 0$ give us the differential parameter changes induced by the replacement step:

$$- \left(\frac{\partial F}{\partial \psi}\right)_{\psi=0} = \left(\frac{\partial F}{\partial \beta}\right)_{\psi=0} \frac{d\beta}{d\psi} + \left(\frac{\partial F}{\partial \mu}\right)_{\psi=0} \frac{d\mu}{d\psi} \ , \tag{13}$$

$$- \left(\frac{\partial G}{\partial \psi}\right)_{\psi=0} = \left(\frac{\partial G}{\partial \beta}\right)_{\psi=0} \frac{d\beta}{d\psi} + \left(\frac{\partial G}{\partial \mu}\right)_{\psi=0} \frac{d\mu}{d\psi} \ , \tag{14}$$

$$\frac{d\rho}{d\psi} = \rho_2 - \rho_1 \ . \tag{15}$$

We will schematically express the solutions of Eqs. (13) and (14) as

$$d\beta = F^{\beta}(\beta_1,\mu_1,\beta_2,\mu_2)d\psi \ , \tag{16}$$

$$d\mu = F^{\mu}(\beta_1,\mu_1,\beta_2,\mu_2)\ d\psi \ . \tag{17}$$

To make the substitution step an iterative process, we simply repeat the procedure done in the electrical case: replace β_1, μ_1, ρ_1 by β,μ,ρ and $d\psi$ by $du=d\psi/(1-\psi)$. The density equation can then be integrated immediately to yield $\rho = (1 - \phi)\rho_s + \phi\rho_f$, with porosity $\phi \equiv \exp (-u)$. The other two differential equations give expressions for $d\beta/du$ and $d\mu/du$ which, when integrated, will yield elastic moduli as a function of porosity. However, it is fairly well known that of the overall total porosity in a rock, a small fraction -- those of small scale pores in the regions of close approach or consolidation between solid grains -- plays an especially important role in determining the magnitude of the rock elastic moduli. This is evidenced by the results of pressure experiments[15] in which the closing of small-scale pores by the application of a confining pressure is shown to result in drastically increased rigidity with only a small accompanying decrease in porosity. Such data suggest that the porosity relevant to the determination of the elastic moduli should be a subset of the total porosity -- that of the small scale pores in the regions of consolidation. If we let $\phi_c = \exp(-u_c)$ denote the small scale porosity, then $u_c = W(u)$ defines the relationship between u (total porosity) and u_c. In this work we will let W take the simple form of $W(u) = cu$, (which is consistent with the requirement that $u_c > u$ ($\phi_c < \phi$) and $u_c = 0$ when $u=0$) where $c > 1$ is a parameter whose value can be determined by comparison with experiment. Physically, letting $W(u)=cu$ corresponds to using hollow, porous shell instead of solid particles as the substituting unit. In that case, since the porous shell has similar elastic moduli as the solid particle, but occupies only a fraction $1/c$ of the total unit volume, the only modification would be that in the replacement step, $d\psi_{actual} = (1-\psi_{actual})d\psi/c$, which results in $W(u)=cu$. From this picture it is easy to see that the introduction of c naturally divides the porosities into two categories: those which do not contribute to the overall rigidity of the rock, such as the pore inside the solid shell, and those which are relevant to the determination of the overall rigidity, such as the pores between the dispersed units. In the above picture we have purposely stated that the shell unit should be porous so that electrically the enclosed pores still contribute to the conductivity.

Combination of all the above considerations yields the following equations:

$$\frac{d\beta}{dW} = \frac{1}{c}\frac{d\beta}{du} = F^\beta(\beta,\mu,\beta_s,\mu_s), \tag{18}$$

$$\frac{d\mu}{dW} = \frac{1}{c}\frac{d\mu}{du} = F^\mu(\beta,\mu,\beta_s,\mu_s), \tag{19}$$

where we have let $\beta_2 = \beta_s$ and $\mu_2 = \mu_s$. To obtain explicit forms of F^μ and F^β one needs to evaluate the derivatives of the effective medium equations[16] at $\psi=0$ (as displayed in Eqs. (13) and (14)). Since for non-spherical units the effective medium equations[16] are themselves fairly complicated, the process of differentiation is extremely lengthy and laborious. In order to insure algebraic accuracy, we have utilized MIT's symbolic manipulation program MACSYMA to carry out the calculation. The resulting form of $F^{\beta,\mu}$ can be written as

$$F^{\beta,\mu} = \beta\frac{\displaystyle\sum_{n,\ell=0}^{4}\left(A_{n,\ell}^{\beta,\mu}\mu_s + B_{n,\ell}^{\beta,\mu}\beta_s\right)\left(\frac{\mu}{\mu_s}\right)^n\left(\frac{\beta}{\mu}\right)^\ell}{\displaystyle\sum_{n,\ell=0}^{4}\left(C_{n,\ell}\mu_s + D_{n,\ell}\beta_s\right)\left(\frac{\mu}{\mu_s}\right)^n\left(\frac{\beta}{\mu}\right)^\ell}, \tag{20}$$

where the coefficients A,B,C, and D are functions of the aspect ratio of the basic microstructural units. For spheres, Eq. (20) can be reduced to relatively simple forms:

$$F^\beta = 3\beta\frac{8(\mu_s - \mu)[4\mu(\mu_s - \mu) + \beta(\mu_s + 2\mu)-3\mu\beta_s]+3\beta(\beta-\beta_s)(2\mu_s + 3\mu)}{(4\mu_s - 4\mu-3\beta_s)(4\mu\mu_s + 6\beta\mu_s - 4\mu^2 + 9\mu\beta)}, \tag{21}$$

$$F^\mu = \frac{15\beta\mu(\mu_s - \mu)}{4\mu\mu_s + 6\beta\mu_s - 4\mu^2 + 9\mu\beta}. \tag{22}$$

However, in order to be consistent with Archie's law description of

the electrical conductivity, we have to let d=1/2, implying that
the basic units are oblate spheroids with an aspect ratio of 4.5.
The numerical values of the resulting coefficients A,B,C, and D are
tabulated in Table I. Again, as in the case of the DEM equation
for the dielectric constant, we note that Eqs. (18) - (22) remain
the same regardless of the starting version[16] of effective medium
theory that one chooses. This is due to the fact that the different versions agree to first order in the dilute limit (ψ=0).

IV. COMPARISON OF ACOUSTIC PREDICTIONS WITH EXPERIMENTS

In order to carry out numerical calculations, we need as
inputs the initial values of ρ, β, and μ and the solid parameters
ρ_s, β_s, and μ_s. For initial values, we use those appropriate to
water: ρ_f = 1g/cm^3, β_f = K + i$\omega(\lambda_\ell$ + 2η), μ_f = i$\omega\eta$, where K = 2.2 x
10^{10} dynes/cm^2 is the bulk modulus, η=1 centipoise is the
viscosity, and λ_ℓ = -2η/3   is the bulk viscosity. For solid
parameters we use ρ_s = 2.65 g/cm^3, and β_s, μ_s are chosen to give
the sonic travel time of $1/V_s$ = 53.5 μsec/ft and Poisson's ratio of
1/3 for sandstones solid matrix material.[17] An imaginary part with
the magnitude 0.005 times the real part is also included for both
β_s and μ_s to account for the small frequency-independent
attenuation observed in dry rock frames.[18] With these as inputs,
Eqs. (18)-(20) were numerically integrated to obtain values of β
and μ as a function of u. In Fig. 6 the calculated sonic travel
time with c=2.5 is plotted against the value of the normalized
resistivity calculated within the same DEM microstructure (R/R_w =
ϕ^{-2},R_w being the water resistivity). The particular value of the
adjustable parameter c is fixed by making the theory and experiment
agree at one data point (R/R_w = 10^2). The dashed line gives the
same correlation where the sonic travel time at any given porosity
is calculated by Wyllie's equation and the electrical resistivity
by Archie's law. Compared with the field data[19] on sandstones, it
is seen that the DEM theory is better than Wyllie's equation in
accounting for the observed experimental correlation.

TABLE I

Coefficients in Eq. (20) evaluated at the aspect ratio of 4.5 for randomly oriented oblate spheroids. Within each square the coefficients are arranged in the following order: top line -- A^B, B^B, middle line -- A^U, B^U, bottom line -- C, D.

n \ ℓ	0	1	2	3	4
0	0.671, -0.503 0.395, -0.296 0.057, -0.043	2.864, -2.148 1.561, -1.170 0.357, -0.267	3.154, -2.365 1.436, -1.077 0.718, -0.539	0.46, -0.345 0., 0. 0.46, -0.345	0., 0 0., 0 0., 0
1	-2.683, 1.509 -1.579, 0.888 -0.229, 0.129	-3.961, 0.502 -2.53, 0.425 -0.398, -0.018	4.803, -6.530 1.052, -2.619 1.232, -1.702	3.319, -2.137 0., 0 1.999, -2.137	0.345, 0 0., 0 0., 0
2	4.024, -1.509 2.368, -0.888 0.344, -0.129	-5.298, 5.44 -1.774, 2.661 -0.946, 0.838	-11.390, 2.623 -4.22, 0.969 -3.044, 0.546	4.910, -3.541 0., 0 0.535, -3.541	2.137, 0 0., 0 0., 0
3	-2.683, 0.503 -1.579, 0.296 -0.229, 0.043	11.025, -3.794 4.895, -1.916 1.659, -0.553	-4.245, 6.272 -0.461, 2.727 -0.479, 1.695	-4.084, -1.477 0., 0 -1.966, -1.477	3.541, 0 0., 0 0., 0
4	0.671, 0 0.395, 0 0.057, 0	-4.63, -2.152, -0.672,	7.678, 0 2.193, 0 1.573, 0	-4.605, 0 0., 0 -1.028, 0	1.477, 0 0., 0 0., 0

Without changing any of the input parameter values, we have
also calculated the sonic attenuation per cycle, $1/Q = \text{Im}(\beta)/\text{Re}(\beta)$,

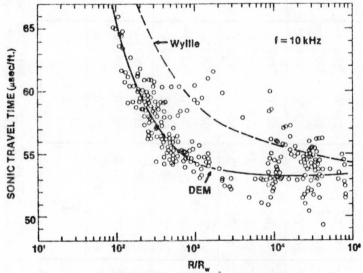

Fig. 6. Correlation between the sonic travel
time and normalized electrical resistivity.
Field data on sandstones are shown as open
circles. Solid line denotes the theoretical
prediction based on the DEM microstructure.
Dashed line denotes the correlation obtained
from Wyllie's equation and Archie's law.

as a function of the scaling variable nf, where f is frequency in
Hertz. In Fig. 7 we compare the theory with experimental data[3,20]
by J. Bulau et al. on Coconino sandstones. The porosity value of
$\phi = 0.1$ has been chosen so that the theoretical attenuation peak
position coincides with that of the experiment. It is seen from
the figure that the present theory accounts well for not only the
magnitude and width of the attenuation peak, but also its associated velocity dispersion. The fact that the data, which were taken
by using either water or glycerin as the filling fluid, seem to
fall on a single curve as a function of nf lends strong support to
the theoretical picture of attenuation by viscous dissipation in
the fluid.[3] For $nf<1$, the experimentally measured attenuation has
been observed to level off. Theoretically, such behavior is consistent with the existence of a frequency-independent attenuation
floor set by the rock frame dissipation. The porosity of the par-

ticular Conconino sandstone sample has been inferred to be 0.19. This value is higher than the theoretical value of 0.1. However,

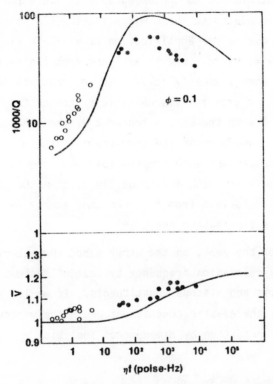

Fig. 7. Attenuation per cycle, expressed in 1000/Q, and normalized acoustic velocity $\bar{V}$ (where the low frequency velocity is taken to be 1) plotted as a function of ηf. Solid line denotes the theory, open circles denote data taken by using water as the filling fluid, and solid circles denote data taken by using glycerin as the filling fluid. (Data from Ref. 3).

in view of the fact that no attempt has been made to fine-tune the theoretical inputs with the purpose of fitting the data, the overall agreement is considered very good.

V. DISCUSSION

There is a close analogy between the physics of the acoustic attenuation peak and that of the dielectric constant enhancement discussed earlier. As we pointed out, the increase in the dielectric constant of a conductor-insulator composite near the percolation threshold is attributed to the appearance of microcracks. If the solid phase is conducting, these microcracks would possess large capacitances due to the amplification of electric field E in the gaps (since the electric field is excluded from the conductor), resulting in large energy density $\varepsilon E^2/2$. If we associate the dielectric constant ε with the viscoelasticity tensor C_{ijkl} and the electric field E with the strain tensor ε_{ij}, then the same amplification effect would occur for the strain in the microcracks provided the microcracks are more compressible than the solid. If the microcracks are filled with a viscous fluid, then the large attenuation naturally follows from the increased energy density $C_{ijkl} \varepsilon_{ij} \varepsilon_{kl}/2$ in a dissipative medium.[21]

The position of the peak, on the other hand, characterizes the viscoelastic stress relaxation frequency typical of systems composed of both elastic and viscous constituents. If we let K denote the bulk modulus of the elastic constituent and η the viscosity of the viscous constituent, then by dimensional analysis

$$f_0 = \frac{K}{\eta} \cdot S \quad , \tag{23}$$

where f_0 is the peak frequency and S is a dimensionless number that depends on geometric factors. In the case of DEM theory, $S \propto \phi_c^3$.

In the above discussion we have noted that one of the requirements for the appearance of a large attenuation peak is that the microcracks have to be very compressible, or compliant under the application of pressure. Such behavior of the microcracks not only is crucial for large sonic attenuation but also is believed to be the basis for sandstones' sensitivity to confining pressure. One of the important elements in the DEM theory is its ability to capture the effects arising from such microcrack behavior. However, another associated aspect of the 2-component DEM model is that the solid constituents (inclusions) in the DEM microstructure are always separated by the fluid (matrix) component.[22] Therefore, whereas physically the contact between solid grains might look like what is schematically depicted in Fig. 8(a), in the DEM model the gap might look like Fig. 8(b), which would certainly be as compressible as (if not more than) the crack in Fig. 8(a). Whereas the difference between Fig. 8(a) and 8(b), i.e. the existence of a small region of solid contact, means only a small difference for the P wave (since the fluid is relatively incompressible), for the propagation of shear waves the absence of solid contacts in the DEM has the effect that the transmission of shear stress relies only on the viscous coupling between solid grains. As a consequence, unless the product $nf > 100$ and

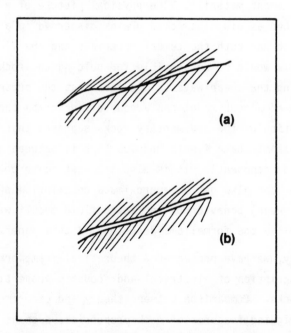

Fig. 8. (a) Schematic picture of a rock microcrack. (b) Schematic picture of a microcrack in the DEM model.

$\phi < 0.2$, the prediction of shear wave velocity within the DEM theory is consistently lower than those experimentally observed. Even in the regime where the value of shear wave velocity is reasonable, its large frequency dependence makes the result unrealistic. Due to this particular shortcoming, the applicability of the DEM theory in its present state is limited to acoustic waves only. We have experimented with various remedies for this situation. Our experience is that if one attempts to solve the shear wave problem by introducing contacts between spherical solid grains, then the increased rigidity of the microcracks would make the attenuation peak disappear and the acoustic velocity essentially flat as a function of porosity. Therefore, it seems that a successful solution would require not only the incorporation of solid-solid contacts into the DEM framework but also the preservation of the crack compressibility. We suggest that a realistic model of the sedmimentary rock may consist of three components: solid, fluid, and the solid cement material. The physical picture of a rock can then be described as disjoint solid grains dispersed in a background which has both the cement materials and the fluid. The cement materials would be responsible for holding the rock together and transmitting the shear waves. The fact that the present simplified two-component model can adequately describe the acoustic velocity variation of the sedimentary rocks suggests that the cement materials may have a bulk modulus that is between that of fluid and solid components. It is also interesting to note within such a model we can also get an approximate description of dry rock (acoustic and shear) behavior by replacing fluid moduli with cement material moduli in the formalisms described in this paper.

In summary, we have presented a theoretical framework for a consistent description of electrical and acoustic properties of sedimentary rocks. Comparison between theory and experiment shows that many intriguing features of rock properties, such as the power law dependence of the conductivity on porosity and the existence of the large frequency peak in acoustic attenuation, are consistent with the characteristics of a fluid-solid composite system that is in the vicinity of the percolation threshold. Besides providing a unified microstructural basis for understanding the observed phenomena, such a physical picture of rock could also serve as a rich source of ideas for future research. For example, by uniformly coating solid rock grains with a thin conducting film, it would be possible to check whether there is indeed a large dielectric constant enhancement in the resulting sample as predicted by the DEM theory. The measurement of electrical conductivity in the same conductor-coated rock may also provide information about solid-solid contacts and could therefore serve as the basis for correlating electrical and shear wave characteristics. It is our hope that the theoretical exploration and speculations presented in this work may serve to generate further interest along these directions.

We wish to acknowledge D. Zwillinger's assistance in using the MACSYMA program and to thank L. Perlovsky, P. Shah, and J. Bulau for providing the data shown in Figs. 6 and 7.

REFERENCES AND FOOTNOTES

1. G. E. Archie, Petroleum Technology $\underline{5}$, No. 1, 1942.

2. M. R. J. Wyllie, A. R. Gregory, and G. H. F. Gardner, Geophysics $\underline{21}$, No. 1, 1956.

3. J. R. Bulau, B. R. Tittmann, and M. Abdel-Gawad, Trans. Am. Geophys. Union, to appear.

4. W. Murphy, J. Acoustical Soc. of Am. $\underline{71}$, 1458 (1982).

5. P. Sheng and A. J. Callegari, to be published.

6. See R. Landauer's review article in Electrical Transport and Optical Properties of Inhomogeneous Media, edited by J. C. Garland and D. B. Tanner, AIP Conference Proceedings No. 40 (American Institute of Physics, N.Y. 1978), p. 14. Also, S. Kirkpatrick's article in the same volume contains a graphical illustration of the geometry near the percolation threshold.

7. P. N. Sen, C. Scala, and M. H. Cohen, Geophysics $\underline{46}$, 781 (1981).

8. K. S. Mendelson and M. H. Cohen, Geophysics $\underline{47}$, 257 (1982); P. N. Sen, Geophysics, to appear.

9. R. Knight, Dielectric Properties of Rocks, unpublished, data in Ph.D. thesis, Stanford University, 1983.

10. A. J. deWitte, Oil and Gas J. March 4, 1957, p. 89.

11. For the general theory of dielectric constant enhancement in a conductor-insulator composite, see D. J. Bergman and Y. Imry, Phys. Rev. Lett. 39, 1222 (1977); and P. Sheng and R. V. Kohn, Phys. Rev. B26, 1331 (1982). For experimental observation of the effect in oxide-coated Ag particle systems, see D. M. Grannan, J. C. Garland, and D. B. Tanner, Phys. Rev. Lett. 46, 375 (1981).

12. R. Burridge and J. B. Keller, J. Acoust. Soc. Am. 70, 1140 (1981).

13. A point in this case means a region of space which is small compared with the wavelength but large compared to pore dimensions.

14. M. A. Biot, J. Appl. Phys. 33, 1482 (1962).

15. K. Winkler and A. Nur, Geophysics 47, 257 (1982).

16. Various versions of the effective medium theory can be found in the following papers: T. T. Wu, Int. J. Solids Structures 2, 1 (1966); G. T. Kuster and M. N. Toksoz, Geophysics 39, 587 (1974); J. G. Berryman, J. Acoust. Soc. Am. 68, 1820 (1980). It should be noted that the formulas contained in the Wu and Kuster papers contain some errors.

17. Schlumberger Log Interpretation, (Schlumberger Ltd., N.Y., N.Y. 1972).

18. 1000/Q for dry rock frames is $\simeq$ 5, see Refs. (3) and (4).

19. L. I. Perlovsky, Report No. EPR 1EX.82, June, 1982, Exxon Production Research Co., Houston, Texas. The data were obtained from a 280 ft. section (interpreted to be sandstones) of sonic and electrical logs.

20. The data were a direct measurement of $Q_E = Im\ (E)/Re(E)$, where E is Young's modulus. However, since Poisson's ratio ν for the samples is small, i.e. $\nu \simeq 0\text{-}0.1$ (see Ref. (4), and J. Bulau, private communication), we have $E{\approx}\beta$, and $Q_E \simeq Q$.

21. The present mechanism of attenuation does not explicitly invoke a particular type of fluid motion (i.e. "squirt") inside the pores as suggested by O'Connell and Budiansky (J. Geophys. Res. 82, 5719 (1977)). However, the concentration of

stress and strain at the microcrack does suggest considerable fluid movement.

22. F. Yonezawa and M. H. Cohen, J. Appl. Phys. 54, 2895 (1983).

A VISCOELASTIC MODEL OF ANELASTICITY OF FLUID SATURATED POROUS ROCKS

Richard J. O'Connell
Harvard University, Cambridge, MA 02138

ABSTRACT

A simple model for porous rocks is proposed based on classification of pores as either crack-like or sphere- or tube-like. Analytic results are used for the strain of each class to obtain expressions for effective moduli. Attenuation results from fluid flow among cracks and pores, and depends on a characteristic frequency. The parameters in the model can be estimated or measured independently. The model gives a very reasonable interpratation or laboratory data on sandstone, where attenuation is due to cracks with a narrow distribution of aspect ratios.

INTRODUCTION

The effect of cracks, pores and fluid saturation on the elastic and anelastic properties of rocks is important for geophysical problems ranging from detecting partial melt in the Earth's mantle to exploring for hydrocarbons. The presence of pores, and in particular thin cracks, can substantially reduce the elastic moduli of solids, and it is hoped that measurement of these can provide information about the nature of the porosity. Fluid saturated rocks may exhibit substantial attenuation of elastic waves, and again measurement of anelastic properties may provide information about both the porosity and properties of the pore fluid, both in the laboratory and *in situ*.

Whereas the determination of the effects of porosity on static elastic properties is relatively straightforward, the identification and analysis of pore fluid related attenuation mechanisms is less so. Marko, Kjartansson and Winkler[1] have reviewed both experimental and theoretical investigations of attenuation; the review by Watt, Davies and O'Connell[2] covers some more basic aspects of calculating effective elastic properties of rocks.

It appears that local fluid flow on the scale of individual pores is the most probable explanation for attenuation of elastic waves observed in a variety of laboratory measurements of water saturated rocks.[1,3] The purpose of this paper is to discuss a simple model that incorporates this mechanism, and is applicable to rocks with relatively large porosities, and to interpret some measurements in terms of the model. The discussion will focus on some basic considerations of modelling, and the analysis of the model and derivation of results is in other papers.[3-6]

We start with some basic definitions and results[7] for a composite with two constituents, present in volume concentration c_1 and c_2. The volume average strain in each is $\bar{e}_1$ and $\bar{e}_2$, and these are related to the average stress in each by

$$\bar{\tau}_1 = C_1 \bar{e}_1 \qquad \text{and} \qquad \bar{\tau}_2 = C_2 \bar{e}_2$$

where C_1 and C_2 are the elastic modulus tensors for each constituent. The effective modulus of the composite $\overline{C}$ is defined in terms of the average stress and strain of the composite

$$\overline{\tau} = \overline{C}\,\overline{e}$$

Since $c_1\overline{e}_1 + c_2\overline{e}_2 = \overline{e}$ and $c_1\overline{\tau}_1 + c_2\overline{\tau}_2 = \overline{\tau}$ it follows that

$$\overline{C} = C_2 - (C_2 - C_1)c_1\overline{e}_1/\overline{e} \tag{1}$$

Thus the determination of the effective modulus of the composite is equivalent to determining the average strain of one of the constituents. (Note that equation 1 is exact.)

The determination of the average strain of the pores in a saturated porous rock is complicated by the complex shape of the pores and the presence of pore fluid. The pressure of the pore fluid will depend on the strain of the pores and will in general be heterogeneous; this will lead to fluid flow, which will in turn be influenced by pore shapes and interconnections. The pore strain will, of course, depend on both the externally applied loads and the internal pore fluid pressure.

Given these complications it is clear that one cannot expect to model the pore strain in very great detail, and that one can only hope to obtain a reasonable estimate of the average pore strain that represents some sort of statistical average over the various pore shapes as well as the range of internal fluid pressures and interconnections among pores. The means of estimating the pore strain should take into account the main characteristics of the pore shape, the variability (if any) of the pore shapes and whatever fluid flow processes that are thought to be important.

The strain of isolated pores can be calculated directly for several idealized pore shapes (e.g. spheres, ellipsoids). Although such idealized pore shapes may be far from those encountered in real rocks, they can provide insight into the dependence of pore strain on shape and pore fluid properties, and form the basis for a rational scheme for estimating the strain of pores of more complicated shape. As an example, consider the volumetric strain θ_1 of an isolated cylindrical pore with an elliptical cross section with semi-axes $\underline{a}$ and $\underline{b}$ where $b/a \leq 1$. The pore strain θ_1 is easily calculated from two dimensional elastic theory,[8] and is

$$\theta_1 = \frac{s}{3(1-2\nu)K}\left[2\left(\frac{a}{b} + \frac{b}{a}\right)(1-\nu^2) + (1-2\nu)^2\right] \tag{2}$$

where s is the isotropic stress applied far from the inclusion, and K and ν are the bulk modulus and Poisson ratio of the matrix.

For circular cylindrical pores ($a = b$), this becomes

$$\theta_1 = \frac{s}{K}\frac{(5 - 4\nu)}{3(1 - 2\nu)} \tag{3}$$

We note first that this result, through equation (1), leads directly to an expression for the effective bulk modulus of a solid with cylindrical pores: for widely separated pores, take the matrix prop-

erties in (3) to be K_2 and ν_2 (i.e. those of the solid matrix); then
with $\bar{\theta} = s/\bar{K}$, (1) gives

$$\frac{\bar{K}}{K_2} = \left[1 + \frac{c_1}{3}\left(\frac{5 - 4\nu_2}{1 - 2\nu_2}\right)\right]^{-1}$$

Alternatively, we can take the matrix properties in (3) to be
those of the composite, $\bar{K}$ and $\bar{\nu}$, which leads to

$$\frac{\bar{K}}{K_2} = 1 - \frac{c_1}{3}\left(\frac{5 - 4\bar{\nu}}{1 - 2\bar{\nu}}\right)$$

which should be a better estimate for $\bar{K}$ when the porosity is large
enough to effectively weaken the matrix surrounding a pore. This
latter approach, termed "self consistent" by Hill,[7] gives the same
result whether one considers the average strain of the inclusions,
as in equation 1, or considers the average stress in the inclusions.[7,9] (In the latter case one obtains an expression for the effective compliance of the composite in a form similar to equation
(1).)

As one indication of the effect of pore shape on strain, compare (3) with the equivalent result for a spherical pore[7,8]

$$\theta_1 = \frac{s}{K} \frac{3}{2}\left(\frac{1 - \nu}{1 - 2\nu}\right) \tag{4}$$

The results are not very different; for $\nu = 1/4$ the values of $K\theta_1/s$
are 2 2/3 and 2 1/4 for the cylinder and sphere respectively. This
similarity suggests that it is not necessary to distinguish between
spherical and circular cylindrical pores in rocks, since either has
a similar effect on the effective modulus. (Similarly, measurements
of the modulus will not be able to determine which shape of pore is
present.)

The case for elliptical cylinders is different. Here the
strain depends strongly on the aspect ratio b/a of the ellipse, and
for small b/a

$$\theta_1 \rightarrow \frac{2s}{3K}\left(\frac{1 - \nu^2}{1 - 2\nu}\right)\frac{a}{b}$$

which becomes large as b/a becomes small. The product of the strain
and the pore volume, however, approaches a constant as $b/a \rightarrow 0$:

$$\theta_1 c_1 = \frac{2s}{3K}\left(\frac{1 - \nu^2}{1 - 2\nu}\right)\pi a^2 \ell$$

where the pore volume is $\pi a b \ell$; ℓ is the length of the cylinder.
This means that the effective bulk modulus will not depend simply
on the pore volume, as was the case for spheres and circular cylinders, but will depend on the parameter $\pi a^2 \ell$ (averaged over all such
pores) which is independent of the thickness, b, of the pores.

This result is similar to that for cracks (of which this is
one case), where the effective modulus depends on a parameter, the
crack density, defined as

$$\varepsilon = N \langle a^3 \rangle$$

for circular cracks of radius $\underline{a}$, and as

$$\varepsilon = N \frac{2}{\pi} \left\langle \frac{A^2}{P} \right\rangle \tag{5}$$

for elliptical cracks;[5,6] N is the number of cracks per unit volume, A is the area, in planform, of the crack, and P the length of the perimeter of the crack. (The two expressions coincide of course for circular cracks.) For such thin, crack-like, pores, the reduction in the modulus is *not* simply proportional to the pore volume, which by itself is thus not a useful predictor of the effective modulus of a cracked solid.

The crack density, however, is a useful parameter for predicting the effective modulus of solid with crack-like porosity. Moreover, the effect of cracks of any elliptic shape is practically identical so long as the crack density is defined as in (5). The fact that the result is the same for shapes as disparate as circles and long thin ellipses (including those represented by letting b/a → 0 in (2)) suggests that similar results would hold for cracks of a wide variety of shapes, and that it is not necessary to specify, or determine, their shapes so long as they are characterized by a crack density defined by (5). We note further that the crack density can be estimated independently by counting and measuring crack traces in a plane section of the cracked solid.[5,6,10]

These two cases represent two distinct types of behavior: pores like spheres or circular cylinders have an effect on the effective modulus proportional to their volume; crack-like porosity has an effect proportional to the crack density, which is independent of the thickness, and hence volume, of the crack. It is thus clear that for a rock containing both types the porosity by itself will not be sufficient to predict its elastic moduli. Pores with shapes intermediate between these extremes will exhibit intermediate behavior. Figure 1 shows the strain of elliptical cylinders, from equation 2, as a function of the aspect ratio of the elliptical cross section. For b/a → 0, the product of the pore strain and volume is a constant, as noted above. This limiting value is nearly attained for b/a = 0.1, and it appears that pores with flatness ratios, b/a, less than ~0.2 will behave like cracks. Similarly the strain of pores with b/a greater than ~0.6 differs little from the value for circular cylinders (b/a = 1). Thus, except for the rather limited range 0.2 < b/a < 0.6, it appears that the classification of cylindrical pores into crack-like (b/a → 0) and tube-like (b/a = 1) should result in little error in predicting the effective modulus, especially considering the uncertainties inherent in any simple representation of pore shape.

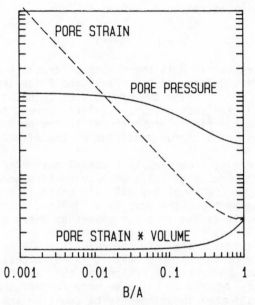

Fig. 1. Pore strain and fluid pressure
for elliptical cylindrical pores as a
function of the aspect ratio b/a of the
elliptical cross section. $K_f/K = 0.1$
and $\nu = 1/4$.

The strain of a fluid filled pore will depend on the fluid
pressure induced in the pore fluid; this will depend on the bulk
modulus of the fluid, and whether the fluid can flow in or out of
the pore in response to pressure changes. For isolated elliptical
cylindrical pores, as before, the fluid pressure induced by external isotropic stress s is

$$p = -s\alpha \left[\frac{K}{K_f} - 1 + \alpha \right]^{-1} \qquad (6)$$

where

$$\alpha = \frac{1}{3(1-2\nu)} \left[2\left(\frac{a}{b} + \frac{b}{a} \right)(1-\nu^2) + (1-2\nu)^2 \right]$$

For crack-like pores $\alpha \to \infty$, and then $p \to -s$; i.e. the pore pressure
is the same as the externally applied pressure. For circular cylindrical pores (b/a = 1) the fluid pressure is less than the external
pressure; for example if $\nu = 1/4$ and $K_f/K = 0.1$, then $-p/s = 8/35 =$
0.23.
    Figure 1 shows the pore pressure as a function of the flatness,
b/a, of an elliptical cylinder, for the case with $\nu = 1/4$ and
$K_f/K = 0.1$. As before, the pressure approaches the value for thin
cracks for b/a less than 0.1, and has a value similar to that for
circular cylindrical tubes for b/a > 0.5. The separation between

crack-like and tube-like behavior is not as sharp as for the strain, but it is nonetheless apparent, and we are again led to consider the pores as members of two distinct classes.

Note that in a general stress field τ_{ij}, the fluid pressure in a thin crack with unit normal $\underline{n}$ will be $p = -\tau_{ij}n_in_j$; it thus depends on the orientation of the crack. Thus even under shear loading, pressures will be induced in cracks, with values depending on the crack orientation.

The different pressures in differently shaped or oriented pores will lead to fluid flow if the pores are interconnected. The geometry of such interconnections must certainly be even more difficult to characterize than the shape of the pores in a rock, yet if we are to include such fluid flow effects in a model, some characterization must be made, if only implicitly. In terms of our two classes of pores, the flow will be primarily between cracks at different orientation to a shear stress (and hence having different fluid pressures) and between cracks and tubular or spherical pores. The simplest assumption is that the rate of fluid flow is proportional to the pressure difference between the pores. The constant relating the two can either be considered an adjustable parameter, or it can be estimated from simple models based on idealized shapes of pores and their interconnections.[3] Such estimates must in any case be considered as only very rough ones, and the utility of the microscopic models lies in using them to identify important geometrical parameters.

The model we are led to consider then is that of a solid permeated with two classes of porosity: crack-like, characterized by a crack density, with fluid pressure equal to the applied normal stress on the crack face and pore-like (i.e. tubes or spheres), characterized by a volume porosity, with fluid pressures substantially less than the applied hydrostatic stress. Fluid will flow between cracks at different orientations and between cracks and pores in response to pressure differences. The model will exhibit visco-elastic behavior, with the unrelaxed (i.e. short time or high frequency) properties corresponding to no fluid flow, and the relaxed properties (long time or low frequency) corresponding to complete equilibration of pore pressure. The transition between these limiting cases will occur at a frequency (or time scale) near a characteristic frequency or time for flow to take place between pores. Owing to the variety of interconnections that may be present, we expect there to be a distribution of characteristic frequencies, perhaps over a considerable range.

In the model, we use analytic results for elliptic cracks[3] to estimate the strain of thin, crack-like pores in a rock, and use analytic results for spherical pores[6,7,11,12] to estimate the strain of more equi-dimensioned or tubular pores. The ultimate utility and accuracy of these approximations is not known, and can only be assessed by comparison with more complex models, and with data on real rocks.

MODEL RESULTS AND DISCUSSION

The results are based on expressions for the strain of cracks and spherical pores that contain a fluid and have been previously derived and presented.[3,4] The parameters are: the crack density ε, defined by equation 5; the porosity of spherical pores ϕ; the fluid bulk modulus, K_f; the bulk and shear moduli of the uncracked, non-porous matrix material, K_M and G_M; and the characteristic frequency for fluid flow between cracks ω_s. We emphasize that all of these, except perhaps ω_s, can be measured or estimated independently of any measurement of the elastic properties of a given porous rock, and are thus not adjustable parameters. The moduli will be a function of frequency ω, and will be complex quantities, the real part representing an effective elastic modulus, and the imaginary part representing anelastic energy dissipation.[13]

The complex bulk modulus K is given by

$$\frac{K}{K_M} = 1 - \frac{\left[1 - \frac{K_f}{K_M}\right]\left[\frac{3}{2}\left(\frac{1-\nu}{1-2\nu}\right)\phi + \frac{16}{9}\left(\frac{1-\nu^2}{1-2\nu}\right)\frac{\varepsilon}{1+i\Omega}\right]}{\left[1 + \frac{K_f}{2K}\left(\frac{1+\nu}{1-2\nu}\right)\right]\phi + \frac{16}{9}\left(\frac{1-\nu^2}{1-2\nu}\right)\left(\frac{K_f}{K}\right)\frac{\varepsilon}{1+i\Omega}} \phi \qquad (7)$$

with

$$\Omega = \frac{16}{9}\left(\frac{1-\nu^2}{1-2\nu}\right)\left(\frac{K_M}{K}\right)\left(\frac{\omega}{\omega_s}\right) \qquad (8)$$

The shear modulus G is determined from Eqs. (9), (10), and (11):

$$\frac{G}{G_M} = 1 - \frac{15(1-\nu')}{7-5\nu'}\phi - \frac{32}{45}(1-\nu')\left[\frac{1}{1+i\Omega'} + \frac{3}{2-\nu'}\right]\varepsilon \qquad (9)$$

$$\frac{K'}{K_M} = 1 - \frac{3}{2}\left(\frac{1-\nu'}{1-2\nu'}\right)\phi - \frac{16}{9}\left(\frac{1-\nu'^2}{1-2\nu'}\right)\frac{\varepsilon}{1+i\Omega'} \qquad (10)$$

where ν' is a fictitious Poisson ratio that satisfies the standard relation

$$\nu' = \frac{3K'-2G}{6K'+2G} \qquad (11)$$

The same expression relates the moduli and Poisson ratio of the porous solid

$$\nu = \frac{3K-2G}{6K+2G} \qquad (12)$$

Equations (9) - (11) are first solved simultaneously, using ν' in (9), to obtain G, and then (7), (8) and (12) are then solved for K and ν. For small values of ε and ϕ the equations can be solved

non-selfconsistently by using K_M and ν_M in the right hand side of
(7) - (10). The derivation of these results, and discussion of the
procedure for solving the equations can be found in the papers by
Budiansky and O'Connell.[3,4]
    The characteristic frequency for fluid flow between cracks, ω_s,
can be estimated by assuming characteristics of the geometry of
crack interconnections and fluid flow. If the rate limiting process
is the escape of fluid from a thin crack, then ω_s can be estimated
from a simple model of flow between two parallel plates moving together.[3] This gives

$$\omega_s \sim 4(K/\eta)(c/a)^3 \qquad\qquad (13)$$

where η is the fluid viscosity and c/a the aspect (thickness to diameter) ratio of the crack. We note that equations (7) - (10) can
be readily adapted to a distribution of characteristic frequencies,
as has been done for cracks alone.[3]

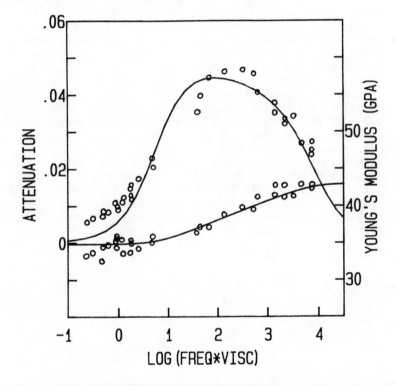

Fig. 2. Model results and data for attenuation and modulus of Coconino sandstone. The upper curve is attenuation
(Q^{-1}), and the lower curve is the modulus.

Figure 2 shows data on Young's modulus and associated attenuation on a sample of Coconino sandstone obtained by Tittmann et

174

al.[14] The data is compared with model results with a crack density $\varepsilon = 0.1$ and porosity $\phi = 0.24$; the matrix moduli are those for quartz,[15] $K_M = 38$ GPa, $E_M = 95$ GPa, and $K_f/K_M = 0.058$ is appropriate for water. The characteristic frequency ω_s was assumed to be distributed uniformly in log ω over three decades, with f_η ranging from 56 to 56000 ($f = \omega/2\pi$). On the basis of equation (13) this corresponds to cracks with aspect ratios ranging between ~10^{-2} and ~10^{-3}.

The fit to the data is surprisingly good; both the magnitude and width of the attenuation peak are fit well, as is the dispersion of the modulus. The value of the crack density is constrained by the observed modulus defect, and the attenuation peak then constrains the distribution of ω_s. The porosity is constrained by the observed value of the modulus in comparison with the matrix value. Thus the parameters are all well constrained by the data.

The model porosity 0.24 is greater than that of the rock sample, which was 0.16.[14] However, if the model were based on tubular pores, with slightly elliptical cross sections (b/a ~ 0.7), then a fit with the proper porosity would have resulted (cf. Figure 1). Perhaps most surprising is the relative narrowness of the attenuation peak and that it can be fit by a relatively simple distribution (the discrepancies in the fit could easily be eliminated by minor adjustments of the distribution of ω_s). In fact, the narrowness of the implied aspect ratio distribution, from 0.001 to 0.01, may indicate that the cracks that account for the observed attenuation have a special origin, such as cracking between grains during coring or sample preparation, and that consequently they may not be an intrinsic property of the rock *in situ*.

We finally note that the model predicts a substantial relaxation and associated attenuation in the bulk modulus, and that measurement of this effect would provide a test of the consistency of the model. In addition, measurements at higher values of frequency times viscosity should indicate attenuation from relaxation of shear stresses in the viscous fluid[3] for $f_\eta \sim 10^8$.

REFERENCES

1. G. Marko, E. Kjartansson and K. Winkler, Rev. Geophys. Space Phys. 17, 1155 (1979).
2. J. P. Watt, G. F. Davies and R. J. O'Connell, Rev. Geophys. Space Phys. 14, 541 (1976).
3. R. J. O'Connell and B. Budiansky, J. Geophys. Res. 82, 5719 (1977).
4. B. Budiansky and R. J. O'Connell, in Solid Earth Geophysics and Geotechnology, S. Nemat Nasser, ed. (Am. Soc. Mechan. Eng., New York, 1980), p. 1.
5. R. J. O'Connell and B. Budiansky, J. Geophys. Res. 79, 5412 (1974).
6. B. Budiansky and R. J. O'Connell, Int. J. Solids Structures 12, 81 (1976).
7. R. Hill, J. Mechan. Phys. Solids 13, 213 (1965).
8. S. P. Timoshenko and J. N. Goodier, Theory of Elasticity (McGraw-Hill, N. Y., 1970).
9. L. J. Walpole, J. Mechan. Phys. Solids 17, 235 (1969).
10. K. Hadley, J. Geophys. Res. 81, 3484 (1976).
11. B. Budiansky, J. Mechan. Phys. Solids 13, 223 (1965).
12. B. Budiansky, J. Compos. Mat. 4, 286 (1970).
13. R. J. O'Connell and B. Budiansky, Geophys. Res. Lett. 5, 5 (1978).
14. B. R. Tittmann, J. R. Bulau and M. Abdel-Gawad (in these proceedings).
15. J. P. Watt and L. Peselnick, J. Appl. Phys. 51, 1525 (1980).

CONTACT MICROPHYSICS AND VISCOUS RELAXATION IN SANDSTONES

**William F. Murphy III, Kenneth W. Winkler,
Robert L. Kleinberg**

Schlumberger-Doll Research
P.O. Box 307
Ridgefield, CT 06877

ABSTRACT

We present a microphysical model for acoustic attenuation and dispersion in sedimentary materials. The theory governs the response of two grains in contact to small sinusoidal loadings. Surface energy and fluid saturation are included explicitly. Grain surfaces are microscopically rough and irregular. We postulate that contact between grains forms numerous small solid-solid contacts and that narrow interconnected gaps remain between the surfaces. The stress relaxation is hydrodynamic. As the grains oscillate, liquid must be squeezed out of and sucked back into the gaps. The theory offers a unified explanation of several heretofore apparently unrelated observations. The resulting equations predict the stiffness and loss as a function of frequency, effective pressure, fluid adsorption, saturation, viscosity, and temperature.   Insofar as the   micromechanical   predictions relate to continuum acoustic properties, the agreement with observation is excellent.

INTRODUCTION

Our aim is to present a micromechanical model for acoustic attenuation and modulus dispersion in sedimentary materials. Recent experiments have stirred considerable interest by demonstrating a strong frequency dependence in sandstones[1-3]. Presented in these Proceedings are measurements by Tittmann[4] which delineate a complete stress relaxation. Velocities and attenuation in sandstones have also been shown to depend strongly on effective pressure[3-7], vapor pressure[2,8-10], pore fluid chemistry[1,8-10], water saturation[2,6,11], viscosity[4], and temperature[1,12].

As yet, no previously published theory has coherently explained these observations[1,2,5,6]. O'Connell and Budiansky[13] [hereafter referred to as OB] have developed a self-consistent effective medium theory for fully saturated rocks. The phenomenological model incorporates several loss mechanisms,

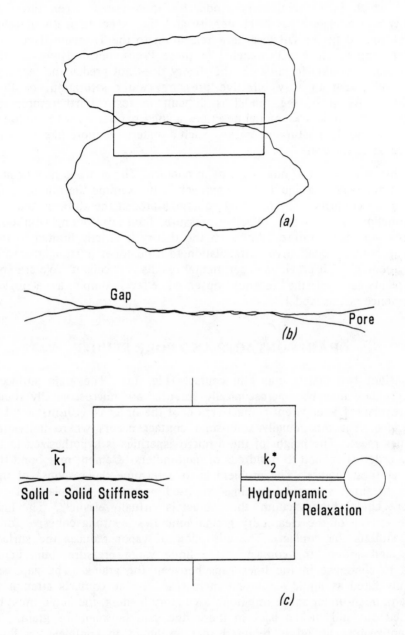

Fig. 1   Grain contact in a sandstone. a) sketch of a natural contact; b) isolation of the sysytem and its components; c) decomposition for the theoretical model.

one of which is a rudimentary model for local flow. Given the fluid viscosity and adjusting the crack density and the aspect ratio distribution, one can indeed fit the OB local flow relaxation to the Tittmann data quite well [see the article by O'Connell[14] in these Proceedings]. However, the mechanism is weakly formulated; the theory does not predict the response should one wish to vary effective pressure, water saturation, or fluid chemistry. As such, the model is difficult to test. Furthermore, the O'Connell and Budanisky model describes a solid permeated with randomly distributed and fluid-saturated cracks. Such a material is more like a granite rather than a sandstone.

Sandstones consist of quartz grains in contact. The contacts may or may not be immersed in a liquid. Our approach is to examine the microphysics of the grain contacts. The resulting equations predict the stiffness and loss as a function of frequency, effective pressure, fluid adsorption, saturation, viscosity, and temperature. Although the theory is strictly limited to two grains in contact, qualitative extrapolation to sandstones is straightforward. The agreement with previous experimental results is excellent. We are able to explain each of the recently observed effects simply as a logical consequence of the model.

GRAIN CONTACTS AND PORE FLUIDS

Consider two quartz grains in contact (Fig. 1a). The grain surfaces, although they may be macroscopically smooth, are microscopically rough and irregular. The apparent contact area is of the order of $(10\mu m)^2$ for 100 μm grains. Yet the actually solid-solid contact occurs where individual asperities meet. The height of these micro-asperities is hypothesized to be on the order of several to hundreds of nanometers. Cement may bond the grains at these points. The problem is to determine the response of this system to small sinusoidal loadings imposed normal to the plane of the contact. Under high vacuum, the contact is virtually elastic[10]. The high surface energy of the clean, dry grains generates a strong cohesive force which stiffens the contact. The adsoption of vapor reduces the surface energy and softens the contact. At a finite vapor pressure, bulk liquid begins to condense in the finer gaps between the grains. The gaps are gradually filled as liquid saturation increases. As the contacts attempt to close and open under small amplitude oscillatory loading, the liquid must be squeezed out and sucked back in these fine gaps between the grains. A sufficiently long period is required for the liquid to complete its flow. Otherwise, the contact cannot relax. The liquid flow is a strong energy dissipator which is clearly frequency dependent.

This conceptual sketch arises directly from the mathematical physics which we developed in detail in Ref. 15. The analysis involves decomposing the contact into two elements (Fig. 1c). The first element is the solid-solid contact. Here the presence of bulk liquid is excluded. We determine the stiffness of two grains in contact under a) mechanical loading due to effective pressure and b) cohesive forces due to van der Waals attractions. The second element is the contact gap. Here, the presence of bulk liquid impedes the oscillatory displacement of the gap walls. The viscoelastic properties of the composite contact are derived by adding the two elements in parallel.

"DRY" SOLID-SOLID STIFFNESS

The contact between two quartz grains in a sandstone is sensitive to effective pressure and gas adsorption. We have developed[15] a model for the contact between two rough grains which relates the stiffness to normal load and vapor pressure. The grain surfaces are assumed to be nominally flat. Apparent contact occurs over an area πl^2, where l is the apparent contact radius. The surfaces themselves consists if ψ elastic micro-asperities. Each asperity has a radius ϵ. For simplicity, we confine our model to micro-asperities of uniform height; the height of the asperities above the nominally flat surface is set at $\dfrac{h_o}{2}$, where h_o is the separation between the nominally flat surfaces. The response of each asperity is elastic. Each asperity possesses a surface energy which we use as a measure of the van der Waals cohesive traction[15].

The total solid-solid stiffness is the sum of all the stiffnesses of the individual micro-asperities, $\tilde{k}_1 = \sum k_{1i} = \psi k_{1i}$. The stiffness of the i-th asperity is[16]

$$k_{1i} = \frac{2\mu_s a_i}{1-\zeta}, \tag{1}$$

where the radius of the i-th micro-contact which is a function of the asperity elasticity, surface energy, and the normal load is[16]

$$a_i^3 = \frac{3(1-\zeta)\epsilon}{8\mu_s}\left\{\frac{F}{Y}+6\gamma_s\pi\epsilon+\left[\frac{12\gamma_s\pi\epsilon F}{Y}+(6\gamma_s\pi\epsilon)^2\right]^{1/2}\right\}. \tag{2}$$

Adsorption of foreign molecules or ions onto the surface reduces the surface energy. Adsorption onto quartz surfaces is a monotonically increasing function of the vapor partial pressure $X=P/P_o$. The form of the dependence varies greatly with the fluid chemistry. We have shown in Ref. 15 that the Gibbs equation can be transformed into an explicit expression for γ_s as a function of X. That expression is $\gamma_s(X) = \gamma_s(0)-\Delta\gamma_s(1)\chi(X)$. $\gamma_s(0)$ is the surface energy of the solid grain in a vacuum which is 450 mJ m^{-2} for quartz (Table 1). $\Delta\gamma_s(1)$ is the total change in surface energy from vacuum to

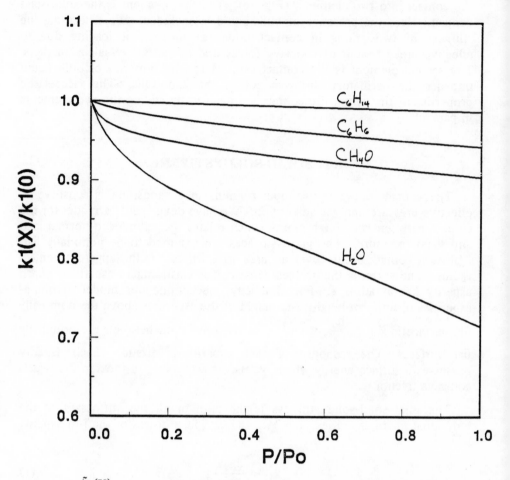

Fig. 2 $\dfrac{\tilde{k}_1(X)}{\tilde{k}_1(0)}$ vs. P/P_0 for four different fluids: water, methanol, benzene, and n-hexane. $\tilde{k}_1(X)$ is normalized to its value calculated at $X=0$, which is 43.12 kN/m. Agreement with data from Clark et al. [1980, Fig. 8] is excellent.

vapor pressure for the given saturating fluid. Measured values of $\Delta\gamma_s(1)$ of quartz for the vapors of interest are given in Ref. 15. χ represents the extent to which the surface is covered normalized to that at vapor pressure (i.e., $X=1$)

$$\chi(X) = \frac{\displaystyle\int_0^X \theta\,\frac{dX}{X}}{\displaystyle\int_0^1 \theta\,\frac{dX}{X}}. \qquad (3)$$

181

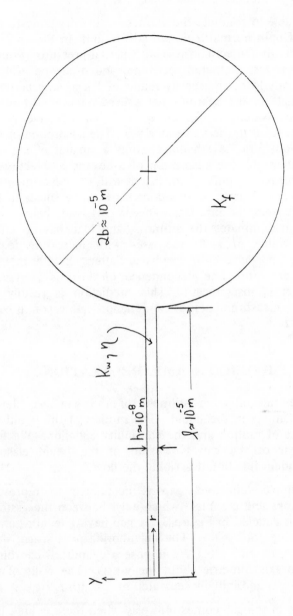

Fig. 3   Definition sketch for the gap closure and hydrodynamic relaxation
problem.

θ is the number of monolayers adsorbed.

One is now able to compute the stiffness of the dry grain-to-grain contact as a function of both normal load and adsorption. In Figure 2, we plot the calculated decline in contact stiffness with partial pressure. Four adsorbants are considered: water, methanol, benzene, and n-hexane. Calculations are made for a 0.1 mN load, an asperity radius of 1 μm, an asperity height of 5 nm, and a density of 0.3 aperities per square micron. 0.1 mN is a small load, roughly equivalent to 0.1 MPa or 1 bar effective pressure. The stiffness is normalized to the value at X=0. The adsorption of water lowers the stiffness about 30%. Methanol exhibits a smaller effect; the effect of benzene is smaller still; the adsorption of n-hexane has relatively no effect at all. This result is qualitatively consistent with the experiments of Clark et al.[9] and of Spencer[1]. Further calculations show that a substantial increase in load literally squashes the interfacial effect[15]. At loads below 10^{-2} mN, the adhesive traction dominates the stiffness, and load has no effect. Above 10^{-2} mN, the value of $k_1(0)$ increases with increasing load, and the dependence on vapor adsorption begins to flatten. By 100 mN (roughly 10 MPa effective pressure), the dependence on load is Hertzian, and the adsorption effect is insignificant. This prediction is readily testable by performing the measurements as a function of vapor pressure under effective pressure.

HYDRODYNAMIC RELAXATION

To calculate the effective stiffness of the gap, we determine the pressure-flow relations in the liquid. The motion of the liquid is governed by the equations of motion and the continuity equation. We find that the effective stiffness of the gap is a sum of the liquid elasticity and a frequency-dependent function describing the flow.

A single simple "effective" gap is postulated to represent all the complicated "nooks and crannies" which exist between the grains. Consider the configuration detailed in Figure 3. A gap having length l and a width h joins a neighboring pore space. The neighboring pore space is represented by a torus of minor radius b. We impose a cylindrical coordinate system (r,Θ,y) which is axisymmetric about the y-axis. The walls of the gap are normal to the y-axis and initially separated by a width h_o.

The response of the gap comes into play when there is bulk liquid in the pores. If the liquid wets the solid, capillarity will draw the liquid into the gap. According to an argument developed in Ref. 15, the liquid droplet has an effective length

$$\frac{l_e^2}{l^2} = S_w \left[1 + \frac{2\pi b^2(l+b)}{l^2 h} \right] , \quad \text{when } S_w \leqslant \frac{1}{1 + \frac{2\pi b^2(l+b)}{l^2 h}}$$

$$l_e = l, \quad \text{when } S_w \geqslant \frac{1}{1 + \frac{2\pi b^2(l+b)}{l^2 h}}, \tag{4}$$

where S_w is the liquid saturation. The acoustic pressure in the liquid is $p(r) = p_1(r) - p_o$ where p_1 is the instantaneous pressure during loading and p_o is the ambient pressure. The acoustic pressure is assumed to remain finite throughout the system. The acoustic load is

$$\Delta F = \int_0^{l_e} \int_0^{2\pi} p \; r d\Theta \; dr = 2\pi \int_0^{l_e} p(r) \; r dr. \tag{5}$$

In response to loading, the walls at $y = \pm \frac{h}{2}$ are free to converge and diverge yet are constrained to remain normal to the y-axis. They are free from connection or restraint at $r=0$ or $r=l$. In other words, h is uniform across the gap in both the radial and azmiuthal directions, and the resistance to wall motion arises solely from the presence of the liquid.

The flow in the gap is parabolic. For liquids of interest[15] and a gap width h_o of 1 μm, the skin depth $\delta = (2\nu/\omega)^{1/2}$ equals the half width at approximately 1 MHz. ν is the kinematic viscosity and ω is the angular frequency. In sandstones, a gap separation of 1 μm is exceptionally large. A smaller width would merely push the transition frequency higher. We conclude that below 1 MHz, *the flow in the contact gap is well described as a Poiseuille flow.* The viscous resistance of the Poiseuille flow D_o is $12\eta/h_o^2$, where η is the liquid viscosity.

The walls of the pore neighborhood are not permitted to deform under external or internal loading. The pore has a capacity C to accept only a finite volume of extra liquid per unit rise in acoustic pressure. Because the walls of the pore neighborhood are assumed to be rigid, C is solely a function of the pore volume and the pore fluid compressibility. That function is

$$C = \frac{2\pi^2(l+b)b^2}{K_f}, \tag{6}$$

where K_f is the effective bulk modulus of the pore fluid[15].

We have shown in Ref. 15 how one may reduce the vector Navier-Stokes and continuity equations relating the pressure and volume flow rate to a single, linear, scalar governing equation for the pressure. The resulting equation is an inhomogeneous, second order, partial differential equation.

The homogeneous part is Bessel's equation of order zero. The complete steady state solution subject to the boundary conditions is

$$p(r,t) = -\frac{K_w}{h_o}\left[1 - \frac{\kappa l_e\, CK_w\, J_o(\kappa r)}{2\pi l_e^2 h_o J_1(\kappa l_e) + \kappa l_e CK_w J_o(\kappa l_e)}\right]\Delta h, \qquad (7)$$

where K_w is the bulk modulus of the liquid, and the functions J_o and J_1 are the Bessel functions of the first kind of zeroth order and first order, respectively. The wavenumber κ consists in general of an inertial term and a viscous resistance term[15]. If we evaluate the wavenumber for the range of values appropriate for a contact gap in a sandstone, we find that the inertial term is very much smaller than the viscous term. In the worst case of a gap of 100 nm at 10 MHz, the ratio of the inertial to viscous terms is 0.1. For the range of interest, the wavenumber κ reduces to $\kappa = \sqrt{-i}\,\beta,$ where $\beta = \left(\dfrac{\omega h_o D_o}{K_w}\right)^{1/2}.$

The impedence or effective stiffness of the contact gap is by definition $k_2^* = \Delta F/-\Delta h$. The effective stiffness, k_2^*, may now be deduced directly from equations 5 and 7. In response to a steady sinusoidal force $\Delta Fe^{-i\omega t}$, the gap separation will vary as $\Delta he^{-i\omega t}$. We find that

$$k_2^*(\omega) = \frac{\pi l_e^2 K_w}{h_o}\left[1 - \frac{2CK_w\, J_1(\kappa l_e)}{2\pi l_e^2 h_o J_1(\kappa l_e) + \kappa l_e CK_w J_o(\kappa l_e)}\right]. \qquad (8)$$

The dependence on saturation enters the effective stiffness through the effective length of the droplet l_e and the effective fluid compressibility $\dfrac{1}{K_f}$ which is contained in the pore volume capacity C (eqn. 6).

RESULTS

We determine the effective stiffness $k^*(\omega)$ for the composite grain contact by adding in parallel the stiffness of the solid-solid contact $\tilde{k}_1$ and the effective stiffness of the contact gap $k_2^*(\omega)$. If $S_w \neq 0$, then the composite stiffness k^* is complex. The resulting expression for k^* is $k^*(\omega) = \tilde{k}_1 + k_2^*(\omega)$. The real part of $k^*(\omega)$ is

$$k'(\omega) = \tilde{k}_1 + k'_2(\omega). \qquad (9)$$

The ratio of minus the imaginary part over the real part determines the fractional energy loss per cycle or the loss tangent.

$$\frac{k''(\omega)}{k'(\omega)} = \frac{k''_2(\omega)}{\tilde{k}_1 + k'_2(\omega)}. \qquad (10)$$

The microphysical model coherently explains the complete set of

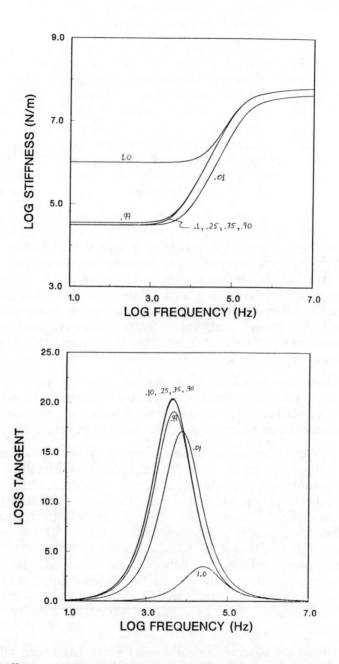

Fig. 4   Stiffness and loss tangent vs. frequency as a function of water
saturation: 0.01, 0.10, 0.25, 0.75, 0.90, 0.99, and 1.00. Agreement
with data from Murphy [1982] is excellent.

experimental observations discussed above. Of course, the absolute magnitude of the relaxation, as exhibited in both k' and $\frac{k''}{k'}$, are not directly comparable to measurements in sandstones. In order to make such a comparison, the individual contact must be embedded in a packing. Our ultimate objective is to obtain the macroscopic or continuum complex frame moduli[18] K_b and N from contact theory [perhaps utilizing techniques described by Schwartz[19] in these Proceedings]. In this paper, we have modelled the contact configuration which is likely to be the most dissipative in a sandstone. Consequently, when the analysis for a packing is complete, the relaxation is expected to be significantly weaker. With that caveat in mind, however, there is no reason why the qualitative prediction of the present formulation should not relate directly to observations in sandstones.

Since ω and η occur in equations 6-8 only as their product $\omega\eta$, the location of the relaxation varies with the product for a given gap geometry. This agrees with the measurements of Tittmann[4] in Coconino sandstone. The viscosity is a thermally activated property of a liquid described by the Arrehenius equation[15]. Increasing the temperature will lower the viscosity, thus shifting the relaxation to a higher frequency. This shift is presumably related to the effect observed by Spencer[1] in Navajo sandstone and Jones and Nur[12] in Berea sandstone. Similar viscosity and temperature dependences can be derived from the OB theory[13-14]. The following predictions are new.

The observed relaxations in sandstones center in the frequency range from 1 to 100 kHz[1,2,6,11]. Our model predicts that gap widths between 5 and 50 nm are responsible. The existance of such gaps is a hypothesis; 5-50 nm gaps in grain contacts have not yet been observed in sandstones.

The micromechanical properties k' and k''/k' are both dependent on liquid saturation. In Figure 4, we plot k' and k''/k' vs. frequency at several water saturations. A modulus dispersion is predicted which varies with saturation. Both the dispersion and loss strengthen from 0.01 to 0.90, yet weaken from 0.90 to full saturation. The weakening of the relaxation results from a dramatic change in the volume capacity C near full saturation. When the saturation is less than 0.90, K_f is small, and the volume capacity of the neighboring pore is effectively infinite. As the liquid saturation approaches 1, the volume capacity rapidly reduces to the same order of magnitude as the volume discharge from the gap. The calculations in Figure 4 exhibit each of the effects which our experimental work[2,6,11] has attributed to partial saturation.

Two effects are observed in sandstones which have been related to the fluid chemistry: the modulus defect measured[9] as a function of P/P_0 and the depression in the relaxation magnitude[1]. Our theory predicts both of these effects. Figure 5 shows the relaxations for a contact saturated with water, ethanol, and n-hexane. The viscosities are roughly similar among the

187

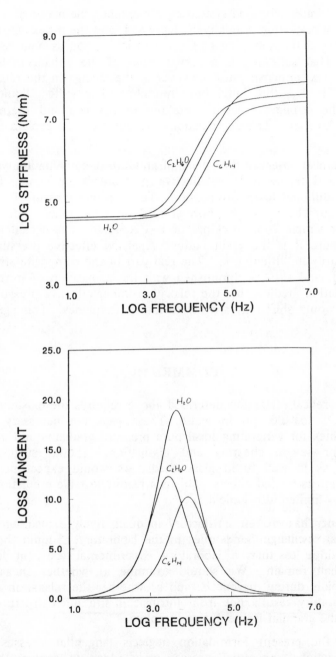

Fig. 5 Stiffness and loss tangent of a liquid saturated contact. Frequency dependence as a function of fluid chemistry: water, ethanol, and n-hexane. Agreement with data from Spencer (1981, Fig. 7] is excellent.

liquids. The water saturated system clearly exhibits the maximal relaxation; the methanol relaxation is relatively depressed; and the n-hexane relaxation is weak. Recall the softening of $\tilde{k}_1(0)$ with adsorption as demonstrated in Figure 2. That softening is a partial cause of the enhancement of the relaxation. The principal cause however of the change in the relaxation is the change in K_w, the liquid bulk modulus. The stiffest liquid, water, produces the strongest pressure buildup in the gap and therefore the maximal relaxation. These predictions are sufficient to explain Spencer's[1] results.

We have also observed the effects of pressure in combination with liquid saturation[6] and frequency[3,4,6]. Effective pressure is universely found to increase moduli and lower attenuation. The effective pressure P_e is simply related in our theory to the normal load on two grains. For instance, $F=4R^2P_e$ for simple cubic packing, or $F=\sqrt{2}R^2P_e$ for a face centered cubic packing, where R is the grain radius. Applying effective pressure would result primarily in stiffening $\tilde{k}_1$. The real part of the composite stiffness, k' is increased, and k''/k' is diminished with the application of normal load. The formulation predicts that the relaxation under effective pressure, while depressed, would shift only slightly to higher frequency. This agrees with observations[4,6].

COMMENTS

The theoretical relaxation described above requires the existence of gap separations 1 to 100 nm in width. These gaps are necessary both as compliant sites for generating local pore pressure gradients and as narrow channels for severe shearing and dissipation. Should such gaps be eliminated, as in well fused glass beads, we would expect neither the relaxation not its related effects. This is a readily testable prediction, and is supported by limited ultrasonic data[3].

The theory has proven satisfactory in qualitatively explaining previous experimental results on sandstones in the laboratory. Should the contact model continue to survive laboratory experimental tests, at least two question shall remain. We should examine a) whether the asperities dissolve rapidly during diagenesis, and b) whether the relaxation observed in the laboratory results not from intrinsic in-situ microstructure but to damage to the granular frame during sampling.

Finally, the present formulation neglects tangential stresses on the contact. Frictional tangential stresses were added to contact theory by Mindlin[20]. These stresses are not crucial to the flow relaxation. The importance of frictional losses has been demonstrated[2,6], but only at high strain amplitudes. Stewart et al.[21] recently extended the Mindlin theory to contact between rough grains, The independent success of the model in describing frictional effects is further evidence that contact between rough surfaces may be a powerful unifying approach to the microphysics of sandstones.

ACKNOWLEDGEMENTS

The authors are grateful for helpful discussions with J.R.A. Pearson, D.L. Johnson, D. Wilkinson, T.J. Plona, M. Gouilloud, and L. Schwartz.

REFERENCES

1. J.W. Spencer, J. Geophys. Res. *86*, 1803 (1981).

2. W.F. Murphy III, J. Acoust. Soc. Am. *71*, 1458 (1982).

3. K.W. Winkler, J. Geophys. Res. *88*, 9493 (1983).

4. B.R. Tittmann, (in these Proceedings).

5. D.H. Johnston, M.N. Toksoz, and A. Timur, Geophys. *44*, 691 (1979).

6. K.W. Winkler and A. Nur, Geophys. *47*, 1 (1982).

7. B.R. Tittmann, H. Nadler, V.A. Clark, L.A. Ahlberg, and T.W. Spencer, Geophys. Res. Lett. *8*, 36 (1981).

8. B.I. Pandit and M.S. King, Canad. J. Earth Sci. *16*, 2187 (1979).

9. V.A. Clark, B.R. Tittmann, and T.W. Spencer, J. Geophys. Res. *35*, 5190 (1980).

10. B.R. Tittmann, V.A. Clark, J.M. Richardson, and T.W. Spencer, J. Geophys. Res. *85*, 5199 (1980).

11. W.F. Murphy III, J. Geophys. Res. (submitted in Oct. 1983).

12. T.A. Jones and A. Nur, Geophys. Res. Lett. *10*, 140 (1983).

13. R.J. O'Connell and B. Budanisky, J. Geophys. Res. *82*, 5719 (1977).

14. R.J. O'Connell, (in these Proceedings).

15. W.F. Murphy III, K.W. Winkler, and R.L. Kleinberg, J. Geophys. Res. (submitted in Sept. 1983).

16. K.L. Johnson, K. Kendell, and A.D. Robert, Proc. Roy. Soc., London, *A 234*, 301 (1971).

17. A.W. Adamson, *Physical Chemistry of Surfaces*, (Wiley, N.Y., 1976) p. 697.

190

18. For a discussion of frame moduli, see T.J. Plona and D.L. Johnson, (in these Proceedings).

19. L.M. Schwartz, (in these Proceedings).

20. R.D. Mindlin, J. Appl. Mech. *ASME 16*, 259 (1949).

21. R.R. Stewart, M.N. Toksoz, and A. Timur, J. Geophys. Res. *88*, 546 (1983).

MOLECULAR MOTIONS AND SURFACE INTERACTIONS
IN CLAY INTERCALATES

M. Lipsicas

Schlumberger-Doll Research
P.O. Box 307, Ridgefield, CT 06877

ABSTRACT

In this paper we review some experimental work on the interaction of simple molecules, and especially water, with the inter-layer surfaces of kaolinite and Na-vermiculite. The effect of the interaction on the internal molecular motions is considered and the application of spectroscopic and thermal analysis techniques in these studies is illustrated.

INTRODUCTION

Clays are a common constituent of rock formations. They are found either in shale beds, which are composite aggregates of fine grain materials such as quartz grains mixed with clay particles, or within the pore spaces of rocks. In general, clays in rocks are made up of one, or more, crystalline clay minerals and the particle size distribution ranges for about 5 microns to 40 microns. Since clay minerals are layered silicates, these small particles are platey (high aspect ratio) and have a very large surface area per unit volume. In addition, the surfaces are usually negatively charged.

The interaction of fluids, and especially water or saline solutions, with clay surfaces has a direct bearing on a number of rock properties of great interest, such as permeability and electrical properties. In order to examine the clay surface fluid interaction at a fundamental level, it is necessary to begin by simplifying the experimental system down to a reasonably well characterized clay surface interacting with simple molecules of a single species, e.g., H_2O. In this paper we review some work of this nature, in which the surface interaction and its effect on molecular motions have been studied by spectroscopic and thermal analysis techniques.

CLAY STRUCTURE

As shown in Figure 1, the structure of each clay layer can be described in terms of two basic building blocks: sheets of silicon tetraheda in which each silicon ion is fourfold coordinated with oxygen and sheets of aluminum, or magnesium, octahedra in which the cation is sixfold coordinated with oxygen and hydroxyls. The apical oxygens of the silicon tetrahedra form a plane which is common to both the octahedral and tetrahedral sheets. In 1:1 structures, Figure 1, the kaolin clays, each layer consists of one tetrahedral and one octahedral sheet. The layer repeat distance along the c axis is, approximately 7Å. In 2:1 structures, Figure 2, smectite (swelling) clays, vermiculites, etc, an octahedral sheet is attached from above and below to a tetrahedral sheet. In the anhydrous state (no swelling), the layer repeat distance is, approximately 10Å.

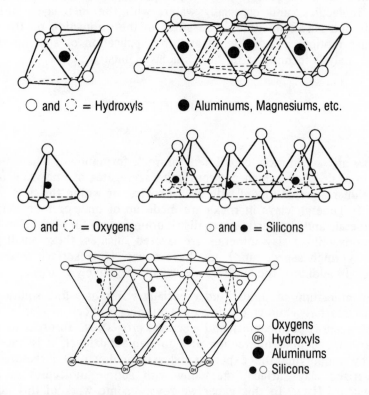

○ and ◌ = Hydroxyls   ● Aluminums, Magnesiums, etc.

○ and ◌ = Oxygens   ○ and ● = Silicons

○ Oxygens
◉ Hydroxyls
● Aluminums
●○ Silicons

Figure 1 - The 1:1 kaolinite clay structure, showing the basic building blocks of clay layers: - sheets of silicon tetrahedra and aluminum, or magnesium, octahedra.

Isomorphous substitution of cations is an important feature of 2:1 clay mineral structures. In particular, aluminum substitutes for silicon in the tetrahedral sheet (vermiculite) and magnesium substitutes for aluminum in the octahedral sheet (montmorillonite). This uncompensated charge substitution leads to excess negative charge centered on oxygen atoms of the clay surface. Exchangeable cations, i.e., non-specific "gegen" cations, which are usually alkali or alkali-earth cations, attach themselves to the clay surface and balance the negative charge. The charge exchange capacity (CEC) of the clay, expressed in milliequivalents per unit weight of clay, is a measure of the concentration of exchangeable cations, and, hence, of the layer surface charge. Exchangeable cations also compensate for the negative charge due to dangling bonds at the cleaved edges of the clay sheets. In the

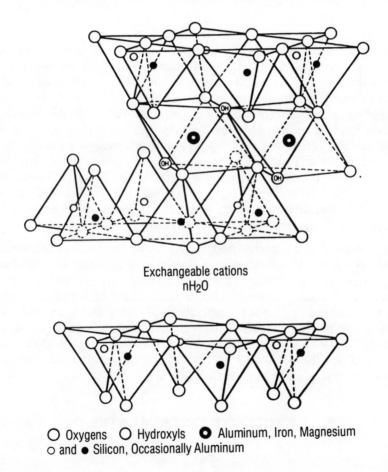

Exchangeable cations
nH_2O

O Oxygens   O Hydroxyls   ◉ Aluminum, Iron, Magnesium
o and ● Silicon, Occasionally Aluminum

Figure 2 - The 2:1 clay structure, as in smectites and vermiculites, showing hydrated exchangeable cations in the inner-layer space.

1:1 clays, where isomorphous cation substitution is infrequent, the CEC is very low and almost entirely due to edge cations. In 2:1 clays, these edge cations are an insignificant contribution to the total CEC.

It should be noted that even the purest natural clay minerals available do contain small amounts (totaling a few percent) of impurity phases, e.g., quartz, iron oxide and other clay minerals. Furthermore, the crystalline structure contains imperfections, especially stacking faults. In the work reviewed here the clay samples used were carefully selected and characterized.

CLAY SURFACES

The outer surfaces of clay particles are usually inhomogeneous and not well characterized. The interlayer surfaces, however, represent a much better defined system and also have a much greater surface area (of order several hundred square meters per gm. of clay), which is of prime concern for experimental measurements. In 1:1 clays, such as kaolinite, Figure 1, the interlayer space is bounded by one hydroxyl bearing surface and one oxygen bearing surface. There are very few, if any, exchangeable cations within this space and in the collapsed, 7Å, phase the layers are held together through "long" hydrogen bonds between these surfaces. In 2:1 clays the situation is quite different. Here, both surfaces are oxygen surfaces of tetrahedral sheets and in swelling clays, such as montmorillonite or vermiculite, there is an appreciable concentration of exchangeable cations.

The interactions of intercalated molecules in the 1:1 clays are dominated by hydrogen bonding. Furthermore, in the case of water intercalation, the surface interaction is between pure water and the clay surface. On the other hand, molecules and, especially, water intercalated into swelling clays may coordinate around the cations (solvation of the cation) as well as form hydrogen bonds with the surface oxygens. The water interaction should be considered that of an ionic solution with a clay surface. We shall illustrate, and expand on, these remarks by reviewing experimental data on hydrated kaolinite and hydrated sodium vermiculite clays.

KAOLINITE INTERCALATES

Very few molecules can be intercalated into kaolinite directly. These are small very polar organic molecules, such as dimethyl sulfoxide (DMSO; $(CH_3)_2SO$) formamide and hydrazine, and in the process of intercalation the

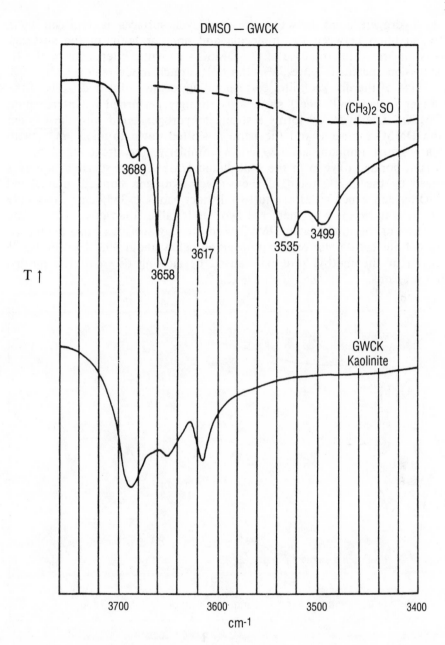

Figure 3 - I.R. transmittance spectrum of the DMSO-kaolinite intercalate (DMSO-GWCK) in hydroxyl stretch region. For comparison, the bulk DMSO spectrum is given above, and the starting GWCK-kaolinite spectrum below, the spectrum of the intercalate.

"long" hydrogen bond between the interlayer surfaces is replaced by a hydrogen bond between the molecule and one, or both, of the surfaces. This is illustrated for the case of the DMSO - kaolinite intercalate by the IR transmission spectra (Figure 3) in the O-H stretch mode region. The 3690 cm^{-1} band of the dry kaolinite, corresponding to the ν_1 for hydroxyls of the interlayer (octahedral sheet) surface, is strongly perturbed by intercalation of DMSO. The hydroxyl forms a stronger hydrogen bond with the oxygen of the DMSO molecule and the band is shifted down to 3658 cm^{-1}, with just a residual remnant at 3689 cm^{-1}. Similarly, the broad band of the hydrogen bonded oxygen in the bulk liquid DMSO, an associated liquid, is replaced by the O-H stretch of the surface hydrogen bonded intercalated DMSO oxygen which gives rise to two distinct bands at 3535 cm^{-1} and 3499 cm^{-1}. It is not clear why there are two bands rather than one. The strong interaction of the intercalated DMSO with the clay surface is also evidenced by partial nuclear dipolar ordering observed below about 200°K in the NMR spectrum of the methyl protons, caused by slowing down of the methyl group rotations.

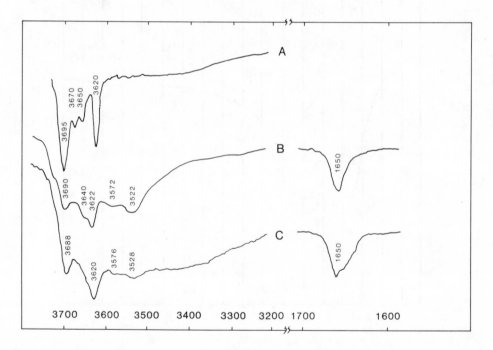

Figure 4 - I.R. transmittance spectrum of kaolinite hydrates. A. The spectrum of kaolinite. (Note the weak broad band centered at about 3400 cm^{-1} due to moisture on the external surfaces of the kaolinite particles.) B. The spectrum of the 8Å monohydrate, showing the bands due to hole water. C. The spectrum of the QS10 dihydrate.

It is possible to intercalate certain other molecules, including water, into kaolinite by an indirect process. Water intercalation into kaolinite, starting with the DMSO-kaolinite intercalate, is discussed elsewhere[1-4]. In particular, samples of kaolinite hydrate which are free of inter-particle (pore) water have been prepared. The fully hydrated material is a dihydrate, (two molecules of water per unit cell of kaolinite), has a c axis spacing, d_{001}, of 10Å and is stable if kept below about 8°C. We refer to it as quasi-stable 10Å (QS10). It spontaneously dehydrates in air at room temperature to a stable monohydrate with $d_{001} \approx 8$Å. With further heating it collapses eventually to the 7Å kaolinite.

The infrared spectrum of QS10 and of the 8Å monohydrate, in the regions of hydroxyl stretch and bend modes, are shown in Figure 4 together with the spectrum of the 7Å starting material. The perturbation of the 3690 cm^{-1} ν_1 band of the kaolinite hydroxyl is considerably weaker than in the DMSO-kaolinite intercalate, indicating that water is not as strongly hydrogen bonded to the interlayer surface as is DMSO. A broad band centered, approximately, at 3400 cm^{-1} in the QS10 spectrum is assigned to associated water. Narrow bands at 3522 cm^{-1} and at 3572 cm^1 (very weak) are evident in both the QS10 and the 8 Å monohydrate spectra. The water bending mode (ν_2) in QS10 can be deconvoluted into a broad band centered at 1635 cm^{-1} and a very narrow band ($\approx$ 20 cm^{-1} width at half height) at 1650 cm^{-1} which is common to both QS10 and the 8Å monohydrate. The

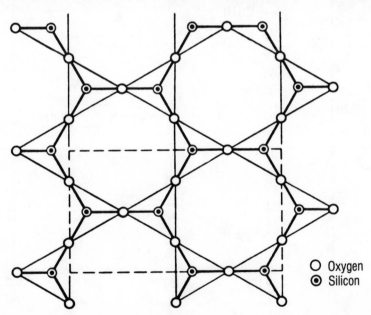

○ Oxygen
◉ Silicon

Figure 5 - Plan view of the tetrahedral sheet, showing the array of ditrigonal holes.

198

IR spectra, coupled with other spectroscopic and thermal analysis data, lead to the conclusion that there are two types of water in the QS10 dihydrate: - (1) a more or less continuous monolayer of associated water molecules and (2) water molecules keyed to ditrigonal holes in the tetrahedral sheet. In Figure 5 we show a plan view of the tetrahedral sheet and the array of ditrigonal holes formed by the silicon tetrahedra. In going from the QS10 dihydrate phase to the 8Å monohydrate, the associated water molecules are desorbed and only the hole water molecules are retained. The hole water molecules form hydrogen bonds with the oxygens of the tetrahedral sheet, but these are weaker than the inter-molecular hydrogen bonds of the monolayer of associated water molecules.

Referring to Figure 6, the specific heat data for the QS10 dihydrate shows a specific heat anomaly above about 240°K, whereas C_p for the hole water in the 8Å monohydrate is not substantially different from that of ice in the temperature range of 100°K to 300°K. In the 8Å phase the water molecules are attached to the silicate layer, keyed to ditrigonal holes and spaced about 5Å apart. No translational motion is possible, although the molecules do undergo internal rotations (as indicated by NMR experiments), and C_p is that of a "frozen" solid but with no melting transition. Proton NMR spin lattice relaxation (T_1) measurements in the

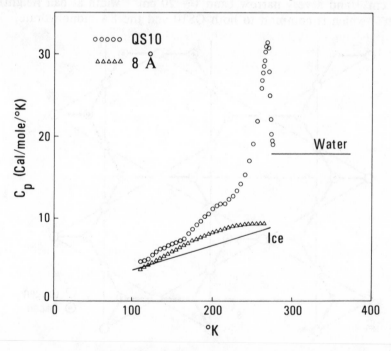

Figure 6 - Specific heat data for the QS10 dihydrate and the 8Å monohydrate, showing the C_p anomaly in QS10.

QS10 dihydrate show that there is only one T_1 value above 250°K, but two T_1 values below this temperature. The second T_1 value is found to be identical to that for the 8Å monohydrate and corresponds to the proton T_1 value for hole water. The T_1 measurements suggest that the specific heat anomaly is associated with exchange of water molecules between the hole water system and the associated water system. At low temperatures, below 200°K, the NMR measurements show half the protons relax as if they were in the hole water phase and the other half relax as if in the associated water phase, in agreement with the dihydrate and monohydrate assignments from the high temperature thermal analysis data[5]. We suggest[6] that at very low temperatures the associated water forms an ordered two dimensional sheet and are currently engaged in a neutron diffraction search for this ordered phase. This suggestion regards the C_p anomaly as a Schottky transition, in which the associated water exchange with hole water molecules at higher temperature causes disorder and a large increase in entropy ("two dimensional melting").

The T_1 data allows a determination of the correlation times for flipping about the C_2 axis of the water molecules in the associated water and hole water phases.

In Figure 7, we plot the correlation times as a function of inverse temperature, assuming the motion is thermally activated with an activation energy H. The corresponding values for H are 4.5 kcal/mole for the associated water and 3.1 kcal/mole for the hole water. Proton spin-spin relaxation (T_2) measurements provide data on the correlation times for the water molecule tumbling motion. They are found to be an order of magnitude slower than the flipping motion, with an activation energy of 2.4 kcal/mole. Thus, the clay surface interaction causes the water molecule internal motion to be anisotropic and considerably slower than in bulk water. There is no indication of nuclear dipolar order in the associated water; the surface interaction does not orient the molecules. The hole water molecules are oriented, as indicated by data from IR dichroic experiments, and we are currently studying the ordering by NMR techniques using deuterated hole water.

HYDRATED VERMICULITE

Llano vermiculite from Texas is a 2:1 swelling clay with a very high CEC ($\approx$ 2 milliequivalents per gm.), mainly due to isomorphous substitution in the tetrahedral sheets, and a very large specific surface area ($\approx$ 800 m²/gm.). The adsorption isotherm for Na-Llano vermiculite was studied by Van Olphen[7] many years ago. He found a two step isotherm which corresponds to two distinct c axis spacings. At relative humidities below

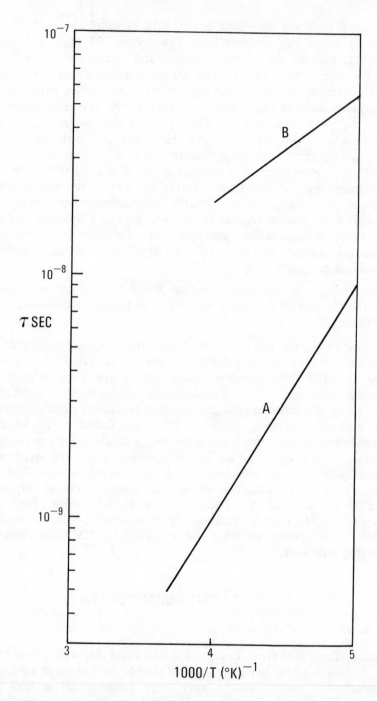

Figure 7 - The correlation times for water molecule flipping about the C_2 axis. A. Associated water molecules. B. Hole water molecules.

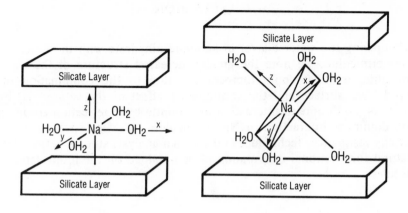

Figure 8 - Na vermiculite. Fourfold and sixfold coordination of water
molecules around the cation.

50%, $d_{001} = 11.8$Å; above 50%, the layers open up further to $d_{001} = 14.8$Å.
It was concluded that the vermiculite interlayer surface was uniformly
charged and that the 11.8Å phase corresponded to one monolayer of water
and the 14.8Å phase to a bilayer. Spectroscopic measurements, especially
EPR[8] and NMR[9] have confirmed Van Olphen's model that the monolayer
phase corresponds to fourfold coordination of water around the cation and
the bilayer to a sixfold, octahedral, coordination (Figure 8). The hydration
water is structured with very little free, non-coordinated, water.

The molecular orientation and proton motions in the bilayer phase were
investigated by NMR[9]. This work was greatly facilitated by the use of
oriented thick films of the Na-Llano vermiculite. A proton and deuteron
NMR Pake doublet signal, characteristic of oriented water molecules, was
observed and the dependence of the doublet separation on the orientation of
the clay sheets with respect to the magnetic field direction was studied.
These measurements showed that the C_2 axes of the water molecules were
tilted at 65° to the crystallographic c axis. At room temperature, the six
water molecules were found to be spinning rapidly about their C_2 axes. In
addition, proton NMR T_1 measurements showed that the cation hydration
shell was characterized by a rotational diffusional motion about a threefold
C_3 axis parallel to c and passing through the center of an equilateral triangle.
The activation energy for this motion is 8.5 kcal/mole and the diffusion
constant at room temperature is about 5×10^{-9} cm^2 sec^{-1}.

202

CONCLUSION

Comparing the water bilayer in kaolinite dihydrate with the water bilayer in Na-vermiculite, we note the greatly increased structure of the water, in vermiculite, even at room temperature, due to the combination of the charged layer surface and the coordinating effect of the cation. Hydrogen bonding is the dominant interaction in kaolinite hydrate; cation coordination is the dominant interaction in Na vermiculite. Modern spectroscopic, and especially resonance, techniques and thermal analysis studies permit detailed structural and motional information to be obtained on the intercalated water molecules.

REFERENCES

1. P. M. Costanzo, C. V. Clemency and R. F. Giese, Clays & Clay Minerals 28, 155, 1980.

2. P. M. Costanzo, R. F. Giese, M. Lipsicas and C. Straley, Nature 296, 549, 1982.

3. P. M. Costanzo and R. F. Giese, Clays and Clay Minerals, in press.

4. R. Raythatha and M. Lipsicas, (private communication).

5. P. M. Costanzo, R. F. Giese and M. Lipsicas, Static and Dynamic Structure of Water in Hydrated Kaolinites: Part I. The Static Structure, (private communication).

6. M. Lipsicas, C. Straley, P. Costanzo and R. F. Giese, Static and Dynamic Structure of Water in Hydrated Kaolinites: Part II. The Dynamic Structure, (private communication).

7. H. Van Olphen, J. of Colloid Science 20, 822, 1965.

8. D. M. Clemenz, T. J. Pinnavaia and M. Mortland, J. Phys. Chem. 77, 196, 1973.

9. J. Hougardy, W. E. E. Stone and J. J. Fripiat, J. Chem. Phys. 64, 3840, 1976.

VOLUME PHASE TRANSITION IN A NON-IONIC GEL

Yoshitsugu Hirokawa* and Toyoichi Tanaka
Massachusetts Institute of Technology, Cambridge, MA 02139
*Permanent Address: Nippon Zeon Co., Ltd., Kawasaki, 210 Japan

ABSTRACT

We report the observation of sharp volume phase transition in the non-ionic N-isopropylacrylamide gel. The finding demonstrates that the phase transition of gels may be general and not confined to ionic gels as was previously considered. It will allow us to separate the electrostatic effects and network-structural effects on the phase transition.

INTRODUCTION

Several polymer gels having ionizable groups are known to undergo a discontinuous volume change upon changes in temperature[1,2], solvent composition[3-6], pH[3], or ionic composition[7]. The volume change was also induced by applying a small electric field across an ionized gel[8]. These phenomena can be interpreted as a phase transition[2,3,9]. This view is supported by observation of critical phenomena in the concentration fluctuations of the polymer network measured by the technique of laser light scattering spectroscopy[10,12].

In this paper we report the preliminary studies on a sharp volume phase transition in the non-ionic N-isopropylacrylamide gel (whether it is discontinuous or not needs more precise experiments). We compare these results with the transition in a non-ionic acrylamide gel which has a continuous volume change.

Theoretical considerations show that whether a gel undergoes a continuous volume change or a first order discontinuous phase transition depends on the proportion of ionizable groups incorporated in the polymer network and on the stiffness of the polymer chains constituting the network[3,9]. The counterions to the ionized groups and the stiffness of the polymer chains increase the osmotic pressure acting to expand the polymer network, resulting in a discontinuous volume change. This situation is similar to a gas-liquid phase transition which can be either continuous or discontinuous depending on the external pressure exerted on the system.

SAMPLE PREPARATION

The N-isopropylacrylamide and acrylamide gels were prepared by free radical polymerization. N-isopropylacrylamide monomer was synthesized from acryloyl chloride and isopropylamine, and purified by distillation, followed by recrystallization from a mixture of petroleum ether and toluene. The purity of the monomer was found to be more than 99.9% by gas chromatography. In particular, we did not find any acrylic acid in the monomer. Five grams of N-isopropylacrylamide and 0.133g of N,N'-methylenebisacrylamide, the crosslinking molecules, were dissolved in pure water to a final volume of 100ml, to which were added 20mg of ammonium persulfate (initiator) and 20mg of sodium bisulfate (accelerator). The gels were made in micropipettes of inner diameter 1.35mm at room temperature and allowed to react for one day. The gels were then removed from the micropipettes and immersed in pure water for one day to wash away unreacted monomers from the polymer network. Finally, the gels were cut into pieces 5mm long to be used in the swelling experiments. The equilibrium time for swelling took from several hours to several days depending on the particular solvent composition used. The same preparation process was employed for the acrylamide gels using the same molar amount of acrylamide as N-isopropylacrylamide. The acrylamide monomer (Biorad, electrophoresis grade) was used without any further purification.

SWELLING EXPERIMENTS

In Figure 1a the degree of swelling of the N-isopropylacrylamide and acrylamide gels is plotted as a function of dimethyl sulfoxide (DMSO) volume percent in mixtures of DMSO and water. The N-isopropylacrylamide gel immersed in mixtures of DMSO composition from 0 to 33 volume percent is slightly swollen compared to the original volume. Above 34% DMSO this gel is collapsed into a compact state. The transition around 33% DMSO is sharp. Above 90% DMSO the gel shows another sharp reswelling. The detailed analysis of this reentry phenomenon will be reported elsewhere[13]. On the other hand, the acrylamide gel shows only a small amount of swelling with no discontinuity.

We also investigated the swelling equilibrium of the N-isopropylacrylamide gel in pure water as a function of temperature. The result is shown in Figure 1b. At low temperatures the gel is swollen, at high temperatures the gel is collapsed. There is a sharp volume transition at approximately $35.0°C$. This behavior is in contrast to the ionized acrylamide gels which are swollen at high temperatures[2]. The total entropy of the gel (polymer network and solvent) must increase at high temperatures. However, the entropy of the polymer network decreases upon its collapse into a more compact and ordered state. The decrease in entropy of the network must be compensated by the entropy increase associated with the solvent molecules, presumably accomplished by the destruction of the solvation structure of water molecules in the vicinity of the polymer chains. Such a reversed temperature dependence was also found in N,N-diethylacrylamide-sodium methacrylate copolymer gels by Ilavsky, Hrouz and Ulbrich[6].

MEAN-FIELD-THEORETICAL CONSIDERATION

The phase transition of a gel can be understood in terms of mean field formula for the osmotic pressure, π of a gel originally derived by Flory and Huggins[14].

$$\Pi = -\frac{NkT}{v}\left[\varphi + \ln(1-\varphi) + \frac{1}{2}\frac{\Delta F}{kT}\varphi^2\right] + vkT\left[\frac{1}{2}\frac{\varphi}{\varphi_0} - \left(\frac{\varphi}{\varphi_0}\right)^{1/3}\right] + vfkT\left(\frac{\varphi}{\varphi_0}\right), \qquad (1)$$

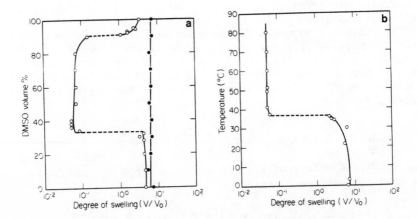

Figure 1: **(a)** The degree of swelling (the ratio of final equilibrium volume to initial volume) of an N-isopropylacrylamide gel (open circles) and an acrylamide gel (filled circles) in mixtures of water and dimethylsulfoxide (DMSO) is plotted as a function of the solvent composition.

(b) The degree of swelling of an N-isopropylacrylamide gel in pure water is plotted as a function of temperature.

206

where N is Avogadro's number, k is the Boltzmann constant, T is
the temperature, v is the molar volume of the solvent, ϕ is the
volume fraction of the network, ΔF is the free energy decrease
associated with the formation of a contact between polymer segments,
ϕ_0 is the volume fraction of the network at the condition the constituent polymer chains have random-walk configurations, ν is the number
of constituent chains per unit volume at $\phi=\phi_0$, and f is the number
of counterions per effective chain. Here we include the effect
of ionization in order to examine the possible elements which determine the discreteness of the gel phase transition.

   The osmotic pressure difference between the inside and outside
of the gel must be zero for the gel to be in equilibrium with the
surrounding solvent. Zero osmotic pressure difference is also
necessary for the free energy of the gel, F, to be minimized, since
$\pi = -\partial F/\partial V$, where V is the volume of the gel. The degree of swelling
is given by

$$\frac{V}{V_0} = \frac{\phi_0}{\phi} \tag{2}$$

where V_0 is the volume of the gel at $\phi=\phi_0$. From Equation (1),
this condition may be expressed as

$$\tau \equiv 1 - \frac{\Delta F}{kT} = -\frac{\nu v}{N\varphi^2}\left[(2f+1)\left(\frac{\varphi}{\varphi_0}\right) - 2\left(\frac{\varphi}{\varphi_0}\right)^{1/3}\right] + 1 + \frac{2}{\varphi} + \frac{2\ln(1-\varphi)}{\varphi^2}, \tag{3}$$

where the parameter τ, the reduced temperature, varies with temperature and solvent composition. Equations (2) and (3) then determine
the equilibrium gel volume and polymer network concentration as
a function of the reduced temperature. For certain values of the
reduced temperature, however, Equation (3) is satisfied by three
values of ϕ, corresponding to two minima and one maximum of the
free energy. The value of ϕ corresponding to the lower minimum
represents the equilibrium value. A discrete volume transition
occurs when the two free-energy minima have the same value. The
criterion which determines whether a volume change of a gel is
discontinuous or continuous can be seen by expanding the logarithmic
term $\ln(1-\phi)$ in Equation (3), retaining terms up to order ϕ^3.
This expansion yields

$$t = S(\phi^{-5/3} - \tfrac{1}{2}\phi^{-1}) - \tfrac{1}{3}\phi . \tag{4}$$

where

$$t \equiv (1 - \Delta F/kT)(2f+1)^{3/2}/2\varphi_0, \tag{5}$$

$$S \equiv (\nu v/N\varphi_0{}^3)(2f+1)^4 \equiv S_0(2f+1)^4, \tag{6}$$

and

$$\rho \equiv (\phi/\phi_0)(2f+1)^{3/2}. \tag{7}$$

Equation (4) is the equation of state of the gel, i.e., the relationship between the renoramlized reduced temperature, t, and the renormalized concentration, ρ. In this approximation, the equation of state is determined by a single parameter S. The parameter S solely determines whether a volume change is continuous or discontinuous. The ratio of the two volumes at either side of the discontinuous transition is also only a function of S. A microscopic interpretation of the parameter S can be seen by the following simple argument[2]. Let the single polymer chain consist of n freely-jointed segments of radius a and persistent length b. Then, the rms end-to-end distance of the single polymer chain is $R \sim n^{1/2}b$. Since R is also the rms distance between neighboring crosslinks, we see that $\nu_0 \sim ba^2/R^3$, and $\phi_0 \sim Nba^2/R^3$. From these relations we have

$$S = (b/a)^4 (2f+1)^4. \tag{8}$$

Equation (8) shows that the S-value depends on two elements, the number of ionized groups per chain, f, and the ratio of persistent length, b, to the effective radius of the polymer chain, a. The ratio b/a reflects the stiffness of the chain. Equation (8) reveals that the S-value changes very rapidly with f and b/a. In order for a gel to have a large S-value and thus to undergo a discontinuous phase transition, the constituent polymer chains must have sufficient stiffness and/or a sufficient amount of ionized groups.

We have seen that the gels of acrylamide and N,N-diethylacrylamide undergo continuous volume change without ionizable groups[3,6]. The volume change becomes discontinuous when ionizable groups are incorporated into the network, indicating the polymer chains of these gels are not stiff enough. The S-value becomes large only when f is increased. N-isopropylacrylamide polymer chains apparently have sufficient stiffness due to the bulky isopropyl groups so the ratio b/a is in itself large enough to induce a discontinuous transition.

CONCLUSION

The findings presented in this report demonstrate that the phase transition of gels is general and not confined to ionic gels. They also indicate the importance of the specific chemical composition of the gel network and solvent. Further study of the phase transition in non-ionic gels is required to allow us to separate the effect of polymer network structure from that of charge. In addition to its scientific importance, an understanding of the volume transition in gels will hasten the application of gel technology to switches, sensors, memories, display units, and mechano-chemical transducers.

We thank G. Swislow for his critical reading of the manuscript. The work has been supported by Nippon Zeon Co., Ltd.

REFERENCES

1. T. Tanaka, Scientific American, 244, 110 (1981).
2. T. Tanaka, Phys. Rev. Letters, 40, 280 (1978).
3. T. Tanaka, D.J. Fillmore, S.-T. Sun, I. Nishio, G. Swislow and A. Shah, Phys. Rev. Letters, 45, 1636 (1980).
4. M. Ilavsky, Macromolecules, 15, 782 (1982).
5. J. Hrout, M. Ilavsky, K. Ulbrich, and J. Kopecek, Europ. Polym. J., 12, 361 (1981).
6. M. Ilavsky, J. Hrouz, and K. Ulbrich, Polymer Bulletin, 2, 107 (1982).
7. I. Ohmine and T. Tanaka, J. Chem. Phys., 11, 5725 (1982).
8. T. Tanaka, I. Nishio, S.-T. Sun, and S. Ueno-Nishio, Science, 218, 467 (1982).
9. K. Dusek and D. Patterson, J. Polymer Sci., A-2, 6, 1209 (1968).
10. T. Tanaka, S. Ishiwata, and C. Ishimoto, Phys. Rev. Letters, 38, 771 (1977).
11. A. Hochberg, T. Tanaka, and D. Nicoli, Phys. Rev. Letters, 43, 217 (1979).
12. T. Tanaka, Phys. Rev., A-17, 763 (1978).
13. S. Katayama, Y. Hirokawa, and T. Tanaka, to be published.
14. P.J. Flory, Principle of Polymer Chemistry, (Cornell University Press, Ithaca, 1953).

ADSORPTION AND ELECTRICAL DOUBLE LAYER PHENOMENA AT MINERAL-WATER INTERFACES

D. W. Fuerstenau
University of California, Berkeley, Ca. 94720

ABSTRACT

This paper summarizes mineral-water adsorption phenomena that can affect the behavior of porous rocks. The nature of the electrical double layer at mineral-water interfaces is briefly reviewed. Phenomena that are affected by the electrical double layer are discussed, particularly in relation to the effect of the electrokinetic or zeta potential on them. Methods to bring the electrokinetic potential to zero are presented for representative mineral systems.

INTRODUCTION

The flow of aqueous solutions through narrow capillaries or porous materials is markedly affected by phenomena that result from adsorption at the solid-water interface. Adsorption of ionic species, either inorganic or organic, results in an electrical double layer at solid-water interfaces, and it is the electrical double layer that can have a controlling effect on the system. For example, in measuring the flow rate of liquids through porous media changes in permeability have been observed for the flow of aqueous electrolyte solutions when the ionic strength or pH have been changed[1]. These effects are probably due to so-called electrokinetic phenomena but may be due to swelling (dispersion) of clay particles, which may migrate and block pore necks. Water structure near interfaces may affect the viscosity in small pores[2]. In addition to the foregoing phenomena, the charge on the surface of a mineral controls adsorption of surfactants and hence may have a significant effect on the wettability of the rock[3]. Even in a more complex situation, the rate of drilling in rocks has been shown to be maximum when the electrokinetic potential of the material is zero[4].

In this paper some of the phenomena that result from the electrical double layer and resultant electrokinetic phenomena will be briefly summarized. Since many of the effects are minimized (or maximized in certain cases) when the electrokinetic potential is zero, the main purpose of this paper is to illustrate how the electrokinetic potential in mineral-water systems can be brought to zero through adsorption. Since the solids constituting natural porous systems are minerals, the most important of which may be oxides (quartz), silicates (clays) or the sparingly soluble salt minerals (calcite), the discussion will center around these types of mineral systems.

THE ELECTRICAL DOUBLE LAYER ON MINERALS

Adsorption phenomena involving minerals in an aqueous environment are controlled by the electrical double layer at the solid-water interface. In this paper, the nature of the double layer on three types of minerals important in reservoir phenomena will be discussed, namely layer silicates, oxides and sparingly soluble salt minerals, such as calcite.

For the salt-type minerals such as calcite or barite, the surface charge arises from the preference of one of the lattice ions for the solid relative to the aqueous phase. Equilibrium is attained when the electro-chemical potential of these ions is constant throughout the system. Those particular ions which are free to pass between both phases and therefore establish the electrical double layer are called potential-determining (P-D) ions[5]. In the case of barite, the P-D ions are then Ba^{++} and $SO_4^=$ or Ca^{++}, CO_3 and HCO_3^- (and H^+ since pH controls the activity of $CO_3^=$ in solution) for calcite. The surface charge, σ_o, on barite is given by the adsorption density, Γ, of Ba^{++} and $SO_4^=$, in mole/cm[2]:

$$\sigma_o = 2F (\Gamma_{Ba}^{++} - \Gamma_{SO_4}^=) \tag{1}$$

where F is the Faraday constant and the 2 comes from the ions being divalent.

For the oxide minerals, hydrogen and hydroxyl ions have long been considered to be potential-determining. Since oxide minerals form hydroxylated surfaces when in contact with water vapor, a hydroxylated surface should be expected when the solid is in equilibrium with an aqueous solution. Adsorption-dissociation of H^+ from the surface hydroxyls can account for the surface charge on the oxide:

$$MOH_{(surf)} + H^+_{(aq)} = MOH^+_{2(surf)}$$

$$MOH_{(surf)} = MO^-_{(surf)} + H^+_{(aq)} \tag{2}$$

The formation of a surface charge by this mechanism, or even by direct adsorption of H^+ and OH^-, would result in a change in the pH of the solution. In any case, the surface charge σ_o on an oxide mineral can be expressed as

$$\sigma_o = F(\Gamma_H^+ - \Gamma_{OH}^-) \tag{3}$$

In the layer silicate minerals such as the clays and micas, because of substitution of Al^{3+} for Si^{4+} in the silica tetrahedra or Mg^{2+} for Al^{3+} in the octahedral layer of the crystal lattice, the surfaces of these crystal faces carry a negative charge that is independent of solution conditions. The magnitude of the surface charge is controlled by the extent of substitution and, for example, is 11.7 microcoulomb/cm[2] in the case of montmorillonite[6]. However, the ends of the crystal sheets behave as complex oxides, making clay particles very heterogeneous in their surface behavior since the faces have a fixed negative charge and the crystal edges have a variable charge controlled by pH.

The single most important parameter that describes the electrical
double layer of a mineral in water is the point of zero surface charge
(PZC). The PZC is expressed as the condition in the aqueous solution
at which σ_0 is zero and this is determined by a particular value of
the activity of the potential-determining ion (a_{pzc}^+ or a_{pzc}^-). In the
double layer model the surface potential ψ_0 is considered to be zero
at the PZC and its value at any activity of P-D electrolyte, a^+, is
given by[5]

$$\psi_0 = (RT/z_+F) \ln (a^+/a_{pzc}^+) \qquad (4)$$

where R is the gas constant, T the absolute temperature, and z_+ the
valence of the potential-determining cation.

The PZC of oxides is controlled by the pH of the solution. Typical values are pH 1-2 for quartz, pH 7 for natural hematite, pH 9 for
alumina, and pH 12.4 for magnesia[7]. If clays exhibit an apparent PZC,
their net zero charge will occur in fairly acidic solution. In the
case of sparingly soluble salts, the PZC will be determined by the
activity of potential-determining ions in solution. Both calcite and
barite exhibit a positive surface charge in water[8]. The PZC of barite
occurs at pBa 6.2 and that of calcite at pCa 3.5 or pH 9.

MODEL OF THE ELECTRICAL DOUBLE LAYER

Adsorption phenomena in charged systems have been explained in
terms of the electrical double layer model. In the simplest case, the
double layer can be regarded as consisting of two regions: 1) a surface
charge, σ_0, and 2) a diffuse layer of counter ions distributed by the
resultant of electrical forces and random thermal motion. The charge
in the diffuse layer, σ_d, must exactly counter balance σ_0 for electro-
neutrality:

$$\sigma_0 + \sigma_d = 0 \qquad (5)$$

Figure 1 illustrates schematically the electrical double layer
showing the surface charge and the diffuse layer of counter ions. The
first layer of counter ions is called the Stern plane, which lies at a
distance δ from the surface. The magnitude of δ depends on whether the
ions are hydrated or dehydrated. The "thickness" of the diffuse layer
of counter ions, $1/\kappa$, is given by the Debye-Hückel relation for a
symmetrical electrolyte ($z_+ = z_- = z$):

$$\kappa^2 = \frac{8\pi c z^2 F^2}{\varepsilon RT} \qquad (6)$$

where c is the concentration of electrolyte in solution and ε the
dielectric constant of the liquid. In aqueous solutions of 1-1 valent
electrolytes, $1/\kappa$ is 10^{-4}, 10^{-5}, 10^{-6} cm in 10^{-7}, 10^{-5} and 10^{-3} molar
solutions, respectively. Thus, increasing the salt concentration in
solutions decreases the extension of the diffuse double layer. The
Debye length, $1/\kappa$, is actually the center of gravity of the distance

212

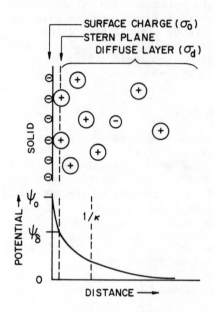

Fig. 1. Schematic representation of the electrical double layer and potential drop across the double layer.

layer, and it is the position where the potential has fallen to $1/e$ of its value at the Stern plane, ψ_δ. The potential drop from the surface, ψ_o, to the Stern plane, ψ_δ, is linear, and from the Stern plane on out into the solution the potential falls off gradually to zero out in the bulk solution.

The diffuse layer charge, σ_d, is given by the Gouy-Chapman theory as

$$\sigma_d = \sqrt{\frac{2\varepsilon RT}{\pi}}\ \sqrt{c}\ \sinh\left(\frac{zF\psi_\delta}{RT}\right) \quad (7)$$

which shows that the adsorption density of counter ions increases with $\sqrt{c}$ if potentials do not change appreciably.

Certain ions strongly adsorb in the inner region of the double layer, that is in the Stern plane, through forces in addition to electrostatic interactions[9]. Such ions are said to specifically adsorb. The adsorption density in the Stern plane is given by a Langmuir-type relation as follows:

$$\frac{\theta}{1-\theta} = \frac{c}{55.5}\ \exp(-\Delta G^o_{ads}/RT) \quad (8)$$

where θ is the fractional coverage (or $\sigma_\delta/\sigma_{max}$) and ΔG^o_{ads} is the standard free energy of adsorption. The quantity $c/55.5$ represents the mole fraction of solute in the aqueous phase. Double layer properties can be strongly influenced by electrolytes that specifically adsorb in the Stern plane. The free energy of adsorption can contain not only electrostatic effects, $z_\pm F\psi_\delta$, but also other terms, called specific adsorption effects:

$$\Delta G^o_{ads} = z_\pm F\psi_\delta + \Delta G^o_{chem} + \Delta G^o_{CH_2} + \Delta G^o_{solv} + \Delta G^o_H + \dots (9)$$

where ΔG^o_{chem} represents chemical bonding at the surface, $\Delta G^o_{CH_2}$ is the free energy associated with hydrocarbon chain association at the surface, ΔG^o_{solv} represents adsorption phenomena controlled by hydration (solvation) of ions and surfaces, ΔG^o_H is the contribution of hydrogen bonding to the adsorption process. If any of the specific adsorption terms are large, they can cause sufficient adsorption that $-\sigma_\delta > \sigma_o$. This behavior can be used to control many of the surface phenomena in solid-liquid systems.

The capacitance of the electrical double layer is strongly dependent on salt concentration and diffuse layer thickness since the double layer model involves two capacitances in series, the inner region of the double layer and the diffuse layer[5]. In concentrated solutions the inner region dominates and in dilute solutions the diffuse layer dominates. The differential capacity of the total double layer, C, is given by $d\sigma_o/d\psi_o$. The differential capacity of the diffuse region of the double layer is given by differentiating Eq. 7,

$$C_d = -d\sigma_d/d\psi_\delta = \frac{\kappa\epsilon}{4\pi} \cosh\left(\frac{zF\psi_\delta}{2\ RT}\right) \tag{10}$$

The differential capacity of the inner region of the double layer (which is essentially an integral capacity) is

$$C_i = \sigma_o/(\psi_o - \psi_\delta) \tag{11}$$

Since the capacity of double layer, C, involves two capacitances in series,

$$\frac{1}{C} = \frac{1}{C_i} + \frac{1}{C_d} \tag{12}$$

the capacitance is large and dominated by C_d in dilute solutions and is low and dominated by C_i in concentrated solutions. Thus, effects that result from capacitance of the double layer at a mineral-water interface can be minimized by increasing the ionic strength of the solution.

CONSEQUENCES OF THE ELECTRICAL DOUBLE LAYER

Electrokinetics

In a charged system where at least one of the phases is fluid and if there is relative motion between the two phases, one observes a number of phenomena called electrokinetic effects. The applied and measured effect depends on whether a mechanical force or an electric field is imposed. If liquid is in a porous rock or capillary, and a pressure is imposed on the liquid, a potential is set up, called the streaming potential. On the other hand, if a potential is applied across the ends of the capillary, liquid will flow in response to the electric field and this is called electroosmosis. If the particles are dispersed solids or oil droplets and the suspension is placed in an electric field, the particles move and this is termed electrophoresis. Relative movement of the fluid causes transport of counter ions in the diffuse layer, giving rise to the various types of electrokinetic phenomena.

Besides the electrokinetic phenomena themselves, these techniques provide a method for measuring the electrical effects due to adsorption. The important potential is the potential at the slipping plane or shear plane, which is the well-known zeta potential, ζ, widely used

214

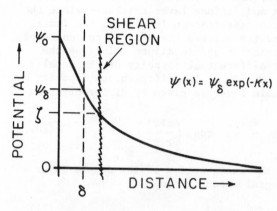

$\psi(x) = \psi_\delta \exp(-\kappa x)$

Fig. 2. Schematic illustration showing
how the zeta potential is determined by
the location of the electrokinetic
slipping or shear plane.

in colloid science, mineral
chemistry and biochemistry.
As can be seen in Figure 2,
the magnitude of the zeta
potential depends on the
location of the slipping
plane. Detailed studies
with micelles indicate that
the slipping plane occurs
very close to the surface
so that taking ζ as a measure of ψ_δ is a reasonably
good approximation[10]. In
the case of adsorbed macro-
molecular polymers, the
slipping plane must necessarily move far from the
surface, thereby reducing
the observed electrokinetic
effects.

The equations relating electrical/mechanical phenomena in elec-
trokinetics all have a similar form where η is the viscosity of the
liquid and λ is its specific conductance:

Streaming Potential

$$\frac{\text{streaming potential}}{\text{pressure drop}} = \frac{E_{st}}{\Delta P} = \frac{\varepsilon\zeta}{4\pi\eta\lambda} \tag{13}$$

Electroosmosis

$$\frac{\text{liquid volume flow}}{\text{current}} = \frac{V}{i} = \frac{\varepsilon\zeta}{4\pi\eta\lambda} \tag{14}$$

Electrophoresis

$$\frac{\text{mobility}}{\text{electric field}} = \frac{v_e}{E} = f(\kappa,a)\,\frac{\varepsilon\zeta}{4\pi\eta} \tag{15}$$

To accurately determine zeta potentials from electrophoretic results,
one must use the functional relation for particle radius, a, and κ
given by Wiersema et al.[11].

Surface Conductance

When measuring the conductance of a fluid inside a capillary or
porous body, the existence of a diffuse double layer gives rise to an
added contribution to the conductivity, known as surface conductance.
Smoluchowski derived an expression for surface conductance, λ_s, in
terms of the zeta potential[12]:

$$\lambda_s = \left(\frac{\varepsilon\zeta}{4\pi}\right)^2 \frac{\kappa}{\eta} \qquad (16)$$

Surface conductance, thus depends on the magnitude of the zeta potential and the thickness of the double layer.

The streaming potential E_{st} that results from the flow of liquid under pressure ΔP through a capillary or porous plug is given by Eq. 13, after Smoluchowski; but if an appreciable amount of current is transported by layers near the wall of a pore of radius, r, then a surface conductivity, λ_s, term must be added[10]

$$\frac{E_{st}}{\Delta P} = \frac{\varepsilon\zeta}{4\pi\eta\lambda\ (1 + 2\ \lambda_s/r\lambda)} \qquad (17)$$

In 1-mm capillaries at concentrations below $10^{-3.5}$ molar, surface conductance becomes appreciable. Thus, for materials with pores in the micron-size range, surface conductance will dominate unless the ionic strength is very high. Figure 3 illustrates schematically the effect of capillary size or particle size on the measured zeta potential (or reduced streaming potential or electroosmotic flow).

Electroviscous Effects

There can be increased resistance to the flow of liquids in capillaries because of electrokinetic interactions between the fluid and solid. A number of relations, of similar form, have been derived that express the apparent increase in viscosity of a liquid in a pore in terms of the zeta potential. An expression, derived by Elton[13], for the apparent viscosity, η_a, of liquid in a porous medium is:

$$\eta_a = \eta + \frac{3}{2}\frac{(\varepsilon\ \zeta)^2}{h^2\ \lambda} \qquad (18)$$

where h is half the thickness of a slit-shaped capillary.

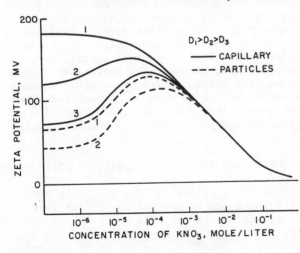

Fig. 3. Effect of pore size and ionic strength on the zeta potential in streaming potential or electroosmosis measurements. D is a measure of capillary diameter.

In the case of the motion of suspensions of fine particles, the viscosity of a dilute suspension, η_s, is given by the well-known expression[14]:

$$\eta_s/\eta = 1 + k_1 \phi \tag{19}$$

where k_1 has a value of 2.5 for spherical particles and ϕ is the volume fraction of particles. Electroviscous effects can cause the viscosity of suspensions to increase, and several relations have been derived[10], one being

$$\eta_s/\eta = 1 + 2.5 \phi \left[1 + \frac{1}{\lambda \, \eta \, a^2} \left(\frac{\zeta \varepsilon}{2\pi} \right)^2 \right] \tag{20}$$

where a is the particle radius. Again, there is the zeta potential squared term operating.

Fine Particle Dispersion

The electrical double layer controls the state of aggregation of fine particles[5]. If two particles have extensive diffuse double layers that overlap, there is a sufficient energy barrier to prevent the particles from coming close enough together that the attractive van der Waals forces can cause them to aggregate. In the simplest case, for two spherical particles the energy of repulsion, V_R, and the energy of attraction, V_A, are given by:

$$V_R = 2 \pi a \, \varepsilon \zeta^2 \exp(-\kappa H); \quad V_A = -\frac{Aa}{12H} \tag{21}$$

H is closest distance between two particles of radius a, and A is the Hamaker constant. The equations for dissimilar particles with different surface potentials and different geometries (such as sphere-plate, plate-plate, etc.) have been derived but need not be given here[15]. We can see that the repulsive energy changes as the square of the zeta potential and also has a double layer thickness dependence. In general, coagulation of particles occurs when the zeta potential drops below about 30 mV. If fine particles, such as clay particles, become dispersed, then as fluid moves in a porous medium, they are transported with the fluid. If the porous medium is made up of cemented mineral grains, the particles can become lodged in the narrow neck of a pore and have a drastic effect on the permeability of the rock to the fluid.

CONTROL OF DOUBLE LAYER PHENOMENA AND THE ZETA POTENTIAL OF MINERALS

The various phenomena that are strongly influenced by the presence of the electrical double layer can be controlled in part by collapsing the extension of the double layer. The double layer can be made thinner by the addition of any electrolyte to the system in accordance with Eq. 6. However, if possible, regulation of the activity of potential-determining ions in solution can bring the mineral to its PZC, and under these conditions there is no double layer at all. Another way to handle problems associated with the presence of double layers is to bring the zeta potential to zero through specific adsorption of surface-active counter ions. Such ions may be inorganic or organic, and the nature of their interaction depends on properties of

the mineral and the electrolyte. If an ion which is charged oppositely to the surface brings the zeta potential to zero, the double layer
is not eliminated but it is compressed into a bimolecular condenser,
consisting of the surface charge and the Stern plane, that is $\sigma_o = \sigma_\delta$.

The types of ions in mineral-water systems can be classified as
to how they affect double layer properties. Some examples follow:

1. Potential-Determining Ions
   These are the ions that can readily pass between the liquid
   and solid phases. They give rise to the surface charge, σ_o,
   and determine the magnitude of the surface potential, ψ_o.

   examples: Ba^{++}, $SO_4^=$ for $BaSO_4$ and H^+, OH^- for oxides.

2. Nonsurface-Active Indifferent Ions
   These ions exist as counter ions in the diffuse part of the
   double layer. Their function is to maintain electrostatic
   neutrality.

   examples: K^+, Na^+, Cl^-, NO_3^- with TiO_2, Fe_2O_3, etc.

3. Surface-Active Inorganic Ions
   These are ions which adsorb specifically in the Stern layer,
   through forces of interaction in addition to simple electrostatic attraction.
   a) Multivalent cations and anions (probably resulting from
      local electrical interactions).
   b) Hydrolyzed metal ions exhibit exceptional surface-activ-
      ity (probably through solvation effects and chemisorption
      effects).

4. Surface-Active Organic Ions
   a) Physisorbing organic ions that adsorb both electrostati-
      cally and through hydrocarbon chain association in the
      Stern layer.
   b) Chemisorbing ions that chemically bond with surface sites.

In the paragraphs that follow, some specific examples of how certain electrolytes can be used to bring the zeta potential to zero will
be discussed.

Potential-Determining Ions

An example of controlling potentials in the double layer by the
addition of an indifferent electrolyte and the potential-determining
ion is given in Fig. 4, where the zeta potential is plotted as a
function of pH in the presence of NaCl as the indifferent electrolyte[16]. At all salt concentrations, only at pH 9.4 is the zeta
potential zero, which is the pH of the PZC. This figure clearly shows
that adding the indifferent electrolyte to the system at constant pH
reduces the magnitude of ζ.

218

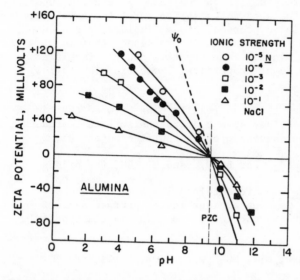

Fig. 4. The zeta potential (and surface potential) of alumina as a function of pH at different concentrations of NaCl.

Multivalent Inorganic Electrolytes

As already indicated, a common way to bring the zeta potential to zero is to add a surface-active counter ion charged oppositely to the surface. If the specific adsorption free energy exceeds the electrostatic component of the adsorption free energy, then $-\sigma_\delta > \sigma_0$ and the zeta potential can be reversed. Figure 5 shows that at a concentration lying between C' and C'', the zeta potential of the mineral can be brought to zero. This can be accomplished with certain inorganic and organic ions.

Although multivalent ions do often exhibit some surface activity[17] hydrolyzed inorganic ions are particularly surface active. Solvation and chemisorption phenomena dominate the adsorption process. Figure 6 presents the electrophoretic mobility of quartz in the presence of cobaltous nitrate as a function of pH[18]. Major changes in the zeta potential (multiplying the electrophoretic mobilities by 13 gives the

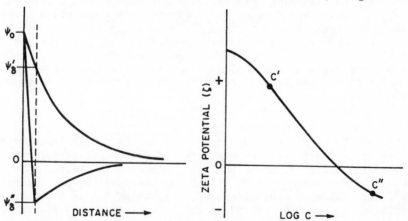

Fig. 5. Schematic representation of potential distribution in the double layer upon addition of an anionic surface-active counter ion, showing the reversal of the Stern plane potential. Typical shape of a ζ-log-c curve upon addition of a surface-active anion.

approximate value of the zeta potential) occur at the pH where $CoOH^+$ ions form in solution. As the pH is further increased, $Co(OH)_2$ appears to precipitate on the surface and the silica behaves as if it were $Co(OH)_2$. The pH at which hydrolysis of any cation begins to occur can be used to predict the conditions at which the zeta potential can be brought to zero by that ion. An interesting phenomenon is that in the presence of ammonia, the zeta potential can be made to reverse at five different pH values in the presence of cobalt or nickel salts[19].

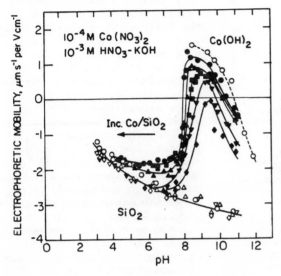

Fig. 6. The electrophoretic mobility of silica as a function of pH in the presence of 10^{-4} M $Co(NO_3)_2$ and 10^{-3} M KOH or HNO_3. ζ reverses its sign at lower pH's as the Co/SiO_2 ratio is increased.

In the case of adding ions to a mineral-water system involving sparingly soluble salts, analysis of solubility relations must be carried out because the surface of a given mineral can be converted to that of a more insoluble salt. Examples include the transformation of the surface of fluorite to calcite in the presence of carbonate ions, the surface of hydroxyapatite to fluorite with fluoride ions, etc. Figure 7 illustrates by means of zeta potential measurements[20] that sodium carbonate reacts at the surface of barite at about pH 10 when the ratio of $(CO_3^=)/(SO_4^=) > 1.05$. Equilibria that control this are the solubility products of the two minerals: the K_{sp} of $BaCO_3 = 1.6 \times 10^{-9}$ and the K_{sp} of $BaSO_4 = 1.5 \times 10^{-9}$. Alkalinity of the solution enters into this behavior because of carbonate/bicarbonate equilibria, namely $HCO_3^- = H^+ + CO_3^=$, $K = 4.8 \times 10^{-11}$.

Organic Ions

At low concentrations, organic ions can adsorb by electrostatic attraction to the charged surface, but at higher concentrations specific adsorption phenomena may occur through association of the hydrocarbon chains of the surfactant.

In aqueous solution, long-chained organic surfactant ions (with hydrocarbon chains greater than 8 carbon atoms) lower their free

220

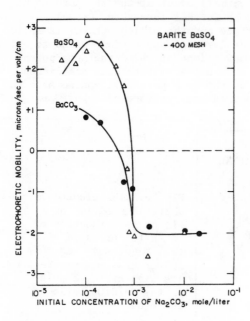

Fig. 7. The transformation of the barite ($BaSO_4$) surface to $BaCO_3$ upon addition of sodium carbonate.

energy through association of their hydrocarbon chains to form micelles[5]. The driving force for organic ions to adsorb at the oxide-water or silicate-water interface is this same tendency for their hydrocarbon chains to associate, thereby escaping from water. Only ions adsorbed in the Stern plane are sufficiently close together that their hydrocarbon chains can interact. Since this behavior at the surface is somewhat similar to micelle formation in solution, except that the association is two-dimensional at the surface, the aggregated surfactant ions at the interface are called hemimicelles[21]. Because the hydrocarbon chain enters into the adsorption process, the adsorption free energy will depend upon the configuration of the hydrocarbon chain. The adsorption free energy for this type of physical adsorption system is

$$\Delta G^o_{ads} = zF\psi_\delta + \Delta G^o_{CH_2} = zF\psi_\delta + N\phi \qquad (22)$$

where N is the number of carbon atoms in the hydrocarbon chain of the surfactant and ϕ is the free energy decrease upon removing one mole of CH_2 groups from water (0.6 Kcal or 1 RT per mole). Figure 8 shows the zeta potential of quartz as a function of the concentration of alkylammonium acetates in aqueous solution[21]. This figure clearly shows that the concentration of alkylammonium salt needed to bring the zeta potential to zero is systematically lowered as the number of carbon atoms is increased. Studies with alkylsulfonates on alumina show identical behavior at pH's below the PZC, where alumina is positively charged. When the solid is negatively charged, the anionic sulfonate ions do not adsorb, a phenomenon of importance in tertiary oil recovery.

In the case of certain systems, surfactant ions strongly chemisorb. An example is the adsorption of anionic oleate (a soap) on hematite, where soap adsorption can occur even when the surface is highly negatively charged[21]. The sparingly soluble salt minerals present a more complex situation in that surface reaction or surface exchange can occur, similar to the case for insoluble inorganic salts. For example, if the mineral cation and the organic anion form insoluble salts, one can predict a sharp uptake of the surfactant

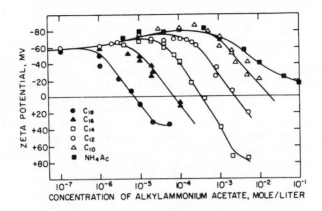

Fig. 8. Effect of chain length on the ζ-potential of
quartz at neutral pH in solutions of alkylamine salts.

under conditions where the surfactant salt is more insoluble than the
mineral. Figure 9 shows such behavior for the uptake of sodium oleate (an 18-carbon group) by calcite[22]. The isotherm exhibits regular
behavior until a concentration of about 3×10^{-5} M oleate is reached,
under which condition the uptake rises steeply. This sharp rise is
the onset of calcium oleate formation on the surface. At pH 7.4, the
zeta potential of calcite can be reversed from positive to negative
with as little as about 5×10^{-6} M sodium oleate[22].

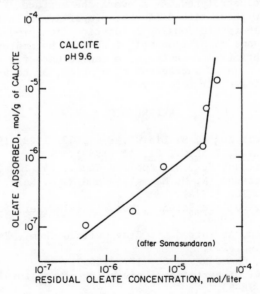

Fig. 9. Adsorption density of oleate on calcite.

222

SUMMARY

Flow of liquid through porous materials is important in many areas. Of technological interest are such things as ground-water hydrology, transport in soils and rocks, osmosis, filtration of particulate solids, oil recovery from reservoirs, slip casting in ceramic processing, drying of fine particulate masses, etc. When ions are present in the fluid, as is the case for aqueous systems, electrical double layer phenomena play a pronounced role in liquid transport in porous media. Movement of fluids in pores manifests itself in electrokinetic phenomena, and the electrical potentials generated can in turn affect the flow of the fluid in the pores through electroviscous and surface conductance effects. Depending on the magnitude of the zeta potential (electrokinetic potential) and the extension of the double layer, the state of aggregation of colloidal clay particles can be altered. The addition of fresh water to a reservoir system can raise double layer potentials and, consequently, clay particles can swell or become dispersed and migrate in the pores of a porous rock, possibly blocking the pore openings and thereby reducing permeability. Furthermore, in certain types of measurements, such phenomena as surface conductance or the capacitance of the double layer may have a pronounced influence on observed behavior.

Most of these phenomena can be controlled by bringing the zeta potential to zero. The general aim of this paper has been to illustrate the principles of adsorption at mineral-water interfaces and to show how adsorption behavior can be used to control double layer potentials, either by changing the concentration of potential-determining ions or by finding conditions where inorganic or organic ions can specifically adsorb at the surface. In case of sparingly soluble salt minerals, electrolytes may convert the surface of the given mineral to a new phase with different properties. In the event that the removal of inorganic ions by adsorption from ground waters is desired, these same adsorption principles can be employed. Similarly, the principles briefly presented here can be used for selecting systems to enhance organic surfactant adsorption, or to prevent it in the case of tertiary oil recovery.

REFERENCES

1. A. S. Michaels and C. S. Lin, I.&E.C., 47, 1249 (1955).
2. W. Drost-Hansen, I.&E.C., 61, 10 (1969).
3. D. W. Fuerstenau, Pure and Applied Chem., 24, 135 (1970).
4. A. R. C. Westwood, N. M. Macmillan and R. S. Kalyoncu, A.I.M.E. Trans., 256, 106 (1974).
5. H. R. Kruyt, Colloid Science, Vol. 1, (Elsevier, New York, 1952), Ch. IV.
6. H. van Olphen, An Introd. to Clay Colloid Chem., 2nd Ed. (Wiley, N.Y., 1977), p. 255.
7. G. A. Parks, Chem. Rev., 65, 177 (1965).
8. Pradip, Ph.D. Dissertation, University of California, Berkeley (1981), pp. 78-83.

9.   D. W. Fuerstenau, in The Chemistry of Biosurfaces, Vol. 1, M. L. Hair, Ed. (Marcel Dekker, N. Y., 1971), Ch. 4.

10. R. J. Hunter, Zeta Potential in Colloid Chemistry (Academic Press, N. Y., 1981), 386 pp.

11. P. H. Wiersema, A. L. Loeb and J. T. G. Overbeek, J. Colloid and Interface Sci., 22, 78 (1966).

12. A. J. Rutgers, M. de Smet and W. Rigole, in Phys. Chem: Enriching Topics from Colloid and Surface Science, H. van Olphen and K. J. Mysels, Ed. (Theorex, La Jolla, CA, 1975), Ch. 21.

13. G. A. H. Elton, Proc. Royal Soc. London, A197, 568 (1949).

14. A. Scheludko, Colloid Chemistry (Elsevier, N. Y., 1966), p. 70.

15. R. Hogg, T. W. Healy and D. W. Fuerstenau, Trans. Faraday Soc., 62, 1638 (1966).

16. H. J. Modi and D. W. Fuerstenau, J. Phys. Chem., 61, 640 (1957).

17. F. J. Hingston, A. M. Posner and J. P. Quirk, J. Soil Sci., 23, 1977 (1972).

18. R. O. James and T. W. Healy, J. Colloid Interface Sci., 40, 42, 53, 65 (1972).

19. K. Osseo-Asare and D. W. Fuerstenau, Int. J. Mineral Proc., 7, 117 (1980).

20. Pradip and D. W. Fuerstenau, Trans. A.I.M.E., to be published in 1984.

21. P. Somasundaran, T. W. Healy and D. W. Fuerstenau, J. Phys. Chem., 68, 3562 (1964).

22. P. Somasundaran, J. Colloid Sci, 31, 557 (1969).

AIP Conference Proceedings

		L.C. Number	ISBN
No.1	Feedback and Dynamic Control of Plasmas	70-141596	0-88318-100-2
No.2	Particles and Fields - 1971 (Rochester)	71-184662	0-88318-101-0
No.3	Thermal Expansion - 1971 (Corning)	72-76970	0-88318-102-9
No.4	Superconductivity in d-and f-Band Metals (Rochester, 1971)	74-18879	0-88318-103-7
No.5	Magnetism and Magnetic Materials - 1971 (2 parts) (Chicago)	59-2468	0-88318-104-5
No.6	Particle Physics (Irvine, 1971)	72-81239	0-88318-105-3
No.7	Exploring the History of Nuclear Physics	72-81883	0-88318-106-1
No.8	Experimental Meson Spectroscopy - 1972	72-88226	0-88318-107-X
No.9	Cyclotrons - 1972 (Vancouver)	72-92798	0-88318-108-8
No.10	Magnetism and Magnetic Materials - 1972	72-623469	0-88318-109-6
No.11	Transport Phenomena - 1973 (Brown University Conference)	73-80682	0-88318-110-X
No.12	Experiments on High Energy Particle Collisions - 1973 (Vanderbilt Conference)	73-81705	0-88318-111-8
No.13	π-π Scattering - 1973 (Tallahassee Conference)	73-81704	0-88318-112-6
No.14	Particles and Fields - 1973 (APS/DPF Berkeley)	73-91923	0-88318-113-4
No.15	High Energy Collisions - 1973 (Stony Brook)	73-92324	0-88318-114-2
No.16	Causality and Physical Theories (Wayne State University, 1973)	73-93420	0-88318-115-0
No.17	Thermal Expansion - 1973 (lake of the Ozarks)	73-94415	0-88318-116-9
No.18	Magnetism and Magnetic Materials - 1973 (2 parts) (Boston)	59-2468	0-88318-117-7
No.19	Physics and the Energy Problem - 1974 (APS Chicago)	73-94416	0-88318-118-5
No.20	Tetrahedrally Bonded Amorphous Semiconductors (Yorktown Heights, 1974)	74-80145	0-88318-119-3
No.21	Experimental Meson Spectroscopy - 1974 (Boston)	74-82628	0-88318-120-7
No.22	Neutrinos - 1974 (Philadelphia)	74-82413	0-88318-121-5
No.23	Particles and Fields - 1974 (APS/DPF Williamsburg)	74-27575	0-88318-122-3
No.24	Magnetism and Magnetic Materials - 1974 (20th Annual Conference, San Francisco)	75-2647	0-88318-123-1
No.25	Efficient Use of Energy (The APS Studies on the Technical Aspects of the More Efficient Use of Energy)	75-18227	0-88318-124-X